Progress in Mathematics

5   GENERAL

Les Murray BA
Senior Teacher and Head of Mathematics, Garstang County High School

Stanley Thornes (Publishers) Ltd

First published in 1987 by Stanley Thornes (Publishers) Ltd, Old Station Drive, Leckhampton, Cheltenham GL53 0DN, UK

British Library Cataloguing in Publication Data

Murray, Les.
 Progress in mathematics.
 5 general
 1. Mathematics—Examinations, questions, etc.
 I. Title
 510'.76   QA43

 ISBN 0-85950-179-5

To JGM

Typeset by KEYTEC, Bridport, Dorset.
Printed and bound in Great Britain by A. Wheaton & Co, Exeter

Preface

This book, the last in the series that leads to the middle level of the GCSE examination, has been written following a detailed analysis of all the available examination syllabuses.

The book contains numerous, carefully graded questions. It is not intended to be worked through from cover to cover; the teacher should be selective in the use of exercises and questions.

Revision sections have been inserted at intervals, questions being based on previous chapters. There is one revision exercise per chapter, thus allowing one topic to be revised at a time. At the end of the book, twelve miscellaneous revision papers have been provided. The first four of these papers each revise a limited number of topics (eight chapters each). Revision Paper 5 covers the whole of the book, while Revision Papers 6 to 12 contain miscellaneous questions for exam practice. This format allows pupils to be introduced gently to an examination situation through the steady progression from one topic to papers containing miscellaneous topics. The course continues to include calculator work, investigations and open-ended questions providing an opportunity for further study.

Photocopy masters are again available to the teacher for exercises where pupils may benefit by their provision. Such exercises have been labelled **M** .

The completion of this book has been dependent on the valued help and advice given to me by many people, in particular Mr J. Britton, Head of Mathematics at Copthall School, London, for his welcome advice and most useful comments; Roger Wilson, Head of Mathematics at Parklands High School and Alan Snelgrove of Tredegar Comprehensive School, for painstakingly working through the text and providing the answers. My thanks also go to the maths staff and the pupils of Garstang County High School, for their interest and co-operation while writing has been in progress; to Casio Electronics and Texas Instruments for the loan of a selection of calculators thus enabling me to consider the different characteristics of calculators in my writing; to Mr G. J. Hindle of the CIS, Mark Gilmartin and Jayne Clarke of the Standard Life Assurance Company and Ian Simpson of I & A Simpson Insurance

Brokers for their invaluable help and advice on insurance and assurance; to the staff of the TSB in Garstang for providing help and information on banking; to Geoff Giles, devisor of Dime Projects Materials for the ideas used in Chapter 10, Exercise 3; to Mitzi Lorenz of London for information on hat sizes; to Eric Hart for advice on building regulations; to the staff of British Rail in Preston for providing timetables and information as and when required; to Booths in Garstang for up-to-date prices and to Lona Bond, Sharan Jeet Shan and Wilbert Garvin for providing lists of names.

Finally I should also like to thank all the staff at Stanley Thornes (Publishers) Ltd.

Les Murray
1987

Acknowledgements

The author and publishers are grateful to the following:

Alan J Richards, *British Birds* (David and Charles) for the pictures of the blackbird on p. 408.

British Railways Board for the timetables on p. 82 and p. 105.

London Transport Museum for the Underground map on p. 81.

National Girobank for the credit slip on p. 178.

The National Dairy Council for the table on p. 104.

Van Nostrand Reinhold Co Ltd for the Arabic manuscript of Pythagoras' Theorem on p. 325.

Contents

1 Sets

1. W = the set of whole numbers that are less than 9. Listing the set, we have W = {0, 1, 2, 3, 4, 5, 6, 7, 8}. List the following sets.
   (a) A = the set of odd numbers that are less than 10
   (b) X = the set of factors of 20
   (c) D = {even numbers that lie between 20 and 35}
   (d) P = the set of even prime numbers
   (e) K = {multiples of 9 that are less than 100}
   (f) R = {prime numbers that lie between 30 and 40}

2. 9 is a square number.
   S = the set of square numbers that are less than 120.
   List set S.

3. 10 is a triangular number. List the set of triangular numbers that are less than 40. Call the set T.

4. List the set of multiples of 4 that are also multiples of 5 and are less than 90.

5. List the set of multiples of 6 that are also multiples of 8 and are less than 75.

1

Exercise 2

1. 45 pupils were asked which of the books A and B they had read. Some of the information obtained is represented in the Venn diagram shown.

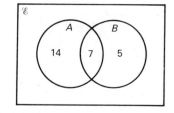

   (a) How many pupils have read book A?
   (b) How many pupils have read both books?
   (c) How many pupils have read only one of the books A and B?
   (d) How many have read neither book?

2. A survey was carried out to find out whether people preferred chocolate P or chocolate Q of two chocolates that were tasted. 55 people tasted the chocolates. The Venn diagram shows some of the information obtained.

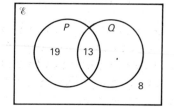

   How many liked:
   (a) chocolate P?
   (b) both chocolates?
   (c) chocolate Q but not P?

3. The Venn diagram shows the results of a survey. C = the set of pupils who like chips and R = the set of pupils who like rice.
   If all the pupils gave a response:

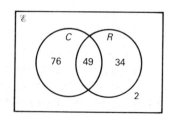

   (a) How many pupils altogether were questioned?
   (b) How many liked only chips?
   (c) How many liked both rice and chips?
   (d) How many did not like rice?

2

4. The Venn diagram gives information about 5th-year pupils at a mixed school:

G = {5th-year girls}
C = {5th-year pupils who cycle to school}

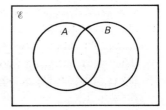

(a) How many 5th-year girls are there?
(b) How many 5th-year girls cycle to school?
(c) How many 5th-year boys do not cycle to school?
(d) How many 5th-year pupils are there altogether in the school?

Exercise 3 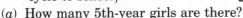 **M**

For each question, copy the Venn diagram then complete it using the information given:

1. 40 pupils were asked which of the television programmes A and B they watched last night:
15 watched both programmes.
4 watched neither programme.
A total of 22 pupils watched programme A.

(a) How many pupils watched programme A but did not watch programme B?
(b) What was the total number of pupils who watched programme B?

2. At a youth club there was a choice between table tennis and snooker. In the Venn diagram, T stands for the set of people who played table tennis and S for those who played snooker. 12 people altogether played table tennis and 3 people played both games. A total of 17 people played at least one of the games, while 2 people played neither.

(a) How many played table tennis but not snooker?
(b) How many played snooker but not table tennis?
(c) How many were there altogether at the youth club?

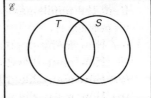

3

3. Meetings were held on Monday and Wednesday of each week. A total of 26 people attended Monday's meeting, 18 attended Wednesday's meeting while 7 attended both meetings. No one missed any meetings.

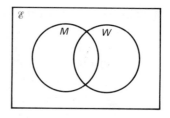

(*a*) How many attended Monday's meeting but missed Wednesday's meeting?

(*b*) How many people altogether attended at least one of the meetings?

(*c*) How many people altogether attended exactly one of the meetings?

4. In the Venn diagram, A = the set of people who are good at art and M = the set of people who can play a musical instrument. 15 people are good at art, 4 people are good at art and play a musical instrument, 21 people are either good at art, play a musical instrument or do both, while 19 are not good at art.

(*a*) How many play a musical instrument?

(*b*) How many do not play a musical instrument but are good at art?

(*c*) How many do not play a musical instrument?

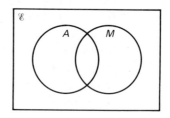

5. Hywel delivers newspapers to 67 households. He delivers the *Daily News* to 32 households and the *Daily Post* to 29 households. 14 households do not take either of these papers.

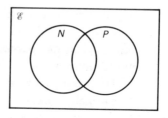

(*a*) How many households take both newspapers?

(*b*) How many households do not take the *Daily Post*?

(*c*) How many households take exactly one of these newspapers?

Exercise 4

1. At a garage doing MOT tests, 11 cars failed due to faulty brakes and 7 cars failed due to faulty suspension. 3 cars that failed had both faulty brakes and faulty suspension. A total of 13 cars did not have faulty brakes.
   (a) How many cars were tested altogether?
   (b) How many cars had faulty brakes only?

2. As a choice of sweet, 17 people chose vanilla ice-cream while 5 people had both vanilla and strawberry ice-cream. 4 people had only strawberry ice-cream while 31 people did not have strawberry ice-cream.
   (a) How many people had strawberry ice-cream?
   (b) How many people had only vanilla ice-cream?
   (c) How many people did not choose vanilla or strawberry ice-cream?

3. Out of 50 people, 5 could play neither chess nor draughts, 29 could play draughts but not chess while a total of 7 people could not play draughts:
   (a) How many could play both chess and draughts?
   (b) How many could not play chess?
   (c) How many could play draughts?

4. In a survey, it was discovered that 66 people liked carrots, 25 people wore glasses and did not like carrots, 57 people did not wear glasses and 9 people neither wore glasses nor liked carrots:
   (a) How many people wore glasses and liked carrots?
   (b) How many people wore glasses?
   (c) How many people were questioned in the survey?

5. Out of 90 people questioned, 39 people used only the alarm on their watch to wake them in the morning, 49 people did not use an alarm clock, while 34 people did not use the alarm on their watch:
   (a) How many people used an alarm clock and the alarm on their watch?
   (b) How many used an alarm clock only?
   (c) How many used neither a watch nor an alarm clock?

6. Out of some people who were questioned, 46 wore gloves; 73 wore gloves, a scarf or both; 36 wore neither a scarf nor gloves; while 48 did not wear a scarf:
   (a) How many people were questioned?
   (b) How many wore both gloves and a scarf?
   (c) How many wore a scarf but no gloves?

7. It was found in a survey that a total of 35 people used either mousse or lacquer or both on their hair, 17 used lacquer but not mousse, 30 did not use lacquer and 35 did not use mousse:
   (a) How many used mousse?
   (b) How many used both mousse and lacquer?
   (c) What was the total number of people questioned in the survey?

8. At a flower show, 18 people showed roses, 9 people showed chrysanthemums, 26 people showed either roses or chrysanthemums or both while 28 people showed neither roses nor chrysanthemums:
   (a) How many showed roses or chrysanthemums but not both?
   (b) How many showed roses only?
   (c) How many people altogether were questioned?

Exercise 5

The Venn diagram shows the number of tourists in a survey who could speak English, set N, French, set F and German, set G:

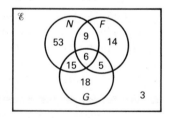

1. How many tourists altogether were questioned in the survey?

2. How many tourists could speak the following languages:
   (a) English, French and German?
   (b) English and German?
   (c) English and German but not French?
   (d) only German?
   (e) neither English, French nor German?

6

2 Approximation

1. Write the following correct to the nearest pound:
    (*a*) £2.75   (*b*) £31.46   (*c*) £82.90   (*d*) £50.09

2. Write the following correct to the nearest penny:
    (*a*) 91.68 p   (*b*) £3.518   (*c*) 23.407 p   (*d*) 8.925 p

3. Write the following correct to the nearest 10 kg:
    (*a*) 47 kg   (*b*) 24.7 kg   (*c*) 536 kg   (*d*) 863 kg

4. Round to two decimal places:
    (*a*) 2.737   (*b*) 0.0782   (*c*) 9.705   (*d*) 2.395

5. Round to one decimal place:
    (*a*) 5.88   (*b*) 9.035   (*c*) 0.159   (*d*) 79.98

6. Round to three significant figures:
    (*a*) 681.8   (*b*) 29 146   (*c*) 0.8029   (*d*) 6201

7. Round to one significant figure:
    (*a*) 4.7   (*b*) 38   (*c*) 6285   (*d*) 0.0567

8. 37.83 ℓ correct to the nearest litre is:
    A. 37.8 ℓ B. 37.80 ℓ C. 40 ℓ D. 38 ℓ

9. 6037.9542 correct to three significant figures is:
    A. 6037   B. 6030   C. 6040   D. 6038

10. 387 people were at a concert. Write the number correct to the nearest ten.

11. 18 749 people went to the match:
    (a) Write the number correct to the nearest thousand.
    (b) Write the number correct to the nearest hundred.

12. 17 862 people went to City's match. Write the number correct to three significant figures.

13. A jar holds 454 g of jam. Write its mass correct to the nearest 10 g.

14. Mont Blanc is 4807 m high:
    (a) Write its height correct to the nearest thousand metres.
    (b) Write its height correct to the nearest hundred metres.
    (c) Write its height correct to the nearest ten metres.

15. A common brick has a mass of 2.58 kg. Write its mass in kilograms correct to one decimal place.

16. A bulk tank for milk holds 2485 ℓ. Write that amount correct to the nearest hundred litres.

17. A 10 p piece has a mass of 11.3104 g:
    (a) Write its mass, in grams, correct to one decimal place.
    (b) Write its mass correct to the nearest gram.
    (c) Write its mass correct to the nearest 10 g.

18. The distance from Manchester to London is about 318 km. Write the distance correct to two significant figures.

19. A piece of material is 2.83 m long:
    (a) Write the length correct to one place of decimals.
    (b) Write the length correct to the nearest metre.
    (c) Write the length correct to two significant figures.

20. A calculator's display shows
    Write this number:

    $$1.5263$$

    (a) correct to three decimal places,
    (b) correct to three significant figures,
    (c) correct to one decimal place,
    (d) correct to one significant figure.

Limits of Accuracy

Exercise 2

A 1. Round the following lengths correct to the nearest centimetre:

(a) 4.8 cm   (c) 5.4 cm   (e) 4.9 cm   (g) 5.49 cm

(b) 5.1 cm   (d) 4.5 cm   (f) 4.86 cm   (h) 5.499 cm

2. Write what you notice about the answers to question 1.

3. (a) What is the smallest length that rounds up to 5 cm when rounded to the nearest centimetre?

(b) Any length that rounds down to 5 cm when rounded to the nearest centimetre must be less than a certain length. What is that certain length?

B 1. Round the following lengths correct to the nearest metre:

(a) 7.1 m   (c) 7.3 m   (e) 6.6 m   (g) 7.499 m

(b) 6.7 m   (d) 6.5 m   (f) 7.49 m   (h) 7.4999 m

2. Write what you notice about the answers to question 1.

3. (a) What is the smallest length which, when rounded to the nearest metre, rounds up to 7 m?

(b) Any length that rounds down to 7 m when rounded to the nearest metre must be less than a certain length. What is that certain length?

C 1. Round the following to the nearest 10 kg:

(a) 59 kg   (c) 62 kg   (e) 55 kg   (g) 64.9 kg

(b) 64 kg   (d) 56 kg   (f) 56.3 kg   (h) 64.999 kg

2. Write what you notice about the answers to question 1.

3. (a) What is the smallest mass that rounds up to 60 kg when rounded to the nearest 10 kg?

(b) Any mass that rounds down to 60 kg when rounded to the nearest 10 kg must be less than a certain mass. What is that certain mass?

D 1. Round the following to the nearest 100 g:

(a) 280 g   (c) 312 g   (e) 250 g   (g) 349 g

(b) 296 g   (d) 251 g   (f) 306.5 g   (h) 349.99 g

2. Write what you notice about your answers to question 1.

3. (a) What is the smallest mass that rounds up to 300 g when rounded to the nearest 100 g?

(b) Any mass that rounds to 300 g when rounded to the nearest 100 g must be less than a certain mass. What is that certain mass?

E 1. Round the following to the nearest 1000:

(a) 27 950   (c) 27 645   (e) 27 500   (g) 28 490

(b) 28 200   (d) 28 015   (f) 27 619   (h) 28 499

2. Write what you notice about the answers to question 1.

3. (a) What is the smallest number that rounds up to 28 000 when rounded to the nearest 1000?

(b) Any number that rounds to 28 000 when rounded to the nearest 1000 must be less than a certain number. What is that certain number?

F 1. Round the following to one decimal place:

(a) 6.79   (c) 6.84   (e) 6.75   (g) 6.8499

(b) 6.82   (d) 6.76   (f) 6.849   (h) 6.849 99

2. Write what you notice about the answers to question 1.

3. (a) What is the smallest number that rounds up to 6.8 when rounded to one decimal place?

(b) Any number that rounds to 6.8 when rounded to one decimal place must be less than a certain number. What is that certain number?

The above lines measure 9 cm when measured to the nearest centimetre.

If a line measures 9 cm, correct to the nearest centimetre, the shortest length it can have is 8.5 cm. Also, its length must be less than 9.5 cm. We can say that its actual length *lies between the limits* 8.5 cm and 9.5 cm.

We can write: 8.5 cm ≤ actual length < 9.5 cm
(That is, the actual length is greater than or equal to 8.5 cm but is less than 9.5 cm.)

A piece of string measures 40 cm when measured to the nearest 10 cm. Its smallest possible length must be 35 cm.
Its biggest possible length must be less than 45 cm.
Its actual length lies between the limits 35 cm and 45 cm.
We can write: 35 cm ≤ actual length < 45 cm

If there are, in a room, 40 people correct to the nearest 10, the smallest possible number of people in the room is 35 and the biggest possible number of people in the room is 44.
We can write: 35 ≤ actual number of people ≤ 44
This is the same as: 35 ≤ actual number of people < 45

Compare the two examples (the string and the people). The measurements of length are *continuous*, but the number of people is a *discrete* value (that is, the number of people is an exact number). Both types of data have an exact lower limit (35 in the example). However, only discrete data has an exact upper limit. (For the string, all we can say is that its length is less than 45 cm; but for the number of people we can give an exact highest possible number, 44 in this example.)

Exercise 3

1. There were, in the hall, 600 people correct to the nearest 100. Write the lowest and the highest possible number of people in the hall.

2. The attendance at a concert was 570 correct to the nearest 10. Write the lowest and the highest possible attendance.

3. The attendance at a match was 16 000 correct to the nearest 1000. Write the lowest and highest possible attendance.

4. The number of sweets in a packet was 25 correct to the nearest 5. Write the lowest and highest possible number of sweets.

5. There were 70 beads in a bag when estimated to the nearest 10. Write the lowest and highest possible number of beads.

6. The conchologist had 60 shells when the number was estimated to the nearest 5. Write the lowest and highest possible number of shells.

7. The numismatist said he had collected 120 coins give or take 10. Write the lowest and highest possible number of coins.

8. A philatelist had collected 12 400 stamps to the nearest 100. Write the lowest and highest possible number of stamps.

Exercise 4

For each value given, write the limits between which the given value lies:

A *e.g.* 14 m to the nearest metre,
14 m lies between the limits 13.5 and 14.5.

1. 18 m to the nearest metre,
2. 6 cm to the nearest centimetre,
3. 50 cm to the nearest 10 cm,
4. 260 km to the nearest 10 km,
5. 800 mℓ correct to the nearest 100 mℓ,
6. 750 yd to the nearest 50 yd,
7. 180 min to the nearest 20 min,
8. 35 ℓ correct to the nearest 5 ℓ.

B *e.g.* State the limits between which 3.8 cm lies.
3.8 cm lies between the limits 3.75 cm and 3.85 cm.

1. 47 kg	**3.** 23 pt	**5.** 326 g	**7.** 96 miles
2. 108 lb	**4.** 54 s	**6.** 8 cm	**8.** 645 m

Exercise 5

1. A length of rope measures 12 m correct to the nearest metre. Write the limits between which the actual length lies.

2. Using a map, a driver estimated a journey to be 170 miles correct to the nearest 10 miles. Write the limits between which the true distance lies.

3. Olwyn bought 150 g of nuts correct to the nearest 10 g. Write the limits between which the actual mass lies.

4. Vince travelled 300 km to the nearest 20 km. Write the limits between which the actual distance lies.

5. A house cost £28 000 to the nearest £1000. Between what limits does its actual cost lie?

6. The potatoes weighed 4.3 kg to the nearest tenth of a kilogram. Between what limits does its true mass lie?

7. Cindy estimated a time of 45 s to within 5 s accuracy. Between what limits did her estimate lie?

8. A builder measured a distance of 56.8 m to the nearest tenth of a metre. Write the limits between which the actual distance lies.

Exercise 6

1. A rectangular room measures 5 m by 4 m, where each measurement is correct to the nearest metre:

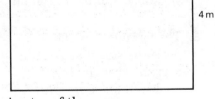

   (a) Write the limits between which the actual length lies.
   (b) Between what limits does the actual breadth lie?
   (c) Calculate the minimum perimeter of the room.
   (d) Calculate the maximum perimeter of the room.
   (e) Calculate the minimum area of the room.
   (f) Calculate the maximum area of the room.

2. Each side of a square measures 7 cm correct to the nearest centimetre:
   (a) Between what limits does the length of each side lie?
   (b) Calculate the minimum perimeter of the square.
   (c) Calculate the maximum perimeter of the square.
   (d) Calculate the minimum area of the square.
   (e) Calculate the maximum area of the square.

3. Each side of a square measures 4 cm correct to the nearest centimetre. Between what limits does:
   (a) the length of each side lie?
   (b) the perimeter lie?
   (c) the area lie?

4. Milk is sold in cartons containing 500 mℓ correct to the nearest 10 mℓ:
   (a) Write the limits between which the amount of milk in each carton lies.

   If Mr Lockwood bought 8 cartons, calculate:
   (b) the maximum possible amount of milk bought,
   (c) the minimum possible amount of milk bought.

5. A circular pond has a radius of 2.4 m correct to one decimal place:
   (a) Between what limits does the true radius lie?
   (b) Between what limits does the true diameter lie?

   Given that the circumference of a circle $= \pi d$ and using $\pi = 3$:
   (c) Calculate the minimum possible circumference of the pond.
   (d) Calculate the maximum possible circumference of the pond.

   Given that the area of a circle $= \pi r^2$ and using $\pi = 3$:
   (e) Calculate the minimum possible area of the pond.
   (f) Calculate the maximum possible area of the pond.

6. The formula $A = 180 - B$ gives the size of angle A in degrees when angle B is known. If angle $B = 52°$ correct to the nearest degree:
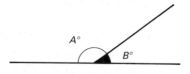
   (a) Between what limits does the actual size of angle B lie?
   (b) Calculate the minimum possible size of angle A.
   (c) Calculate the minimum possible size of angle B.

7. 8.5 and 6.2 are both correct to two significant figures:
   (a) Between what limits does 8.5 lie?
   (b) Between what limits does 6.2 lie?

   Calculate the limits of accuracy of the calculations:
   (c) $8.5 + 6.2$ (e) 8.5×6.2
   (d) $8.5 - 6.2$ (f) $8.5 \div 6.2$

8. The formula $v = \frac{s}{t}$ gives the average velocity v km/h of a car that travels s km in t h. A car travels 110 km give or take 2 km, in a time of 2 h to the nearest half hour.

(a) Between what limits does the distance lie?

(b) Between what limits does the time lie?

(c) Calculate the minimum possible velocity.

(d) Calculate the maximum possible velocity.

Exercise 7

A rectangular garden measures 19.8 m by 13.6 m:

1. (a) Write between which limits the actual length lies.

(b) Write between which limits the actual breadth lies.

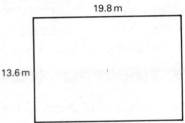

19.8 m

13.6 m

2. (a) Use the given measurements to find the area of the garden. Use a calculator and give all the digits shown.

(b) Write the area correct to three significant figures.

(c) Write the area correct to two significant figures.

3. (a) Calculate the minimum possible area of the garden using a calculator. Give all the digits shown on the calculator.

(b) Write the minimum possible area correct to three significant figures.

(c) Write the minimum possible area correct to two significant figures.

4. (a) Calculate the maximum possible area of the garden using a calculator. Give all the digits shown on the calculator.

(b) Write the maximum possible area correct to three significant figures.

(c) Write the maximum possible area correct to two significant figures.

5. Compare the answers to questions 2, 3 and 4. To how many significant figures are all these answers the same?

15

Exercise 7 shows that it is not sensible to give an answer to too many significant figures. An answer can be too accurate. It is more sensible to consider the accuracy of the numbers used in a calculation and to round an answer accordingly.

Exercise 8   Approximations to Obtain Reasonable Answers

Where appropriate, round an answer to make it sensible:

1. An answer was shown on a calculator as:

$$\boxed{91.86}$$

If the answer was in pence, round it to make it sensible.

2. A pack of 6 cards cost 59 p. Find the cost of one card.

3. A pack of 12 coloured pencils cost £1.99. Find the cost of one coloured pencil.

4. 24 felt-tipped pens cost £3.40. What is the cost of one pen?

5. A pack of 4 one-litre cartons of orange juice was sold for £1.95. Find the cost of one carton.

6. A pack of 4 bars of soap cost 99 p. Find the cost of one bar of soap.

7. A pack containing 5 tubes of sweets cost 79 p. Find the cost of one tube of sweets.

8. A pack of 8 cartons of yoghurt cost £1.79. Find the cost of one carton.

Exercise 9

Throughout this exercise, work with one significant figure:

1. Anthea saved £8.95 per month for 8 months. Estimate the total amount saved.

2. Estimate the cost of 21 m² of carpet at £9.85 per square metre.

16

3. A bus driver drove 794 miles in 4 days. Estimate the average distance travelled per day.

4. Mr Baines obtained two estimates, one for £871.50 and the other for £683. Estimate the difference between the estimates.

5. Niall saved the following sums of money:
   £13.25, £28.40, £19.70, £38.60, £20.52
   Estimate his total savings.

6. It was estimated that each pupil would use 5 sheets of paper in an exam. Estimate the number of sheets of paper needed by 913 pupils.

Appropriate Checks of Accuracy

One check of accuracy is to *estimate* an answer as in the previous exercise.

Another check of accuracy is to find the limits between which an answer should lie, as in Exercise 6, or to estimate some limits as in book 3G, pp. 16–18.

A further check of accuracy is to work out what the last digit in the answer to a calculation should be.

For example, consider the calculation 2.9×3.7

$$9 \times 7 = 6\underline{3}$$

Since $9 \times 7 = 6\underline{3}$, the last digit in the answer to 2.9×3.7 is $\underline{3}$.

The last digit in the answer to 46×84 is $\underline{4}$

$$\text{Since } 6 \times 4 = 2\underline{4}$$

Another check of accuracy is to reverse a calculation. However, this check entails as much work as working out the question.

For example, $2.9 \times 3.7 = 10.73$
then $10.73 \div 3.7$ should equal 2.9,
and $10.73 \div 2.9$ should equal 3.7.

Consider the calculation 4.8×7.2 (Answer $= 34.56$). Using some of the above checks:

$4.8 \times 7.2 \approx 5 \times 7 = 35$ Estimate $= 35$
Since $8 \times 2 = 1\underline{6}$ Last digit $= 6$

$4 \times 7 = 28$ and $5 \times 8 = 40$. The answer lies between 28 and 40. These checks suggest that the answer, 34.56, is correct.

Since $34.56 \div 7.2 = 4.8$, the answer is definitely correct.

Exercise 10

A Write the units digits of the answers to the following calculations:

1. 27×32	**5.** 86×451	**9.** $649 - 286$
2. 15×83	**6.** $413 + 728$	**10.** $592 - 347$
3. 98×47	**7.** 145×94	**11.** 203×56
4. 62×96	**8.** $396 + 507$	**12.** 762×649

B Write the last digit of the answer to each calculation:

1. 4.3×6.9	**5.** 3.2×7.5	**9.** 50×1.7
2. 6.8×24	**6.** 81×4.7	**10.** 30.6×8.8
3. 9.5×3.6	**7.** 74.5×65	**11.** 23.2×92.4
4. 2.4×5.1	**8.** 93×2.7	**12.** 69.4×35.7

C Write whether the given statement is 'TRUE' or 'FALSE':
1. The answer to 54×29 ends in 6.
2. The answer to 1.7×3.5 ends in 0.
3. The answer to 6.7×16 ends in 8.
4. The answer to 3.86×2.9 ends in 4.
5. The answer to 5.02×9.8 ends in 2.

D Choose the correct answer:

1. $59 \times 38 = \boxed{?}$
   A. 1572   B. 7215   C. 222   D. 2242

2. $84 \times 1.6 = \boxed{?}$
   A. 134.4   B. 84.24   C. 104.8   D. 84.16

3. $75 \times 69 = \boxed{?}$
   A. 5175   B. 4249   C. 4245   D. 465

4. $2.3 \times 94 = \boxed{?}$
   A. 181.2   B. 216.6   C. 216.2   D. 181.8

Exercise 11

Check each answer by reversing the calculation:

e.g. 1 $34.65 + 129.87 = 164.52$
$164.52 - 129.87 = 34.65$ <u>CORRECT</u>

e.g. 2 $3.9 \times 7.6 = 29.64$
$29.64 \div 7.6 = 3.9$ <u>CORRECT</u>

e.g. 3 $2.4 \times 3.8 = 10.32$
$10.32 \div 3.8 \neq 2.4$ <u>WRONG</u>

1. $5.9 \times 3.7 = 21.83$
2. $857 + 548 = 1405$
3. $784 - 288 = 486$
4. $23.5 + 14.9 = 38.4$
5. $200.3 - 185.4 = 24.9$
6. $47.6 \div 8.5 = 5.6$
7. $547.8 + 682.7 = 1130.5$
8. $96 \times 3.4 = 316.4$
9. $620.7 - 299.8 = 320.9$
10. $7.548 \div 1.02 = 7.9$

3 Types of Number

1. Consider the numbers 2, 3, 5, 8, 12, 17:
   - (a) Which of the numbers are even?
   - (b) Which of the numbers are prime?
   - (c) Which of the numbers are multiples of 3?
   - (d) Which of the numbers are factors of 24?
   - (e) Which three of the numbers add up to 27?
   - (f) If the numbers in the given order form a sequence, what are the next two numbers in that sequence?

2. The first four triangular numbers are 1, 3, 6, 10:
   - (a) What is the fifth triangular number?
   - (b) Draw diagrams to show why these numbers are called triangular numbers.

3. Write down all the even numbers that are factors of 72.

4. 1, 7 and 203 are all factors of 203. Write down another factor of 203.

5. Consider the numbers 3, 9, 15, 18, 22, 30, 41, 45, 57, 68:
   - (a) Which of the numbers are multiples of 5?
   - (b) Which of the numbers would become multiples of 5 if 3 was added?
   - (c) Which of the numbers are prime?
   - (d) Which of the numbers would be prime if 4 was added?
   - (e) Which of the numbers have 3 as a factor?

6. The sum of the digits of a 2-digit prime number is 8. Find three such prime numbers.

7. What is the smallest number that should be added to 93 to make it a multiple of 8?

8. Consider the numbers 86, 53, 21, 41, 45, 56, 31, 42:

    (a) Which pair of numbers in the list total 77?

    (b) 53 + $\boxed{?}$ = a multiple of 5. Find the missing number from the given list of numbers.

9. Write all the factors of 36. Underline those that are prime numbers.

10. Which one of the following numbers is prime?

    A. 39   B. 49   C. 57   D. 67   E. 81

11. Write all the multiples of 9 that lie between 100 and 150.

12. Write each of the following numbers as a product of prime factors:

    (a) 40   (b) 42   (c) 64   (d) 225   (e) 420

Exercise 2

1. Consider the numbers 2, 5, 8, 10 and 12:

    (a) Find a number n in the list such that $n = \sqrt{25}$.

    (b) Find numbers p and q in the list such that $p = 4q$.

2. Consider the numbers 1, 2, 4, 6, 7, 8, 9, 12.

    From the given numbers, write:

    (a) a prime number,

    (b) five factors of 56,

    (c) three multiples of 4,

    (d) a number x where $x = \sqrt{64}$,

    (e) a number y where $y^2 = 81$,

    (f) two numbers p and q where $p = \sqrt{q}$ and $q = \sqrt{16}$.

3. Consider the numbers 2, 3, 4, 7, 9, 11, 15.

    From the given numbers, find:

    (a) numbers a and b such that $3(a - b) = 27$,

    (b) numbers c and d such that $2c - d = 10$,

    (c) numbers e, f and g such that $e(f + g) = 24$.

Exercise 3   Divisibility

1. Which of the following numbers are exactly divisible by 9?

    (a) 63   (b) 84   (c) 112   (d) 127   (e) 144   (f) 172   (g) 189

2. Consider the numbers:

2, 4, 6, 9, 12, 15, 18, 24, 27, 30, 32, 38, 42, 51, 55, 56, 62, 69, 78
Which of the given numbers are exactly divisible by:
(*a*) 5?   (*b*) 3?   (*c*) 4?   (*d*) 6?

3. Consider the numbers:

14, 16, 21, 25, 45, 52, 84, 96, 108, 125, 140, 164, 192, 286
Which of the given numbers are exactly divisible by:
(*a*) 5?   (*b*) 3?   (*c*) 4?   (*d*) 6?

Exercise 4   Common Factors and Common Multiples

A 1. (*a*) List the factors of 18.
     (*b*) List the factors of 30.
     (*c*) List the factors of 18 that are also factors of 30 (that is, the common factors of 18 and 30).
     (*d*) Write down the highest common factor of 18 and 30.

2. (*a*) List the factors of 15.
     (*b*) List the factors of 30.
     (*c*) List the common factors of 15 and 30.
     (*d*) Write down the highest common factor of 15 and 30.

3. List the common factors of:
     (*a*) 20 and 28,   (*b*) 72 and 84,   (*c*) 60 and 75.

4. Write down the highest common factor of each pair of numbers in question 3.

B 1. (*a*) List the multiples of 6 that are less than 100.
     (*b*) List the multiples of 5 that are less than 100.
     (*c*) List the multiples of 6 that are less than 100 and are also multiples of 5 (the common multiples of 6 and 5).

2. List the common multiples of the following (only list the common multiples as far as 100):
     (*a*) 5 and 8,   (*b*) 9 and 15,   (*c*) 10 and 20.

3. Write the lowest common multiple of each pair of numbers in question 2.

Exercise 5

1. Here is a number line that shows some different types of number:

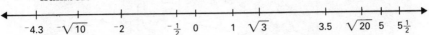

From the numbers marked on the above line, write the:
   (a) natural numbers,
   (b) whole numbers,
   (c) positive integers,
   (d) integers,
   (e) non-negative integers,
   (f) rational numbers,
   (g) positive rational numbers,
   (h) irrational numbers.

2. Copy the following number line:

On your number line mark and label:
   (a) the natural numbers 3 and 5,
   (b) the integers $^-4$, $^-1$ and 2,
   (c) the rational numbers $\frac{3}{4}$, $^-0.5$, 4.5 and $^-2\frac{3}{4}$,
   (d) the irrational numbers $^+\sqrt{2}$, $^+\sqrt{8}$, $^+\sqrt{14}$, $^-\sqrt{5}$ and $^-\sqrt{22}$.

Exercise 6

For each statement, write whether it is 'ALWAYS ODD', 'ALWAYS EVEN' or 'COULD BE ODD OR EVEN':

1. the sum of two odd numbers,

2. the sum of two even numbers,

3. the sum of an odd and an even number,

4. the product of two odd numbers,

5. the product of two even numbers,

6. the product of an even and an odd number,

7. the sum of three consecutive integers,

8. the sum of four consecutive integers.

Directed Numbers in Practical Situations

Exercise 7

Zone times are the standard times kept on land and sea compared with 12 noon Greenwich Mean Time (GMT). Daylight saving time is not shown on the map.

Time Zones

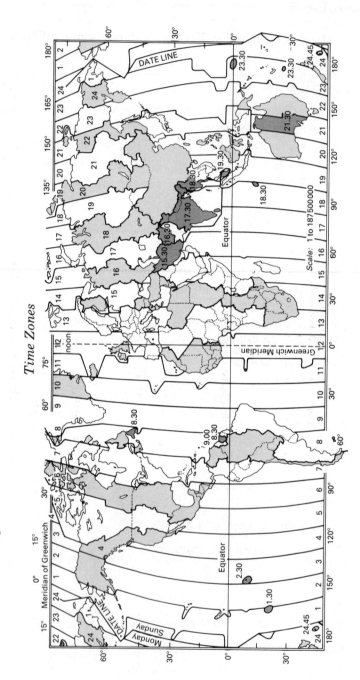

Zone Times

Abu Dhabi	+ 4	Bern*	+ 1	Copenhagen*	+ 1
Adelaide*	+ 9½	Bombay	+ 5½	Dubai	+ 4
Algiers	+ 1	Brussels*	+ 1	Helsinki*	+ 2
Amsterdam*	+ 2	Bucharest*	+ 2	Honk Kong	+ 8
Athens*	+ 2	Budapest*	+ 1	Istanbul	+ 3
Auckland*	+12	Buenos Aires	− 3	Jerusalem*	+ 2
Beijing	+ 8	Cairo*	+ 2	Karachi	+ 5
Beirut*	+ 2	Calcutta	+ 5½	Lagos	+ 1
Belgrade*	+ 1	Cape Town	+ 2	Lima	− 5
Berlin*	+ 1	Chicago*	− 6	Lisbon*	0

Los Angeles*	− 8	Paris*	+ 1	Stockholm*	+ 1
Madras	+ 5½	Perth*	+ 8	Sydney*	+10
Madrid*	+ 1	Prague*	+ 1	Tehran	+ 3½
Melbourne*	+10	Rangoon	+ 6½	Tokyo	+ 9
Mexico City	− 6	Rio de Janeiro	− 3	Toronto*	− 5
Moscow*	+ 3	Rome*	+ 1	Tunis	+ 1
Nairobi	+ 3	San Francisco*	− 8	Vancouver*	− 8
New York*	− 5	Santiago*	− 4	Vienna*	+ 1
Oslo*	+ 1	Singapore	+ 8	Warsaw*	+ 1
Ottawa*	− 5	Sofia*	+ 2	Winnipeg*	− 6

Answer the following questions using the table above (ignore daylight saving time):

1. Which place is 5 h ahead of GMT?

2. Which places are 6 h behind GMT?

3. How many hours behind GMT is New York?

4. How many hours behind Rio de Janeiro is San Francisco?

5. How many hours behind Sydney is Paris?

6. How many hours behind Jerusalem is Toronto?

7. How many hours ahead of Budapest is Perth?

8. How many hours ahead of Vancouver is Buenos Aires?

9. How many hours ahead of Lima is Athens?

10. Write the names of the places that are behind Santiago in time and, next to each name, write how many hours behind Santiago that place is.

World Standard Times (compared with GMT)
In certain areas*, daylight saving time operates for part of the year. As with British Summer Time, this is generally one hour ahead of local standard time, from March to October (October to March in the southern hemisphere).

Exercise 8

The table shows the share prices of several stores (correct at the time of writing).

High	Low	Company	Price	+/-	High	Low	Company	Price	+/-
95	58	Aquascutum	68	− 1	316	183	Harris Qwy	195	− 5
240	160	Ashley (L)	183 1/2	− 1 1/2	33	23	Helene Lon	29 1/2	
208	130	Bentalls	154	− 2	231	169 1/2	Marks & Sp	203	− 4
287 1/2	219	Boots	274 1/2	− 3 1/2	297	188	Next	287	+ 1
354	244	Burton	251	− 9	385	250	Reed (Aus)	365	− 5
265	149	Comb Eng	222	− 8	131	101	Ryman	128	− 1
438	218 1/2	Dixons	331 1/2	− 6 1/2	148 1/2	104	Sears	129 1/2	− 1/2
18 1/2	4	Eagle Tst	18 1/4		364	240	Smith (WH)	305	− 5
226	136	Empire Sts	194	− 1	365	256 1/2	Storehouse	291	− 10
225	106	Fine Art	223	− 1	146 1/2	133	Virgin	140 1/2	− 1 1/2
£16 7/8	880	GUS	£16 3/8	− 1/8	925	438	Woolworth	751	− 9

The highest price of one WH Smith share was 364 p, while the lowest price was 240 p. One WH Smith share now costs 305 p. Yesterday it cost 310 p. Its price has fallen 5 p (shown by ⁻5 in the table).

Answer the following from the given table:

1. (a) What was the highest price of one Burton share?
   (b) What is the current price of one Burton share?
   (c) What was yesterday's price of one Burton share?

2. (a) What is the current price of one Woolworth share?
   (b) What was yesterday's price of one Woolworth share?

3. What was yesterday's price of:
   (a) one Next share?   (c) one Dixons share?
   (b) one Marks & Spencer (d) one Boots share?
   share?

4. (a) One Great Universal Stores (GUS) share is now priced at £16$\frac{3}{8}$. Write that amount in pounds and pence correct to the nearest penny.
   (b) What was yesterday's price, in pounds and pence, of one GUS share?

5. If you owned 1000 Austin Reed (Reed (Aus)) shares, what would your 'loss' be when comparing yesterday's prices with today's?

6. On Monday, a share was priced at 328 p. Throughout the week the daily changes were ⁻3, ⁻5, ⁺1, ⁻4, ⁺2. What price was the share after the changes?

Exercise 9

1. Write the temperatures shown on the given thermometers:

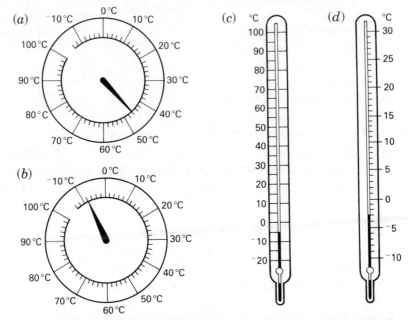

2. The temperature fell from 2 °C to ⁻5 °C. Through how many degrees had it fallen?

3. A thermometer showed the temperature to be ⁻3 °C. If it then rose by 8 °C, what would the new temperature be?

4. The temperature in Helsinki was ⁻15 °C. If it then dropped by 8 °C, what was the new temperature?

5. The temperature was 3 °C. During the night the temperature dropped by 7 °C. What was the new temperature?

6. Consider the temperatures:
    ⁻4 °C, 7 °C, ⁻2 °C, ⁻1 °C, 3 °C
   (a) Which of the temperatures are less than ⁻3 °C?
   (b) Which is the third highest temperature shown?

7. Consider the temperatures:
    4 °C, ⁻5 °C, 1.6 °C, ⁻0.8 °C, ⁻3.4 °C, 2 °C, ⁻1.7 °C
   (a) Which of the temperatures are less than ⁻2 °C?
   (b) Write the temperatures in order, giving the coldest first.
   (c) Which is the third lowest temperature?

8. The table shows the maximum and minimum temperatures at five places during 24 h in January:

Place	Max. temp. (°C)	Min. temp. (°C)
Edinburgh	3	$^-5$
Manchester	4	$^-4$
Dublin	5	$^-1$
Tenby	6	$^-2$
Penzance	7	$^-1$

(a) Which place recorded the lowest temperature?

(b) What is the difference between Tenby's highest and lowest temperatures?

(c) Calculate the mean of the maximum temperatures at the five places.

(d) Calculate the mean of the minimum temperatures at the five places.

Exercise 10   The Idea of Inequality of Numbers

A Copy the following but replace each box with the words 'IS EQUAL TO', 'IS LESS THAN' or 'IS GREATER THAN' to make the statement correct:

1. $^-6$? 2

2. 2.5 ? $2\frac{1}{2}$

3. 3.5 ? $^-3\frac{1}{2}$

4. 2 ? $^+\sqrt{7}$

5. $4\frac{3}{4}$? 4.6

6. $^-2\frac{3}{4}$? $^-2.6$

7. $^-\sqrt{12}$? $^-4$

8. $^-3$? $^-\sqrt{9}$

9. $\frac{2}{3}$? 0.67

B Copy the following but replace each box with the symbol =, < or > to make the statement correct:

1. $^-9$? $^-4$

2. $^-2.8$? $^-3$

3. $^-4\frac{1}{4}$? $^-4.25$

4. $^+\sqrt{9}$? $^-3$

5. $^-0.6$? 0.2

6 0.125 ? $\frac{1}{8}$

7. $^-3\frac{3}{4}$? $^-3.8$

8. $^-\sqrt{20}$? $^-4$

9. 5 ? $^-\sqrt{25}$

Simple Number Patterns and Sequences

Exercise 11 ════════════════════════════════ **M**

1. Look at the given number pattern:

$$1 \times 2 + 1 = 1^2 + 2$$
$$2 \times 3 + 2 = 2^2 + 4$$
$$3 \times 4 + 3 = 3^2 + 6$$
$$4 \times 5 + 4 = 4^2 + 8$$
$$5 \times a + 5 = b^2 + c$$

(a) What number does the letter a stand for?
(b) What number does the letter b stand for?
(c) What number does the letter c stand for?
(d) Write down the next line in the pattern.

2. The following pattern can be made with matches:

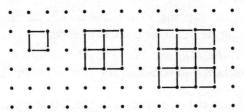

(a) On dotty paper, draw the next diagram in the pattern.
(b) Copy and complete the table to show the pattern:

Number of small squares	1	4	9	16	25
Number of matches used	4	12			

(c) Try to explain how to find the number of matches used for any size square without just simply counting.
(d) How many matches are used when there are 100 small squares in the pattern?

Exercise 12

A The following six numbers are written in order of size and form a pattern:

1, 7, 17, 31, 49, 71

1. The difference between the first and second numbers is $7 - 1 = 6$. The difference between the second and third numbers is $17 - 7 = 10$.
Find the difference between:
(a) the third and fourth numbers,
(b) the fourth and fifth numbers,
(c) the fifth and sixth numbers.

2. (*a*) Form a new sequence by writing down the differences obtained in question 1, that is, write:

6, 10, (*a*), (*b*), (*c*), . . .

answers to question 1

(*b*) Find the next two terms of the new sequence obtained in part (*a*).

(*c*) By considering the above answers, find the seventh and eighth terms in the original sequence:

1, 7, 17, 31, 49, 71, ⎡?⎤, ⎡?⎤

(*d*) Explain how you obtained the two terms in part (*c*).

B Write down the next two numbers in the following patterns:

1. 4, 7, 12, 19, 28, . . .
2. 3, 9, 19, 33, 51, . . .
3. 2, 3, 6, 11, 18, . . .
4. 10, 20, 40, 80, . . .
5. 5, 14, 27, 44, 65, . . .
6. 192, 96, 48, 24, 12, . . .
7. 1.2, 1.8, 2.4, 3, 3.6, . . .
8. 0.36, 0.48, 0.6, 0.72, 0.84, . . .

Exercise 13   Rules for Generating a Pattern or Sequence ▪ **M**

A Write the first six terms of each sequence:

1. *Rule*   Multiply by 3 then add 1.
Use the numbers {1, 2, 3, 4, 5, 6}.
The sequence starts 4, 7, . . .

2. *Rule*   Double then subtract 3.
Use the numbers {4, 5, 6, 7, 8, 9}.

3. *Rule*   Multiply by 6 then subtract 4.
Use the numbers {1, 2, 3, 4, 5, 6}.

4. *Rule*   Divide by 2 then add 3.
Use the numbers {2, 3, 4, 5, 6, 7}.

5. *Rule*   Square then add 4.
Use the numbers {1, 2, 3, 4, 5, 6}.

B In the right-angled triangle shown, $p^2 = m^2 + n^2$ (Pythagoras).

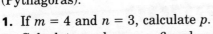

1. If $m = 4$ and $n = 3$, calculate p.
2. Calculate p when $m = 6$ and $n = 8$.
3. Calculate p when $m = 8$ and $n = 15$.
4. Copy the table:

m	n	p
4	3	
6	8	
8	15	
10	24	
12		37
	48	50
16		65
18	80	
20	99	
	120	122
24		145

5. Use your answers to questions 1, 2 and 3 to fill in the values of p in the first three rows of your table.
6. By considering the patterns in the rows and columns of the table, complete the table.
7. What is the length of the hypotenuse of a right-angled triangle whose other sides measure 1.8 cm and 8 cm?
8. What is the length of the shortest side of a right-angled triangle whose other sides measure 5 cm and 4.8 cm?

4 Computation

Efficient Use of an Electronic Calculator

Since different makes of calculator work in different ways, the explanation of some of the keys (as given in book 3G) is repeated in this book*.

Exercise 1

Carry out the following using a calculator. Always start by clearing the display.

A For each question, compare the answers to parts (*a*) and (*b*) and write what you notice:

1. Work out £6.75 − £2.25:
   (*a*) Write the answer as shown on the calculator.
   (*b*) Write the answer as an amount of money in the correct way.

2. (*a*) Key in: $\boxed{3}\boxed{\cdot}\boxed{5}\boxed{0}\boxed{+}\boxed{2}\boxed{\cdot}\boxed{7}\boxed{0}\boxed{=}$
   (*b*) Key in: $\boxed{3}\boxed{\cdot}\boxed{5}\boxed{+}\boxed{2}\boxed{\cdot}\boxed{7}\boxed{=}$

3. (*a*) Key in: $\boxed{0}\boxed{\cdot}\boxed{6}\boxed{+}\boxed{0}\boxed{\cdot}\boxed{8}\boxed{=}$
   (*b*) Key in: $\boxed{\cdot}\boxed{6}\boxed{+}\boxed{\cdot}\boxed{8}\boxed{=}$

4. (*a*) Key in: $\boxed{0}\boxed{\cdot}\boxed{0}\boxed{2}\boxed{+}\boxed{0}\boxed{\cdot}\boxed{7}\boxed{0}\boxed{=}$
   (*b*) Key in: $\boxed{\cdot}\boxed{0}\boxed{2}\boxed{+}\boxed{\cdot}\boxed{7}\boxed{=}$

B Work out the following using the fewest number of keys possible. Write the number of keys pressed.

1. £7.60 − £4.30
2. £8.70 − £1.80
3. £0.70 + £0.10
4. £0.40 + £0.08

* See Appendix 1, p. 465.

Exercise 2

Carry out the following on a calculator. Always start by clearing the display.

1. Key in: $\boxed{7}\ \boxed{\times}\ \boxed{=}$

If you obtained 49, then you can answer this question.

(a) $\boxed{4}\ \boxed{\times}\ \boxed{=}$ (c) $\boxed{5}\ \boxed{\times}\ \boxed{=}$ (e) $\boxed{1}\ \boxed{0}\ \boxed{\times}\ \boxed{=}$

(b) $\boxed{6}\ \boxed{\times}\ \boxed{=}$ (d) $\boxed{8}\ \boxed{\times}\ \boxed{=}$ (f) $\boxed{1}\ \boxed{2}\ \boxed{\times}\ \boxed{=}$

Explain what the calculator does when $\boxed{\times}\ \boxed{=}$ are pressed.

2. (a) Key in: $\boxed{3}\ \boxed{\times}\ \boxed{5}\ \boxed{=}$

    (b) Key in: $\boxed{3}\ \boxed{\times}\ \boxed{4}\ \boxed{C}\ \boxed{5}\ \boxed{=}$
                         ↑

           This might be labelled $\boxed{CE}$ or possibly $\boxed{ON|C}$.

(If you obtained the same answer to parts (a) and (b), then pressing $\boxed{C}$ must clear the previous number keyed in.)

3. (a) Key in: $\boxed{7}\ \boxed{+}\ \boxed{5}\ \boxed{=}$

    (b) Key in: $\boxed{7}\ \boxed{-}\ \boxed{+}\ \boxed{5}\ \boxed{=}$

    (You probably obtained the same answer as in part (a). If so, it shows that the previously keyed in operator is cancelled by another operator.)

Exercise 3   Calculator Constants

The following questions will not work on all calculators. Some questions will work on some calculators and other questions on other calculators. You will probably find that the whole of one section will work. It is unlikely that you should need to answer questions from both sections A and B. If nothing works you will need to read your calculator's instruction booklet. Try this first:

Key in: $\boxed{AC}\ \boxed{5}\ \boxed{\times}\ \boxed{2}\ \boxed{=}\ \boxed{4}\ \boxed{=}$

If your answer is 20 (or 8) then try section A, otherwise try section B.

A 1. If $\boxed{AC}\ \boxed{5}\ \boxed{\times}\ \boxed{2}\ \boxed{=}\ \boxed{4}\ \boxed{=}$ gives 20 than the constant 5 has been stored by the calculator together with the instruction to multiply. Any number keyed in followed by $\boxed{=}$ will then automatically be multiplied by 5. (An answer of 8 means that the stored multiplying constant is 2.)

2. Key in: $\boxed{\text{AC}}\ \boxed{5}\ \boxed{+}\ \boxed{2}\ \boxed{=}\ \boxed{4}\ \boxed{=}$

If the answer is 6 then 'add 2' has been stored as the constant. Any number keyed in followed by $\boxed{=}$ will automatically have 2 added to it. (An answer of 9 means that 'add 5' is the constant, while an answer of 4 means that this method has not worked.)

3. Key in: $\boxed{\text{AC}}\ \boxed{5}\ \boxed{-}\ \boxed{2}\ \boxed{=}\ \boxed{4}\ \boxed{=}$

An answer of 2 means that 'subtract 2' has been stored, so any number keyed in followed by $\boxed{=}$ will have 2 subtracted from it.

4. Key in: $\boxed{\text{AC}}\ \boxed{5}\ \boxed{\div}\ \boxed{2}\ \boxed{=}\ \boxed{6}\ \boxed{=}$

An answer of 3 means that 'divide by 2' has been stored, so any number keyed in followed by $\boxed{=}$ will be divided by 2.

B In the following, if your calculator has a constant key $\boxed{\text{K}}$ then follow the first example, otherwise key in the second:

1. Key in: $\boxed{\text{AC}}\ \boxed{5}\ \boxed{\times}\ \boxed{\text{K}}\ \boxed{2}\ \boxed{=}\ \boxed{4}\ \boxed{=}$

    or $\boxed{\text{AC}}\ \boxed{5}\ \boxed{\times}\ \boxed{\times}\ \boxed{2}\ \boxed{=}\ \boxed{4}\ \boxed{=}$

If the answer is 20 then 'multiply by 5' has been stored by the calculator. Any number keyed in and followed by $\boxed{=}$ will be multiplied by 5. (An answer of 8 means that the stored multiplying constant is 2.)

2. Key in: $\boxed{\text{AC}}\ \boxed{5}\ \boxed{+}\ \boxed{\text{K}}\ \boxed{2}\ \boxed{=}\ \boxed{4}\ \boxed{=}$

    or $\boxed{\text{AC}}\ \boxed{5}\ \boxed{+}\ \boxed{+}\ \boxed{2}\ \boxed{=}\ \boxed{4}\ \boxed{=}$

If the answer is 9 then 'add 5' has been stored by the calculator. Any number keyed in followed by $\boxed{=}$ will have 5 added to it. (An answer of 6 means that 'add 2' has been stored.)

3. Key in: $\boxed{\text{AC}}\ \boxed{5}\ \boxed{-}\ \boxed{\text{K}}\ \boxed{2}\ \boxed{=}\ \boxed{4}\ \boxed{=}$

    or $\boxed{\text{AC}}\ \boxed{5}\ \boxed{-}\ \boxed{-}\ \boxed{2}\ \boxed{=}\ \boxed{4}\ \boxed{=}$

If the answer is ⁻1 then 'subtract 5' has been stored, so any number keyed in followed by $\boxed{=}$ will have 5 subtracted from it. (In the above example, $4 - 5 = {}^-1$). (Note that an answer of 2 means that 'subtract 2' has been stored.)

4. Key in: $\boxed{\text{AC}}\ \boxed{5}\ \boxed{\div}\ \boxed{\text{K}}\ \boxed{2}\ \boxed{=}\ \boxed{4}\ \boxed{=}$

    or $\boxed{\text{AC}}\ \boxed{5}\ \boxed{\div}\ \boxed{\div}\ \boxed{2}\ \boxed{=}\ \boxed{4}\ \boxed{=}$

If the answer is 0.8 then 'divide by 5' has been stored, so any number keyed in followed by $\boxed{=}$ will be divided by 5. (In the above example, $4 \div 5 = 0.8$). (Note that an answer of 2 means that 'divide by 2' has been stored.)

C Practise whichever method works on your calculator. Use some examples of your own.

D Try these. List the numbers shown on the calculator's display and write what you notice about them.

1. (a) $\boxed{\text{AC}}\ \boxed{2}\ \boxed{\times}\ \boxed{=}\ \boxed{=}\ \boxed{=}\ \boxed{=}\ \boxed{=}\ \boxed{=}\ \boxed{=}$

    (b) $\boxed{\text{AC}}\ \boxed{2}\ \boxed{\times}\ \boxed{\text{K}}\ \boxed{=}\ \boxed{=}\ \boxed{=}\ \boxed{=}\ \boxed{=}\ \boxed{=}$

    (c) $\boxed{\text{AC}}\ \boxed{2}\ \boxed{\times}\ \boxed{\times}\ \boxed{=}\ \boxed{=}\ \boxed{=}\ \boxed{=}\ \boxed{=}\ \boxed{=}$

2. (a) $\boxed{\text{AC}}\ \boxed{2}\ \boxed{+}\ \boxed{=}\ \boxed{=}\ \boxed{=}\ \boxed{=}\ \boxed{=}\ \boxed{=}\ \boxed{=}$

    (b) $\boxed{\text{AC}}\ \boxed{2}\ \boxed{+}\ \boxed{\text{K}}\ \boxed{=}\ \boxed{=}\ \boxed{=}\ \boxed{=}\ \boxed{=}\ \boxed{=}$

    (c) $\boxed{\text{AC}}\ \boxed{2}\ \boxed{+}\ \boxed{+}\ \boxed{=}\ \boxed{=}\ \boxed{=}\ \boxed{=}\ \boxed{=}\ \boxed{=}$

Exercise 4   Using a Calculator's Memory

A If your calculator does not have the keys used in this exercise, then see Appendix 1 on p. 465. Clear the memory and the display of your calculator before answering each question.

1. Key in: $\boxed{4}\ \boxed{\text{M+}}\ \boxed{\text{M+}}\ \boxed{\text{M+}}$

Press $\boxed{\text{MR}}$ to read what is stored in the memory. Try to explain why that number is stored in the memory.

2. Key in: $\boxed{1}\ \boxed{0}\ \boxed{\text{M+}}\ \boxed{\text{M+}}\ \boxed{\text{M+}}\ \boxed{\text{M+}}$

Read the memory and give a reason for the number being stored there.

B Total the following supermarket till receipts using the method given in the example:

e.g. To add the column of figures shown, first clear the memory and the display of your calculator then key in:

$\boxed{\cdot}\ \boxed{4}\ \boxed{6}\ \boxed{\text{M+}}\ \boxed{2}\ \boxed{\cdot}\ \boxed{1}\ \boxed{7}\ \boxed{\text{M+}}\ \boxed{\cdot}\ \boxed{8}$

$\boxed{\text{M+}}\ \boxed{\cdot}\ \boxed{4}\ \boxed{9}\ \boxed{\text{M+}}\ \boxed{\text{M+}}\ \boxed{\text{M+}}\ \boxed{1}\ \boxed{\cdot}\ \boxed{3}\ \boxed{\text{M+}}$

$\boxed{\cdot}\ \boxed{7}\ \boxed{6}\ \boxed{\text{M+}}\ \boxed{\text{M+}}\ \boxed{\cdot}\ \boxed{2}\ \boxed{5}\ \boxed{\text{M+}}\ \boxed{\text{MR}}$

0.46
2.17
0.80
0.49
0.49
0.49
1.30
0.76
0.76
0.25

Total = £7.97

1. 0.85	**2.** .42	**3.** 2.50	**4.** 0.92
0.29	.42	.91	0.26
0.29	.76	.36	0.31
1.76	.89	.36	0.75
3.42	2.40	.36	0.84
0.51	.16	1.87	0.84
0.51	.16	1.87	0.75
0.51	1.07	.09	0.58
2.60		.74	0.44

C Find out what is left in your calculator's memory after carrying out the following steps. Do not forget to clear the memory and the display before each question.

1. $\boxed{8}$ $\boxed{\text{M+}}$ $\boxed{\text{M−}}$

2. $\boxed{7}$ $\boxed{\text{M+}}$ $\boxed{\text{M+}}$ $\boxed{\text{M+}}$ $\boxed{\text{M−}}$

3. $\boxed{6}$ $\boxed{\text{M+}}$ $\boxed{9}$ $\boxed{\text{M+}}$ $\boxed{\text{M−}}$ $\boxed{8}$ $\boxed{\text{M+}}$

4. $\boxed{2}$ $\boxed{\cdot}$ $\boxed{7}$ $\boxed{\text{M+}}$ $\boxed{3}$ $\boxed{\cdot}$ $\boxed{2}$ $\boxed{6}$ $\boxed{\text{M+}}$ $\boxed{\text{M−}}$ $\boxed{3}$ $\boxed{\cdot}$ $\boxed{2}$ $\boxed{5}$ $\boxed{\text{M+}}$

Explain what $\boxed{\text{M−}}$ does.

Order of Operations

Exercise 5

A Find, without a calculator, the value of:
1. (*a*) 3 lots of 5,   (*b*) 3 × 5.

2. (*a*) 4 added to 3 lots of 5,   (*b*) 4 + 3 × 5.

B Key the following into a calculator in the given order, then press $\boxed{=}$ to find the answers:
1. (*a*) 4 × 3 + 6   **3.** (*a*) 4 + 12 ÷ 2
     (*b*) 6 + 4 × 3   (*b*) 12 ÷ 2 + 4

2. (*a*) 7 + 5 × 2   **4.** (*a*) 18 ÷ 3 + 6
     (*b*) 5 × 2 + 7   (*b*) 6 + 18 ÷ 3

If you got the same answers to parts (*a*) and (*b*) of each question, then your calculator must sort out the correct order of operations for you.

If you got different answers, then you may need to rearrange the order before using the calculator.

For example, $8 + 7 \times 3$ becomes $7 \times 3 + 8$.

Note Multiplication is worked out *before* addition.

Also $2 + 8 \div 4$ becomes $8 \div 4 + 2$

Note Division is worked out before addition.

Exercise 6

A Calculators should not be used in this part of the exercise:

1. (*a*) Work out $9 - 3 + 4$.   (Work from the left.)
   (*b*) Work out $9 - (3 + 4)$.   (Work out the brackets first.)

2. (*a*) Work out $15 \div 3 + 2$.
   (*b*) Work out $15 \div (3 + 2)$.

3. (*a*) Work out $24 \div 3 \times 2$.
   (*b*) Work out $24 \div (3 \times 2)$.

B Part A shows how the use of brackets can affect the answer to a calculation. If your calculator has parentheses (brackets) on it then repeat part A using a calculator.

C Work out the following:

1. $9 + 14 \div 2$

2. $30 - 7 \times 3$

3. $(30 - 7) \times 3$

4. $26 - 8 - 3$

5. $41 - (19 - 2)$

6. $(12 + 8) \div 4$

7. $40 \div (20 \div 4)$

8. $9 + 4 \times 6 - 11$

9. $(8 - 5) \times (2 + 7)$

10 $(21 + 9) \div (11 - 5)$

D Copy the following. *Where necessary*, insert brackets to make the statements correct.

1. $4 + 6 \times 3 = 30$

2. $7 + 2 \times 4 = 15$

3. $19 - 8 - 3 = 14$

4. $5 \times 9 - 4 = 25$

5. $12 \div 6 + 2 = 4$

6. $24 - 15 + 3 = 6$

7. $7 \times 4 + 2 = 30$

8. $48 \div 6 \times 2 = 16$

9. $32 \div 8 \div 2 = 8$

10. $36 - 12 \div 3 - 1 = 7$

11. $8 - 3 \times 2 + 4 = 30$

12. $12 - 5 \times 10 - 3 = 49$

E 1. The statement $9 \times (8 + 4) = 36$ is incorrect. Copy it, but change one operator to make it correct.

2. $(7 - 3) \times (5 + 2) = 70$ is incorrect. Copy it, but change one operator to make it correct.

3. Selina used a calculator to work out $(9 - 3) \times (4 + 8)$:
    (*a*) What should the answer be?
    (*b*) If she accidently pressed $\boxed{+}$ instead of $\boxed{-}$, what answer did she get?

4. (*a*) Work out $7 \times 4 + 3$.
    (*b*) What would the answer be to the calculation in part (*a*) if the operators $\times$ and $+$ were interchanged?

5. Albert worked out $(9 + 3) \times (7 - 4)$ on a calculator:
    (*a*) What answer should he have got?
    (*b*) If Albert forgot to key in the brackets (and his calculator gave the correct answer to that which was keyed in), what answer was shown on the calculator?

Vulgar, Decimal and Percentage Fractions

Exercise 7

1. Write the following vulgar fractions (i) as decimals (ii) as percentages:

(*a*) $\dfrac{13}{20}$ (*b*) $\dfrac{7}{8}$ (*c*) $\dfrac{27}{45}$ (*d*) $\dfrac{21}{56}$ (*e*) $\dfrac{2}{3}$

2. Change the following decimals (i) to vulgar fractions (in their simplest form) (ii) to percentages:

(*a*) 0.8   (*b*) 0.96   (*c*) 0.625   (*d*) 0.675   (*e*) 0.005

3. Change the following percentages (i) to decimals (ii) to vulgar fractions in their simplest form:

(*a*) 78%   (*b*) 48%   (*c*) 49%   (*d*) 6%   (*e*) 12.5%

4. Write the following percentages as decimals:

(*a*) 37%   (*b*) 8%   (*c*) 5.9%   (*d*) 8.71%   (*e*) 15.08%

5. Three-quarters of the pupils were learning a foreign language. What percentage was that?

6. At a certain school, 6 lessons out of 40 are maths lessons. What percentage is this?

7. Alice did two tests. In the first she got 33 out of 40, and in the second she got 22 out of 25.
   (a) Write the first mark, $\frac{33}{40}$, as a percentage.
   (b) Write the second mark, $\frac{22}{25}$, as a percentage.
   (c) In which test did Alice do better?

8. There were 450 seats in a school hall. 360 people attended a concert in the hall.
   (a) What fraction of the seats were filled? (Give the answer in its simplest form.)
   (b) What percentage of the seats were filled?

9. A car lost 45% of its value. Write this percentage as a vulgar fraction in its simplest form.

Exercise 8 ================================== **M**

Give answers in their simplest forms:

1.

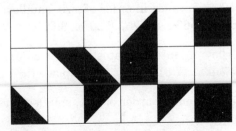

   (a) What fraction of the rectangle is shaded?
   (b) What fraction is unshaded?
   (c) Copy the given diagram.
      Shade some more parts of your copy so that, altogether, $\frac{2}{3}$ of the rectangle is shaded.

2. (a) What fraction of the clock-face has been shaded?

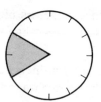

(b) Copy the diagram and shade some more sectors of your diagram so that, altogether, $\frac{1}{3}$ of the clock-face is shaded.

3. The diagrams show two different nets of a cube. For each, write what fraction of the whole diagram has been shaded:

(a)

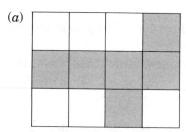

(b)

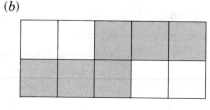

4. What percentages of the rectangles in question 3 have been shaded?

Exercise 9

1. Write these numbers in order of size, smallest first:
0.442, 0.44, 0.424, 0.404, 0.448

2. Write these percentages in order of size, smallest first:
8.76%, 8.56%, 8.67%, 8.65%, 8.57%

3. Write the following interest rates in order of size, highest first:
7.56% p.a., 7.61% p.a., 7.52% p.a., 7.6% p.a.

4. Write these fractions in order of size, smallest first:
$$\frac{3}{8}, \frac{5}{16}, \frac{7}{8}, \frac{3}{4}, \frac{1}{2}, \frac{1}{8}, \frac{1}{4}, \frac{9}{16}$$

5. By first changing the given vulgar fractions to decimals, find which of the two is the larger:

(a) $\frac{1}{20}$ or $\frac{5}{80}$ (b) $\frac{17}{20}$ or $\frac{21}{25}$ (c) $\frac{5}{12}$ or $\frac{2}{5}$

Since $\frac{3}{4}$ can be changed to a decimal by working out $3 \div 4$
and since $8\frac{3}{4} = 8 + \frac{3}{4}$

then $8\frac{3}{4} = 8 + 3 \div 4$

This can be worked out on a calculator by keying in:

$\boxed{3}\ \boxed{\div}\ \boxed{4}\ \boxed{+}\ \boxed{8}\ \boxed{=}$ (or $\boxed{8}\ \boxed{+}\ \boxed{3}\ \boxed{\div}\ \boxed{4}\ \boxed{=}$ if your
calculator sorts out the order of the calculation for you).
Try both methods. (The answer should be 8.75.)

Exercise 10

A Write the following mixed numbers as decimals. If an answer has more than three decimal places, round it off to three decimal places.

1. $2\frac{3}{4}$ **2.** $1\frac{7}{8}$ **3.** $5\frac{4}{9}$ **4.** $9\frac{2}{5}$ **5.** $5\frac{2}{7}$

B 1. A manufacturer made hats in the following sizes:

$$7\frac{1}{4},\ 8,\ 6\frac{3}{4},\ 7\frac{1}{2},\ 7\frac{3}{4},\ 7$$

Write these sizes in order, giving the smallest first.

2. A shop sold the following sizes of hats:

$$6\frac{7}{8},\ 7\frac{1}{8},\ 7\frac{1}{4},\ 6\frac{5}{8},\ 7,\ 6\frac{3}{4},\ 7\frac{1}{2}$$

Write these sizes in order, giving the largest first.

3. Write the following interest rates in order of size, giving the smallest first:

$$8\frac{3}{4}\%,\ 8.7\%,\ 8.68\%,\ 8\frac{7}{8}\%,\ 8\frac{5}{8}\%,\ 8.71\%$$

4. Which of the following numbers are bigger than $12\frac{3}{4}$?
12.71, 12.8, 12.70, 12.57, 12.76, 12.97

5. I have a set of drill bits. Their sizes range from $\frac{1}{16}$ in to $\frac{1}{4}$ in.
If the sizes increase in intervals of one thirty-second of an inch:
(*a*) How many drill bits are there in the set?
(*b*) What size is the third largest drill bit?

41

MISCELLANEOUS QUESTIONS USING THE FOUR RULES

Number

Exercise 11 M

1. Copy the following, but write the correct numbers in place of the question marks:

(a)
```
    ?  7  9  ?
 +  6  1  ?  8
 ─────────────
 1  0  ?  8  1
```

(c)
```
    ?  8  ?  6
 ×           7
 ─────────────
 1  9  ?  5  ?
```

(b)
```
    6  ?  3  7
 -  2  5  ?  4
 ─────────────
    ?  6  5  ?
```

(d)
```
          5  9  ?
 4) 2  ?  7  2
```

2. (a) There were 9 rows of 14 desks set out for an exam. How many desks was that altogether?
   (b) If the desks in part (a) were set out in 18 equal-length rows, how many desks would there be in each row?

3. A football team got an average of about 20 000 spectators to each of their matches. At that rate, how many matches would it take for the total attendance to reach three million?

4. There were three different choices of fruit juice for a school lunch. The number of cartons sold during a particular week are shown in the table below.

	Mon	Tue	Wed	Thur	Fri
Orange	67	52	48	64	
Apple	45	38	44		49
Pineapple	39	49		35	32
Daily totals	151		148	147	140

(a) What were the total sales for Tuesday?

(b) How many cartons of pineapple juice were sold on Wednesday?

(c) How many cartons of apple juice were sold on Thursday?

(d) How many cartons of orange juice were sold on Friday?

(e) What was the total number of cartons sold in the week?

(f) What was the average (mean) daily number of cartons of orange juice sold during the week?

(g) What was the average daily number of cartons sold?

(h) Find the average daily number of cartons of apple juice sold, giving your answer to the nearest whole number.

(i) Find the average daily number of cartons of pineapple juice sold, giving your answer correct to the nearest whole number.

Exercise 12

A Answer these without using a calculator:

1. $\dfrac{8 + 7}{5}$

2. $7 \times 9 - 5 \times 4$

3. $\dfrac{90}{3} - 12$

4. $50 + \dfrac{42}{6}$

5. $\dfrac{35}{(9 - 2)}$

6. $\dfrac{40 - 4}{8 + 1}$

7. $\dfrac{9 \times 8}{15 - 9}$

8. $\dfrac{18 - 6}{18 \div 6}$

B Here are two calculator methods of working out $\dfrac{9 + 12}{9 - 2}$.

(*Note* You may not be able to use both methods on your calculator.)

Method 1 (Using brackets)

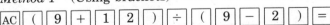

Method 2 (Using the memory)

$\boxed{\text{AC}}\ \boxed{9}\ \boxed{-}\ \boxed{2}\ \boxed{=}\ \boxed{\text{Min}}\ \boxed{9}\ \boxed{+}\ \boxed{1}\ \boxed{2}\ \boxed{=}\ \boxed{\div}\ \boxed{\text{MR}}\ \boxed{=}$

Try the above on your calculator. You should obtain 3.

Now use your calculator to work out the answers to the questions in part A.

C Use a calculator to work out the following:

1. $65 \times 42 - 40 \times 34$

2. $(82 + 12) \times (76 - 14)$

3. $\dfrac{47 + 26}{16}$ (to 2 d.p.)

4. $\dfrac{57}{23} + 15$ (to 2 d.p.)

5. $\dfrac{138}{29 - 12}$ (to 3 s.f.)

6. $\dfrac{78 - 49}{12 \times 8}$ (to 3 d.p.)

Exercise 13   Decimals

A Work out the following:

1. $4.96 + 17.8$
2. $29.031 - 7.845$

3. 8.2×1.7
4. $1.295 \div 3.7$

B Use a calculator throughout:

1. (a) Find the exact value of $\dfrac{12.9 \times 1.8}{3.2}$.

   (b) Write the answer to part (a) correct to two decimal places.

2. (a) Find the value of $\dfrac{58.7 + 69.4}{0.24}$.

   (b) Write the answer to part (a) correct to the nearest whole number.

3. (a) Calculate the exact value of $\dfrac{2.8 \times 6.7}{9.9 - 3.5}$.

   (b) Write the answer to part (a) correct to two significant figures.

4. (a) Find $\dfrac{57.33 + 23.07}{4.48 \div 0.35}$.

   (b) Write the answer to part (a) correct to one decimal place.

C Find two different numbers which make 4.5 when:

1. added,   2. subtracted,   3. multiplied,   4. divided.

44

Vulgar Fractions

Exercise 14

A Work out the following:

1. $3\frac{1}{2} + 2\frac{7}{8}$

2. $1\frac{2}{5} + 1\frac{1}{2}$

3. $4\frac{3}{4} - 1\frac{5}{16}$

4. $7\frac{1}{2} - 3\frac{1}{3}$

5. $2\frac{1}{6} \times 3$

6. $2\frac{2}{5} \times 1\frac{7}{8}$

7. $5\frac{1}{4} \div 2\frac{4}{5}$

8. $7\frac{1}{2} \div 2\frac{1}{4}$

B $3\frac{1}{2} + 4\frac{3}{4}$ can be worked out on a calculator by pressing the keys
$\boxed{3}\ \boxed{\cdot}\ \boxed{5}\ \boxed{+}\ \boxed{4}\ \boxed{\cdot}\ \boxed{7}\ \boxed{5}$.
Try it. (The answer is 8.25.) Work out the following in the same way. If an answer fills the calculator display then write that answer correct to one decimal place.

1. $5\frac{1}{2} + 2\frac{4}{5}$

2. $2\frac{1}{8} - 1\frac{3}{4}$

3. $3\frac{3}{4} \times 1\frac{1}{5}$

4. $3\frac{3}{8} \div 4\frac{1}{2}$

C $5\frac{2}{3} - 2\frac{3}{4}$ can be worked out on a calculator in the following different ways. (You will need to try the methods on your calculator to check whether or not they work.)

Method 1
$\boxed{3}\ \boxed{\div}\ \boxed{4}\ \boxed{+}\ \boxed{2}\ \boxed{=}\ \boxed{\text{Min}}\ \boxed{2}\ \boxed{\div}\ \boxed{3}\ \boxed{+}\ \boxed{5}\ \boxed{-}\ \boxed{\text{MR}}\ \boxed{=}$
Try it. The answer should be 2.917 (to three decimal places).

Method 2
$\boxed{2}\ \boxed{+}\ \boxed{3}\ \boxed{\div}\ \boxed{4}\ \boxed{\text{Min}}\ \boxed{5}\ \boxed{+}\ \boxed{2}\ \boxed{\div}\ \boxed{3}\ \boxed{-}\ \boxed{\text{MR}}\ \boxed{=}$
Try it. (Method 2 will only work if your calculator sorts out the order of the calculation for you.)

Method 3
(Try this if your calculator has parenthesis keys $\boxed{(}$ and $\boxed{)}$.)
$\boxed{5}\ \boxed{+}\ \boxed{2}\ \boxed{\div}\ \boxed{3}\ \boxed{=}\ \boxed{-}\ \boxed{(}\ \boxed{2}\ \boxed{+}\ \boxed{3}\ \boxed{\div}\ \boxed{4}\ \boxed{)}\ \boxed{=}$
(*Note* $\boxed{=}$ causes the calculation so far to be worked out.)

Work out the following using one of the above methods. Where necessary give an answer correct to three decimal places.

1. $4\frac{2}{5} + 4\frac{1}{4}$ **2.** $6\frac{5}{16} - 2\frac{7}{10}$ **3.** $5\frac{3}{5} \times 3\frac{1}{8}$ **4.** $4\frac{1}{4} \div 3\frac{1}{2}$

D Work out the following:

1. $4\frac{3}{4} + 2\frac{1}{2} - 3\frac{5}{8}$

2. $5\frac{1}{2} - 2\frac{4}{5} + 1\frac{1}{4}$

3. $3\frac{5}{6} + 1\frac{1}{8} \times 4\frac{2}{3}$

4. $2\frac{2}{5} \times \left(3\frac{5}{8} - 1\frac{3}{4}\right)$

5. $\frac{3}{10} \times 1\frac{3}{5} \div 2\frac{2}{5}$

6. $3\frac{1}{5} \div \left(2\frac{2}{3} + 1\frac{3}{5}\right)$

Exercise 15   Fractions of a Quantity

1. $\frac{2}{5}$ of 120 pupils are boys. How many girls are there?

2. (a) Monica was given two thousand and seventy pounds. She saved one third of the money. How much did she save?
   (b) Elias saved £180 out of £240. What fraction of his money did he save?

3. Cedric travelled 276 km. If $\frac{3}{4}$ of his journey was by train and the remainder by bus:
   (a) How far did he travel on the train?
   (b) How far did he travel on the bus?

4. (a) What fraction of £3 is 75 p?
   (b) Write the answer to part (a) as a percentage.

5. (a) Find the cost of $\frac{1}{4}$ lb of sweets at £1.80 a lb.
   (b) $\frac{1}{2}$ lb of sweets cost 86 p. Find the cost of 2 lb of sweets.

6. Mrs Robson received $\frac{24}{80}$ of her average salary as a pension. If her average salary was £7800, work out her pension.

7. (a) Geoffrey had £4.80 to spend. He spent $\frac{1}{4}$ of the money in one shop and $\frac{1}{2}$ of the remainder in another. If he then spent a further 72 p, how much money would he have left?
   (b) Marcus spent $\frac{1}{4}$ of his total spending money in one shop and $\frac{1}{2}$ in another. If he had £3 left, how much did he start with?
   (c) Yvette spent $\frac{1}{4}$ of her money in one shop and $\frac{1}{2}$ of the remainder in another. If she had £3 left, how much did she start with?

8. A 2 m post is driven 60 cm into the ground:

    (*a*) What fraction of the post is in the ground?

    (*b*) What fraction of the post is above the ground?

Exercise 16   Problems using Fractions

1. $\frac{5}{8}$ of my garden is lawn and $\frac{1}{4}$ is used for growing vegetables. What fraction is left?

2. Mrs O. N. Holliday worked $7\frac{3}{4}$ h each day for 6 days. Find the total time worked in hours.

3. Which costs more money, 3 kg of potatoes at 39 p per kg or $2\frac{1}{2}$ kg of potatoes at 48 p per kg?

4. A piece of wood is $14\frac{3}{4}$ in long. If a piece measuring $6\frac{13}{16}$ in is cut off, what length remains?

5. Mrs Pascoe needed two lengths of tape, one measuring $1\frac{2}{3}$ yd and the other $2\frac{1}{4}$ yd:

    (*a*) What is the total length needed?

    (*b*) If the two pieces of tape were cut off from a piece measuring $5\frac{1}{2}$ yd, what length was left?

Exercise 17   Remainders

1. (*a*) What is the remainder when 11 is divided by 4?

    (*b*) Using a calculator, try to find the remainder when 11 is divided by 4.

2. (*a*) What is the remainder when 34 is divided by 9?

    (*b*) Using a calculator, try to find the remainder when 34 is divided by 9.

3. (*a*) What is the remainder when 23 is divided by 7.

    (*b*) Using a calculator, try to find the remainder when 23 is divided by 7.

4. Explain your method of finding the remainder to a division calculation on a calculator.

5. Find the remainder in each calculation:

    (*a*) $2057 \div 18$ (*b*) $9614 \div 85$ (*c*) $2065 \div 99$

Exercise 18   Calculations with Directed Numbers

Carry out the following calculations:

1. $6 + {}^-3$
2. $5 + {}^-4$
3. $5 + {}^-7$
4. $3 + ({}^-4)$
5. $1 + ({}^-3)$
6. $2 + (-11)$
7. $({}^-2) + 3$
8. $({}^-5) + ({}^-3)$
9. $(-12) + 4$
10. ${}^-1 + 2$

11. ${}^-6 + {}^-4$
12. ${}^-8 + 1$
13. $6 - 3$
14. $6 - {}^-3$
15. $5 - (-2)$
16. ${}^-9 - 5$
17. ${}^-9 - {}^-5$
18. $({}^-3) - 6$
19. $({}^-3) - ({}^-6)$
20. ${}^-2 - {}^-4$

21. $6 \times {}^-4$
22. ${}^-2 \times {}^-7$
23. $({}^-5) \times 3$
24. $({}^-9) \times ({}^-5)$
25. ${}^-8 \times 4$
26. $8 \div {}^-2$
27. $10 \div ({}^-5)$
28. $({}^-9) \div (3)$
29. ${}^-14 \div {}^-7$
30. ${}^-15 \div 3$

5 Angles and Tessellations

Angles

Exercise 1

Answer the following:

1. For the quadrilateral shown:
  (*a*) Using a protractor, measure angle *p*.
  (*b*) Calculate the size of angle *q*.
  (*c*) Angle *q* is a reflex angle.
      What sort of angle is angle *p*?
  (*d*) What sort of angle is angle *r*?

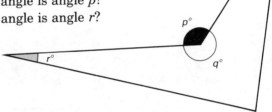

2. *Calculate* the size of each labelled angle:
  (*a*)

  (*c*)

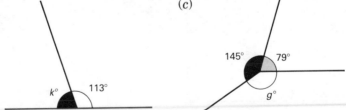

  (*b*)

49

3. (a) Calculate x:

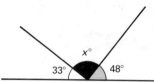

(b) Calculate the value of y:

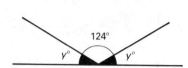

Exercise 2   Angles and Triangles

A Calculate the size of each labelled angle:

1.

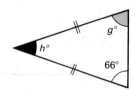

2.

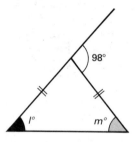

3.

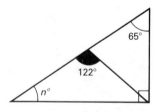

4.

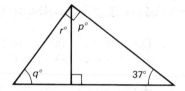

5.

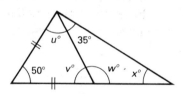

6.

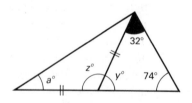

B **1.** (a) *Trace* the given diagram.
  (b) The six angles are 90°, 110°, 70°, 20°, 35° and 35°. Without measuring, mark on your copy which angle is which.

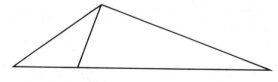

2. Investigate the statement: 'The largest angle in any triangle is always opposite the longest side.'

3. In △XYZ, YZ is longer than XZ but is shorter than XY. Which angle could be 105°?

4. In △LMN, LM = MN. Which two angles are equal?

5. One angle of an isosceles triangle is given. Write down all the possible sizes of the other angles.
   (a) 50°   (b) 120°   (c) 58°

Exercise 3 Miscellaneous Problems

1. Through how many degrees does the minute hand of a clock turn between 09.15 and 09.50?

2. How many degrees are there between the hour and minute hands of a clock at half-past three? (Give the smaller angle.)

3. The movable part of a reading lamp can swing from its lowest position, making an angle of 25° with a fixed upright, to its highest position, making an angle of 140°. Through how many degrees can it swing in moving from its lowest to its highest position?

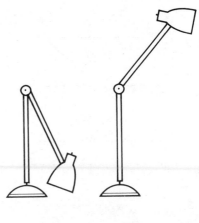

4. The paper tray of a copier makes an angle of 28° with the horizontal. What angle does it make with the vertical?

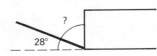

5. Part of a room's ceiling slopes down to a wall. If the sloping part makes an angle of 130° with the wall as shown, what angle does it make with the horizontal part of the ceiling?

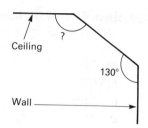

Exercise 4   Angles and Parallels

For each question, calculate the angles labelled with letters:

1.

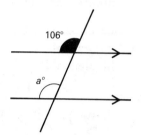

4.

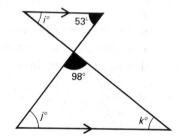

2.

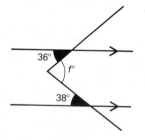

5.

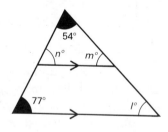

3.

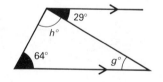

6.

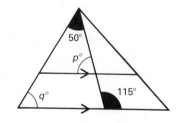

52

Exercise 5   Angles and Quadrilaterals

1. Using a protractor, measure:
   (a) BĈD
   (b) AD̂C
   (c) AB̂C
   (d) By *calculating*, find
      BÂD.

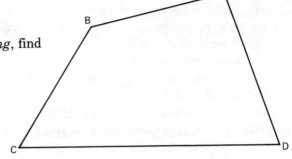

2. A diagonal of a rectangle makes an angle of 32° with a long side of the rectangle:
   (a) What angle does the diagonal make with a short side?
   (b) Calculate the acute angle between the diagonals.
   (c) Calculate the obtuse angle between the diagonals.

3. Calculate the angles labelled with letters:

   (a)
   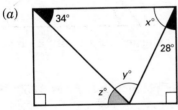

   (b)
   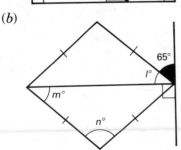

   (c)
   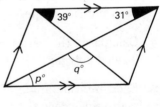

   (d)
   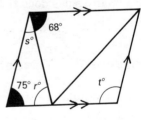

4. Three interior angles of a quadrilateral measures 115°, 85° and 97°. What is the size of the fourth angle?

5. One angle of a parallelogram measures 71°. Write the sizes of the other three angles.

53

Exercise 6   Angles of Regular Polygons

1. A regular polygon is shown:
   (a) Write its name.
   (b) Calculate the size of each interior angle.
   (c) If vertices B and E are joined with a straight line, what sort of triangle would ABE be?
   (d) Calculate the size of angle ABE.
   (e) If side CD is produced to a point P to form exterior angle EDP, calculate the size of ∠EDP.

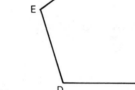

2. ABCDEFGHIJ is a regular 10-sided polygon. Calculate the size of:
   (a) ∠DEF   (b) ∠EFD

3. A regular hexagon is cut in half to form a trapezium as shown. Calculate the size of each interior angle.

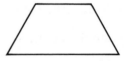

4. Calculate the size of each exterior angle of a regular 9-sided polygon.

5. Each interior angle of a regular polygon measures 135°. How many sides does the polygon have?

Exercise 7   Tessellations   **M**

1. An equilateral triangle is shown.
   (a) What is the size of each interior angle?
   (b) In a tessellation of equilateral triangles, how many of the triangles fit together around one point?

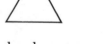

2. (a) What size is each interior angle of a regular hexagon?
   (b) How many regular hexagons fit together around one point in a tessellation of regular hexagons?

3. A regular 12-sided polygon, a regular hexagon and a square all fit together at a point without leaving any gaps:

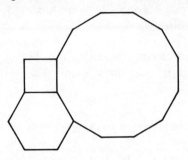

Calculate the interior angle of each of these shapes and use your answers to show why there are no gaps when they are placed together.

4. A manufacturer made some concrete paving stones in the shape of hexagons that were symmetrical but not regular. The sketch shows one.

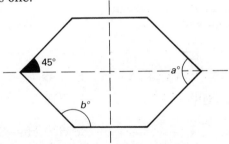

   (*a*) How many lines of symmetry has it?
   (*b*) Find the values of *a* and *b*.
   (*c*) Make several copies of the hexagon. Stick them on to paper to show that it tessellates.
   (*d*) How many hexagons meet at one point?
   (*e*) Choose one point where the hexagons meet. Mark the size of the angles at that point. Now explain why the hexagons tessellate.

5. (*a*) Draw a hexagon of your own, having the same number of axes of symmetry as the one in question 4 but different-sized angles.
   (*b*) In question 4, two different methods were used to prove that the hexagon would tessellate—a practical method and a calculation method.

Either make several copies of your hexagon and use a practical method to show that it tessellates,

or measure the angles of your hexagon, then explain why it tessellates.

6. Do all hexagons having the same number of axes of symmetry as the hexagons in questions 4 and 5 tessellate? Explain your answer.

Angles and Circles

Exercise 8

A **1.** Draw a circle with a radius of about 35 mm.

2. Draw any chord and label it AB.

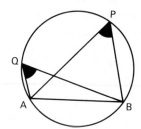

3. Mark a point P anywhere on the circumference of the circle.

4. Join AP and BP.

5. Measure ∠APB.

6. Mark a point Q elsewhere on the circumference of the circle but in the same segment.

7. Join AQ and BQ.

8. Measure ∠AQB.

9. (*a*) Mark some more points on the circumference of the circle and in the same segment.
(*b*) Join each point to A and to B.
(*c*) Measure the angle *subtended** at each point by the chord.

10. Write what you notice about the angles measured in questions 5, 8 and 9.

11. Repeat questions 1 to 10 for a different circle.

* See the glossary, p. 470.

12. Copy the following sentence:
'Angles in the same segment are equal.'

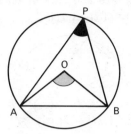

B 1. Draw a circle having a radius of about 35 mm. Label the centre O.

2. Draw any chord and label it AB.

3. Mark a point P anywhere on the circumference of the circle on the same side of AB as the centre, O.

4. Join AO and BO, AP and BP.

5. Measure $A\hat{P}B$ and $A\hat{O}B$ and write what you notice about the sizes of the two angles.

6. Repeat questions 1 to 5 using a different-sized circle, drawing a chord anywhere in the circle and marking a point P anywhere on the circle on the same side of the chord as the centre.

7. Copy the following sentence:
'In any circle, the angle at the centre is twice the angle at the circumference.'

Some reminders

1 The perpendicular bisector of a chord passes through the centre of the circle.

2 The angle between a tangent and a radius is 90°.

3 Tangents drawn from one point to a circle are equal in length.

4 The bisector of the angle between two tangents passes through the centre of the circle.

5 Angles in a semi-circle equal 90°.

6 Angles in the same segment are equal.

7 In any circle, the angle at the centre is twice the angle at the circumference.

Exercise 9

Calculate the size of each angle labelled with a letter. (O is the centre of the circle.)

1.

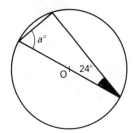

6.

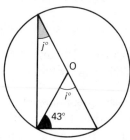

2.

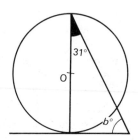

7.

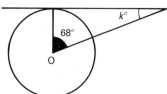

3.

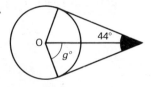

8.

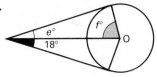

4.

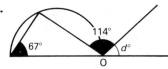

9.

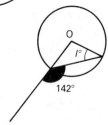

5.

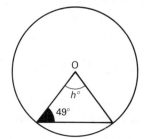

10.

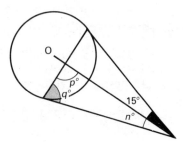

58

11.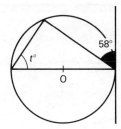

12.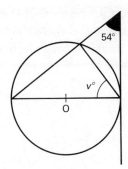

Exercise 10

1. TB is a tangent to the circle centre O.
∠BAC = 42° and
∠BTA = 44°.
Calculate the size of:
(a) ∠BAT   (b) ∠CBT

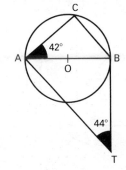

2. The diagram shows triangle PQR inscribed in a circle centre O. PQ is a diameter and ∠RPQ = 32°. S lies on PQ such that ∠QRS = 43°. Find the value of x.

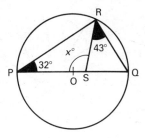

3. PT is a tangent to a circle centre O. TS is a diameter.
PT̂R = 38°. Calculate:
(a) RT̂O   (d) RÔS
(b) RŜT   (e) RÔT
(c) OR̂S   (f) OR̂T

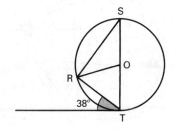

4. In the diagram, O is the centre of the circle. Calculate the angles labelled with letters.

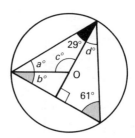

Exercise 11

Calculate the angles labelled with letters. O is the centre of the circle.

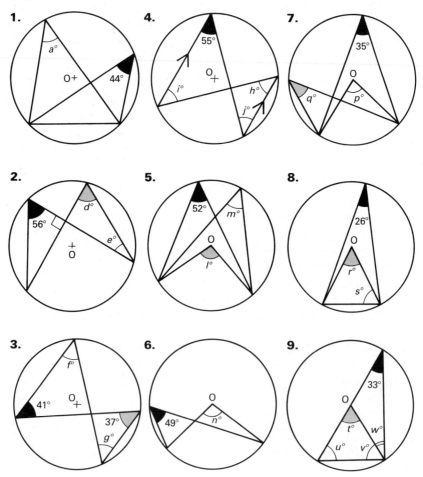

1.

2.

3.

4.

5.

6.

7.

8.

9.

Exercise 12

A Calculate the angles labelled with letters. O is the centre of the circle.

1.

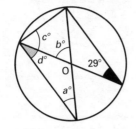

2.

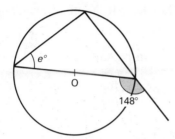

3. TA and TB are tangents.

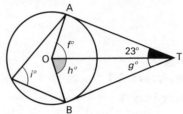

4. TX and TY are tangents.

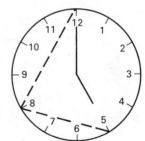

B 1. A clock-face is given.
   (*a*) What time is shown, if it is evening? Give your answer in the 24-hour clock notation.
   (*b*) What size is the obtuse angle between the hands?
   (*c*) If a line is drawn from the 12 position to the 8 and a line is drawn from 8 to 5, what is the size of the angle created?

2. In the given diagram, calculate the size of:
   (*a*) angle *a*,
   (*b*) angle *b*.

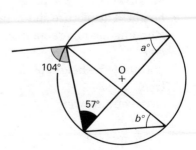

6 Units of Measurement

Length

Exercise 1

1. A piece of string is 6 m long. What length is left after 4.7 m is cut off?

2. How many 40 cm lengths of string can be cut from 20 m?

3. Using the ruler shown in the diagram, find the length of the key in centimetres:

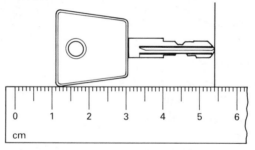

4. Brendan estimated a length to be 4.65 m long. The true length was 4.57 m.
   By how many centimetres was his estimate inaccurate?

5. Mr Haworth is of average height. The picture shows him standing near a crab-apple tree.
   Estimate the height of the tree.
   Give your answer:
   (a) in feet,
   (b) in metres.

6. Draw two different rectangles each having a perimeter of 18 cm. One should have an area of 20 cm². Write the area of the other rectangle.

7. The diagram shows the front view of a piece of wood:

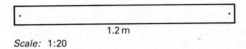

1.2 m

Scale: 1:20

The wood is 1.2 m long and it has screw holes marked 3 cm from each end. The wood is to be fixed to a wall using four equally spaced screws.
(*a*) Copy the diagram. (Use the same scale.)
On your copy, accurately mark the positions of the other two screws.
(*b*) How far apart should adjacent screws be?

8. The net of a shoe box is shown. The box is 32 cm long and 16 cm wide. The net was made by cutting four corner pieces from a rectangular piece of card measuring 54 cm by 38 cm.

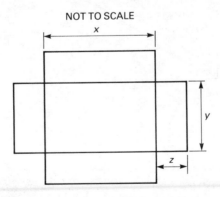

NOT TO SCALE

(*a*) Write the size of measurement x.
(*b*) Write the size of measurement y.
(*c*) Write the size of measurement z.
(*d*) What would be the height of the box that is made from this net?
(*e*) Calculate the area of the net.

63

Here is a map showing Cornwall and part of Devon. (The marked distances are in miles.)

A route diagram can be drawn from the map:

The same information can be shown on a distance chart:

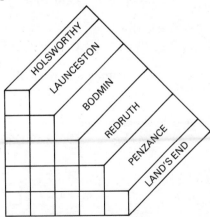

1. (*a*) How far is it from Tavistock to St Austell?

(*b*) How far is it from Truro to Callington?

2. (*a*) Copy the following route chart. Complete it using the map opposite.

Land's End   Penzance   Redruth   Bodmin   Launceston   Holsworthy

(*b*) Copy and complete the distance chart:

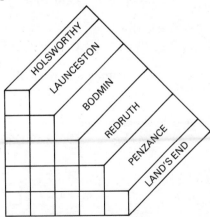

(*c*) How far is it from Bodmin to Land's End?

(*d*) How far is it from Penzance to Launceston?

65

(e) A motorist travelled directly from Land's End to Holsworthy. Her odometer (distance meter, sometimes referred to as mileometer) at the start of the journey showed:

$$4\,2\,3\,5\,6$$

Copy and complete the distance meters for the rest of her journey.

Penzance $4\,2$

Redruth

Bodmin

Launceston

Holsworthy

Exercise 3   Metric Conversions

A Choose the correct answer:

1. A length of 1426 mm is the same as a length of:
   A. 142.6 m   B. 14.26 m   C. 1.426 m   D. 0.1426 m

2. A mass of 2649 g is the same as a mass of:
   A. 26.49 kg   B. 2.649 kg   C. 0.2649 kg   D. 0.026 49 kg

3. A capacity of 4.73ℓ is the same as:
   A. 473 mℓ   B. 4730 mℓ   C. 0.0473 mℓ   D. 47 300 mℓ

4. A mass of 10.8 kg is the same as a mass of:
   A. 0.0108 g   B. 1800 g   C. 1080 g   D. 10 800 g

5. A mass of 12.47 t is the same as:
   A. 124.7 kg   B. 1247 kg   C. 12 470 kg   D. 124 700 kg

B Copy and complete:

1. 26 cm = ? mm

2. 72.3 cℓ = ? mℓ

3. 31.7 g = ? mg

4. 54 ℓ = ? cℓ

5. 0.57 kg = ? g

6. 0.39 ℓ = ? cℓ

Exercise 4

1. How many 120 mℓ coffee mugs can be filled from 6 ℓ of coffee?

2. If 600 mm square paving stones each weigh 40 kg:
   (a) Find the total mass of 18 of the paving stones.
   (b) How many paving stones weigh 1 t?

3. A nurse recorded the mass of two new-born babies and also the circumference of their heads. Derek weighed 2.84 kg and had a head circumference of 33.9 cm, while Beverley weighed 3.73 kg and had a head circumference of 34.7 cm.
   (a) How much heavier was Beverley? (Give your answer in grams.)
   (b) How much smaller was the circumference of Derek's head? (Give your answer in millimetres.)

4. Telegraph poles are spaced 80 m apart. How far will I walk if I walk from the first to the tenth pole?

5. 2 parcels each have a mass of 375 g, while a third parcel weighs 340 g. Find the total mass of the parcels, giving your answer in kilograms.

6. A bag of flour weighs 1.5 kg. How many grams are left after 0.65 kg have been used?

7. 10 people had 2 glasses of wine each. If each glass held 150 mℓ, how many litres of wine were used?

8. An empty box weighs 750 g. When half full it weighs 3.47 kg. Find its mass when full.

9. If wine is bought in 1 ℓ bottles for £3.25 and is then sold at 90 p per 150 mℓ glass, calculate the profit on every 6 ℓ of wine sold.

10. Post Office parcel restrictions are:
    Mass must not be greater than 22.5 kg.
    Length must not be greater than 1.5 m.
    Length + girth must not be greater than 3 m.

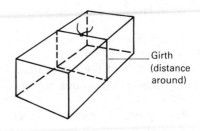

Girth
(distance around)

67

(*Note*   The girth is the distance around the parcel measuring in the direction of the width.)

   (*a*) A parcel has a girth of 1.7 m, what is the maximum length it could be for posting?

   (*b*) A parcel has a girth of 2.45 m, find its maximum allowed length for posting. Give your answer in centimetres.

   (*c*) A parcel has a length of 1.2 m. Find its maximum allowed girth for posting.

   (*d*) A parcel in the shape of a cuboid is to be posted. Its length is 86 cm and its breadth is 59 cm. Work out the maximum allowed height.

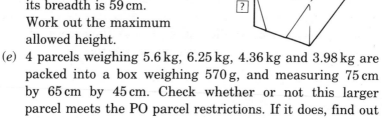

   (*e*) 4 parcels weighing 5.6 kg, 6.25 kg, 4.36 kg and 3.98 kg are packed into a box weighing 570 g, and measuring 75 cm by 65 cm by 45 cm. Check whether or not this larger parcel meets the PO parcel restrictions. If it does, find out how much smaller and lighter it is than the maximum sizes. If it does not, find out by how much it is over the maximum allowance.

Imperial Units

> *Reminders*
> 12 in = 1 ft   16 oz = 1 lb   8 pt = 1 gal
> 3 ft = 1 yd   14 lb = 1 st
> 1760 yd = 1 mile   2240 lb = 1 ton

Exercise 5

   1. Mr and Mrs Green's garden is 23 yd 2 ft long. How long is that in feet?

   2. Rajinder Singh weighs 8 st 7 lb. How many pounds is that?

   3. 1 lb 4 oz of flour was used to bake a cake. How many ounces of flour would be left out of a bag containing 3 lb?

   4. A piece of wood is 5 ft 4 in long. It is cut in half. How long is each piece?

5. There are $7\frac{1}{2}$ pt of shampoo in a container:

    (a) If the container had contained 1 gal of shampoo, how much has been used?

    (b) If the $7\frac{1}{2}$ pt of shampoo is poured into 4 bottles, an equal amount in each, how much shampoo will there be in each bottle?

6. What was the total distance run in the 4×440 yd relay?

7. In 1974, Allan Feuerbach of the USA put a shot 51 ft 5 in with his left hand and 70 ft $1\frac{3}{4}$ in with his right hand. What is the total of these two distances?

8. Mr O'Driscoll wants a fence along one side of his garden, a distance of 55 ft. He wants to use 6 ft wide panels and 3 in wide posts. How many of each should he buy?

Exercise 6   Temperature

The diagram shows a circular thermometer marked in degrees Celsius and degrees Fahrenheit.

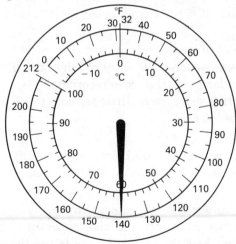

1. What temperature does it show:

    (a) in degrees Celsius?   (b) in degrees Fahrenheit?

2. If the temperature rises by 25 °C:

    (a) What is the new Celsius reading?

    (b) What is the new Fahrenheit reading?

Time and the Calendar

Exercise 7

1. Two clocks are shown. The first clock shows the time that Timothy went to sleep last night, while the second shows the time he woke up this morning.

(a) Write both times using the 12-hour clock notation.
(b) Write both times using the 24-hour clock notation.
(c) Calculate the length of time Timothy slept.

2. An aeroplane was due at Manchester Airport at 16.20. Find its time of arrival if it was 35 min early.

3. Dilwyn switched on his video recorder to record a film at 19.20. The video was switched off at 20.55 when the film finished.
(a) For how long was the video recording?
(b) If Dilwyn used a new 3 h tape, how much recording time would be left?

4. A ship left Penzance at 09.15 and sailed to the Isles of Scilly. The journey took 2 h 35 min. At what time did it reach Scilly?

5. Mrs Goulding decided to tile a bathroom wall. She thought it would take her 3 min per tile plus an extra half an hour. At that rate, how long would it take her to tile the wall using 108 tiles?

6. Mr Sharpe needed 25 min to lay each box of floor tiles plus an extra 10 min. If a job took him 1 h 25 min, how many boxes of tiles did he use?

7. The last complete programme at a cinema commenced at 20.15. The supporting film lasted 35 min. There was an interval of 15 min, then the main film was shown for 1 h 36 min. At what time did the show end?

8. Ms Downe set off for work. She had a 5 min walk to the bus stop where she waited for 3 min for a bus. The bus journey took 10 min. She got off at the bus stop next to the railway station and had a 7 min wait for the train. Her train journey took 24 min. From the station, after a 4 min walk, she arrived at work at 08.55. At what time did she set off that morning?

Exercise 8

1. Penelope wrote W/E 13 May to stand for the week ending on 13 May. Write the next ten weeks following 13 May in the same way.

2. A watch shows the date as 2—21. To which month is it referring?

3. 19 October was the first night of a play. It was staged once each evening up to the last night on 4 December of the same year.
   (a) How many performances were there?
   (b) If the total takings over that period of time were £97 995 what were the average (mean) takings per performance?

4. Astrid went on a 10-night holiday. If she set off on 28 July, on what date did she return?

5. If 6 March is a Monday, write the dates of all the Mondays in March.

6. If 1 January is a Wednesday, what day is the first of each month:
   (a) if it is not a leap year?
   (b) if it is a leap year?

7. Annie was 16 years old on 18–12–86. When was she born?

8. The dates of birth (d.o.b.) of several people are given. In each case, calculate the age in years and months correct to the nearest month from the d.o.b. to the date given.

(*a*) Jeremy's d.o.b. is 11.6.71. How old was he on 6 September 1986?

(*b*) Paramjit Kaur was born on 3 October 1975. What was her age on 14 January 1986?

(*c*) Mr Kerslake's d.o.b. was 24/4/45. What was his age on 1 September 1984?

(*d*) Iris was born on 2 December 1927. How old was she on 19 May 1963?

7 Everyday Applications

Mathematical Language Used in the Media

Exercise 1

The following sentences use words that are frequently used by the media. Re-write the sentences using the correct words. Choose the words from:
{cylindrical, Celsius, faces, rectangle, negative, cuboidal}

1. The temperature is 4 degrees Centigrade.

2. The temperature last night was minus 2 degrees Centigrade.

3. In drawing a plan of his garden, Mr Plant drew an oblong.

4. Fatima carried her cake in a round tin, while Don carried his cake in a square tin.

5. A cube has 6 sides while a square-based pyramid has only 5 sides:

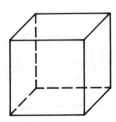
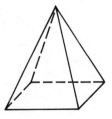

Reading Clocks, Dials, Scales, Tables and Charts

Exercise 2

1. Write the meter reading shown on the following dials:

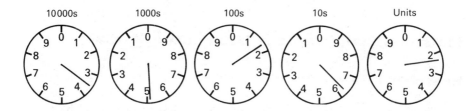

2. Copy the boxes and fill in the reading shown on the gas meter:

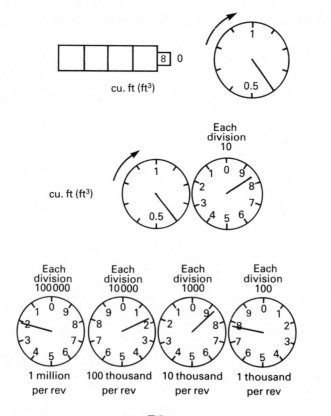

3. Mrs Power was asked to read her electricity meter and write the reading on a meter card. Here are the dials she read.

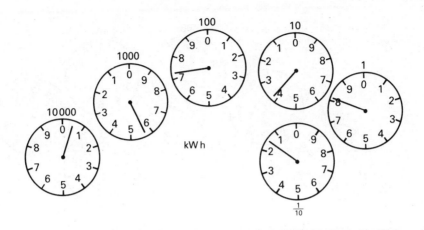

Copy the following meter card and complete it to show the reading on the dials above. (Ignore the $\frac{1}{10}$ kWh dial.)

Meter reading	10 000s	1000s	100s	10s	Units

Exercise 3   M

On copies of the following dials, show the readings given on the digital meters:

1.

| 1 | 4 | 2 | 8 | 6 |

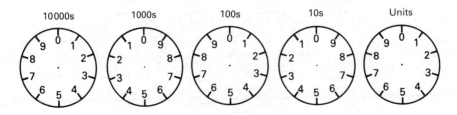

2.

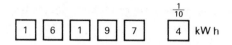

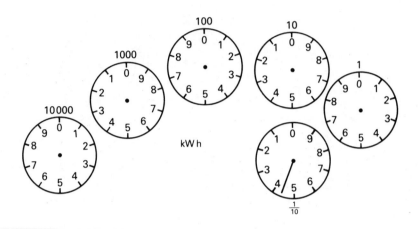

3.

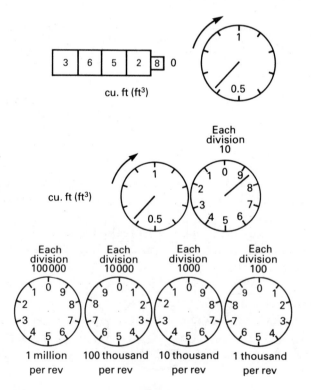

Exercise 4

1. Here is a copy of an electricity bill:

METER READINGS PRESENT	PREVIOUS	UNITS	TARIFF	PENCE PER UNIT	AMOUNT (£)	VAT %
13 287	12 316	?		5.700	?	ZERO
		Quarterly charge			6.60	ZERO
				Total due		
			£	?		

   (a) From the two given meter readings, work out the number of units used during that quarter.
   (b) Calculate the cost of the units used at 5.7 p per unit.
   (c) Calculate the total amount due.

2. Here is an electricity bill for a customer on Economy 7 tariff:

METER READINGS PRESENT	PREVIOUS	UNITS	TARIFF	PENCE PER UNIT	AMOUNT (£)	VAT %
ECONOMY 7 TARIFF		?	D56	5.850	?	ZERO
15833	14750	?	N16	1.900	?	ZERO
3770	3528	Quarterly charge			8.80	ZERO
				Total due		
			£	?		

Economy 7 charges are split into two parts, namely the daytime tariff D56 at 5.85 p per unit and the cheaper night-time tariff N16.
   (a) How many units were used at the daytime rate?
   (b) How many units were used at the night-time rate?
   (c) Calculate the cost of the units at the daytime rate.
   (d) Calculate the cost of the units at the night-time rate.
   (e) Calculate the total amount due.
   (f) What was the total number of units used?
   (g) What would the total cost be if *all* the units were charged at a rate of 5.7 p per unit?
   (h) How much is saved on Economy 7?

3. If electricity costs 5.7 p per unit plus a fixed charge of £6.60 per quarter:
  (*a*) Calculate the total cost of 863 units used in a quarter.
  (*b*) Calculate the number of units used when the total quarterly bill comes to £57.33.

4. The dials show the number of cubic feet of gas used by March and by June:

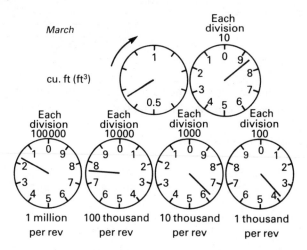

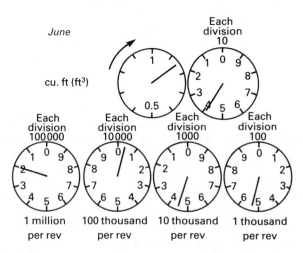

Ignoring the upper pair of dials on each:
(*a*) Write the reading for March.
(*b*) Write the reading for June.

(c) How many cubic feet of gas have been used during the given quarter?

(d) To calculate the number of therms, multiply the volume of gas supplied in hundreds of cubic feet (the difference between the readings) by the calorific value (1026 BTU's/ft^3 in this case), then divide by 1000. For the two dials shown, calculate the number of therms used.

(e) If gas costs 38.00 p per therm plus a standing charge of £8.20, calculate the total cost of gas used from March to June.

Exercise 5

The table shows the nutritional value of 100 g of a cereal:

Typical Nutritional Composition per 100 g

Energy	302 kcal
	1285 kJ
Protein (N × 5.7)	10.2 g
Fat	1.1 g
Dietary fibre	15.2 g
Available carbohydrate	66.9 g
Vitamin C	35.0 mg
Niacin	16.0 mg
Riboflavin (B_2)	1.5 mg
Thiamin (B_1)	1.0 mg
Vitamin D	2.8 μg
Iron	40.0 mg
Vitamin B_6	1.8 mg

1. How many milligrams of Niacin does 100 g of cereal contain?

2. How many milligrams of B_6 are there in 400 g of cereal?

3. What percentage of 100 g of cereal is dietary fibre?

4. Write the amount of vitamin C to the amount of iron as a ratio in its simplest terms.

5. How many grams of cereal contain 70 mg of vitamin C?

6. How much cereal contains 100 mg of iron?

7. How much protein is there in 1 kg of the cereal?

Routes on a Map, Timetabling and Scheduling

Exercise 6

A map of the London Underground is shown opposite. Use the map to answer the following questions.

1. Which line would you travel on if you travelled from:
   (a) Edgware to Camden Town?
   (b) North Ealing to Uxbridge?
   (c) Lancaster Gate to Bethnal Green?
   (d) Bond Street to Wembley Park?
   (e) Baker Street to Notting Hill Gate?
   (f) Baker Street to Royal Oak?

2. Which line would you travel on if you travelled from Embankment to:
   (a) Liverpool Street?   (d) Whitechapel?
   (b) Oxford Circus?   (e) Euston?
   (c) Earls Court?   (f) High Street Kensington?

3. If you travelled from Green Park to Brixton, on which line would you travel and through which stations would you pass?

4. If you travel from Mansion House to Westminster, on which lines could you travel?

5. If you travel from Preston Road to Great Portland Street, on which line would you travel and through which stations would you pass?

6. Explain how to travel from Blackfriars to Leyton. (Give two alternative routes.)

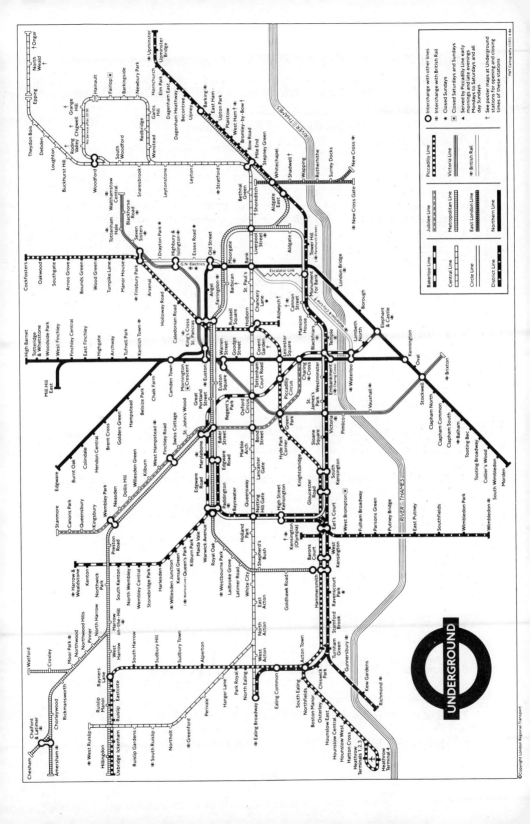

Part of a timetable of trains travelling from Hastings to Eastbourne is shown below:

Hastings → Eastbourne

Mondays to Fridays

km	Miles								☕			
0	0	Hastings	d	05 21	06 26	07 00	07 21	08 00	08 15	08 32	09 06
1.2	$\frac{3}{4}$	St Leonards Warrior Sq	d	05 23	06 28	07 02	07 23	08 02	08 17	08 34	09 08
7.24	$4\frac{1}{2}$	Bexhill	d	05 34f	06 38h	07 10	07 30	08 12j	08 24	08 41	09 15
8.45	$5\frac{1}{4}$	Collington	d	05 36	....	07 12	07 32	....	08 26	....	09 17
10.86	$6\frac{3}{4}$	Cooden Beach	d	05 39	06 42	07 15	07 35	08 16	08 29	08 45	09 20
13.68	$8\frac{1}{2}$	Normans Bay	d	05 43	....	07 18	07 38	....	08 32	....	09 24
16.90	$10\frac{1}{2}$	Pevensey Bay	d	05 46	06 47	07 22	07 42	..	08 36	..	09 27
18.11	$11\frac{1}{4}$	Pevensey and Westham	d	05 48	06 49	07 24	07 44	08 22	08 38	08 51	09 29
22.93	$14\frac{1}{4}$	Hampden Park (Sussex)	d	05 54	06 55	07 30	07 50	..	08 44	..	09 35
26.15	$16\frac{1}{4}$	Eastbourne	a	05 58	06 59	07 34	07 53	08 31	08 47	09 00	09 39

a	Arrival time	f	Arr. 05 30
d	Departure time	h	Arr. 06 35
		j	Arr. 08 09

☕ Buffet counter or trolley service of drinks and cold snacks available for whole or part of journey

1. At what time does the 07.21 train from Hastings arrive at Normans Bay?

2. Mrs Tansley got to Bexhill station at 06.58. How long did she wait for the train, if it was on time?

3. (a) Which is the first train you can catch from Hastings after 6 o'clock in the morning?
   (b) At what time does the train in part (a) arrive at Hampden Park station?

4. If you need to be in Eastbourne before 08.45:
   (a) Which train should you catch from Hastings?
   (b) Which train should you catch from Collington?

5. At what time does the 8 o'clock train from Hastings arrive in Bexhill?

6. How many miles is it from Collington to Pevensey and Westham?

7. How many miles is it from Cooden Beach to Pevensey Bay?

8. How many kilometres is it from Bexhill to Eastbourne?

The following route chart shows four villages on a road that leads to the town of Carlton:

A bus company decided to start a bus service along the above route. They measured the distances between villages and the times needed to travel along the route. This information is written on the route chart.

Assume that you work for the bus company and are asked to draw up a timetable to show three journeys in each direction. You must take into consideration that some people need to travel to work in Carlton to be there before 08.30, and that they need to return home leaving Carlton after 5 o'clock in the evening.

Draw up a timetable as follows:

Westby to Carlton			
Westby			
Altby			
Todwick			
Worden			
Carlton			

Carlton to Westby			
Carlton			
Worden			
Todwick			
Altby			
Westby			

Complete your timetable by considering the given information.
Give reasons for the decisions you make.

Exercise 9 Holidays

Some prices of holidays in Lido di Jesolo are shown below:

Prices per person in pounds including airport charges—no surcharges														
Hotel and board arrangements		MIAMI (HB)		Child reduction	SANT ELENA (BB)				Child reduction	AQUILEIA (HB)				Child reduction
Hotel code		LLI			LSS					LLB				
Fights available		All Venetian Riv flights			All Venetian Riv flights					All Venetian Riv flights				
Nights in hotel		7	14		7	10	11	14		7	10	11	14	
DEPARTURES ON OR BETWEEN	1 May–8 May	126	171	35%	107	124	126	132	50%	135	164	169	187	70%
	9 May–15 May	131	177	35%	112	129	131	138	50%	140	170	175	194	70%
	16 May–26 May	148	198	25%	129	147	151	159	30%	160	191	197	218	50%
	27 May–5 June	160	212	25%	141	160	164	173	30%	173	204	210	230	50%
	6 June–19 June	167	221	25%	148	168	172	182	30%	177	212	219	239	50%
	20 June–3 July	171	225	25%	152	173	176	186	30%	181	214	221	243	50%
	4 July–10 July	180	243	25%	161	190	194	204	30%	190	232	239	262	50%
	11 July–17 July	185	257	15%	166	202	206	218	20%	195	246	253	276	40%
	18 July–10 Aug	192	271	15%	173	216	220	232	20%	203	259	267	290	40%
	11 Aug–24 Aug	185	257	15%	166	206	210	218	20%	194	241	249	273	40%
	25 Aug–31 Aug	180	238	15%	161	186	191	199	20%	189	229	236	255	40%
	1 Sept–30 Sept	167	214	25%	148	165	168	175	30%	177	206	213	234	50%
PLEASE QUOTE FLIGHT CODE, HOTEL AND NUMBER OF NIGHTS REQUIRED														
Remember to add any flight supplement and insurance: 7 nights £9.20; 10, 11, 14 nights £10.80														

Second child discounts (2–11 years inclusive, under 2 years—free):
1–15 May, 1–31 Oct —30%
16 May–10 July, 1-30 Sept—20%
11 July–31 Aug —15%

Italy: Venetian Riviera (Venice Airport)

Departure airport and flight-time	No. of nights	Day of departure	Departures	Approx. take-off time	Approx. home landing	Boeing 787 flight	Flight code	Supplement per person
Gatwick 2h	Sat	7/14	3 May–20 Sept	16.15	21.00		6265	£16
	Sat	11	3 May–13 Sept	16.15	22.15(Wed)		6265	£0
	Wed	7/14	7 May–17 Sept	17.30	22.15		6266	£0
	Wed	10	7 May–17 Sept	17.30	21.00(Sat)		6266	0
Luton 2h	Sat	7/14	3 May–20 Sept	15.45	20.30		6267	£19

Italy: Venetian Riviera (Venice Airport)

Departure airport and flight-time	No. of nights	Day of departure	Departures	Approx. take-off time	Approx. home landing	Boeing 787 flight	Flight code	Supplement per person
Manchester $2\frac{1}{4}$ h	Sat	7/14	3 May–20 Sept	15.00	04.00(Sun)		6268	£18
	Sat	11	3 May–13 Sept	15.00	13.30(Wed)		6268	£13
	Wed	7/14	7 May–17 Sept	08.00	13.30		6269	£13
	Wed	10	7 May–17 Sept	08.00	04.00(Sun)		6269	£2
Newcastle $2\frac{1}{2}$ h	Sat	14 F'ntly	3 May–6 Sept	22.30	20.30		6270	£29
Edinburgh ∅ $2\frac{3}{4}$ h	Sat	14 F'ntly	10 May–13 Sept	22.15	21.00		6271	£36

∅ Edinburgh departures: Add £12 on all holiday lengths, 5th July

1. Copy and complete the following to find the total cost for two adults to stay at the Aquileia for 11 nights flying from Manchester on a Saturday between 6 June and 19 June:

		£	p
Brochure price	2 @ £219	?	?
Flight supplement	2 @ £13	?	?
Insurance	2 @ £10.80	?	?
	Total cost	£ ?	?

2. (a) Find the cost for two adults to spend 14 nights at the Hotel Miami, including full insurance, if they travel between 11 Aug and 24 Aug and fly from Newcastle.
   (b) On what day do the adults in part (a) fly?
   (c) How long is the flight?

3. Mr and Mrs Williams took their 10-year-old son, Dafydd, to stay at the Saint Elena for 10 nights. They flew from Gatwick. If they set off during the first week in August, find:
   (a) the price per adult as printed in the brochure,
   (b) the amount of child reduction,
   (c) the amount payable for their son (not including insurance),
   (d) the total cost of their holiday including insurance,
   (e) the day of their outward flight.

4. Why do the Saint Elena's prices appear to be much cheaper than the other two hotels?

5. (a) If Mr and Mrs O'Neil went on holiday for 11 nights, setting off on 25 June, on which date will they have returned?
   (b) If Mr and Mrs Vidler went on holiday for 10 nights, setting off on a Wednesday, on which day of the week will they have returned?

6. Mr and Mrs Hurley and their two children, Christina and Alexandra, aged 4 and 7 years, stayed at the Hotel Aquileia for 14 nights flying from Luton on 18 Aug:
   (a) Find the brochure price per adult.
   (b) Find the child reduction for their first child.
   (c) Find the child reduction for their second child.
   (d) Find the total cost of the holiday including insurance.

8 Indices, Standard Form and Roots

Indices

Exercise 1

A Find the value of:

1. 3^2
2. 8^2
3. 0.3^2
4. 0.8^2
5. 2^5
6. 2^{10}
7. 3^5
8. 10^6

B Find the value of:

1. 3×2^2
2. $4^2 + 7$
3. $9^2 \div 3^2$
4. $2^4 - 2^3$
5. 4×10^3
6. $8^2 + 6^2$

C 1. Which has the greater value, 3^4 or 2^6?

2. Write the following in order of size giving the largest first:
   3^7, 2^8, 5^4, 6^4

3. Use a calculator to find the value of:
   (a) 18^2 (b) 2.4^2 (c) 9^4 (d) 5×7^3

4. If $y = x^2 + 8$, find the value of y when x equals:
   (a) 3   (b) 5   (c) 10   (d) 8   (e) 0

5. If $t = 2$, find the value of:
   (a) t^4 (b) $4t$ (c) $t + t + t + t$ (d) $t \times t \times t \times t$

6. Find the value of $p^3 - p^2$ when p equals:
   (a) 1   (b) 2   (c) 0   (d) 5   (e) 4

Exercise 2

1. Find the value of:
   (a) $(^-4)^2$ (b) $(^-2)^2$ (c) $(^-2)^3$ (d) $(^-10)^3$

2. If $n = {}^-3$, find the value of:
   (a) n^2 (b) n^3 (c) $2n^2$

3. If $x = {}^-5$, find the value of $2x^2$.

4. If $k = {}^-4$, find the value of $k^2 - 9$.

5. If $y = 3t^2 - 2$, find the value of y when $t = {}^-2$.

Exercise 3

e.g. 1   Express $7^4 \times 7^5$ as a single power of 7.
$$7^4 \times 7^5 = \underline{\underline{7^9}}$$

e.g. 2   Express $\dfrac{4^8}{4^2}$ as a single power of 4.
$$\frac{4^8}{4^2} = \underline{\underline{4^6}}$$

e.g. 3   Express $\dfrac{5^2 \times 5^7}{5^4}$ as a single power of 5.
$$\frac{5^2 \times 5^7}{5^4} = \frac{5^9}{5^4} = \underline{\underline{5^5}}$$

1. Express $2^5 \times 2^2$ as a single power of 2.

2. Express $8^4 \times 8^8$ as a single power of 8.

3. Express $\dfrac{3^8}{3^5}$ as a single power of 3.

4. Express $6^9 \div 6^5$ as a single power of 6.

5. Express $\dfrac{9^4 \times 9^5}{9^6}$ as a single power of 9.

6. Express $\dfrac{4^{10}}{4^3 \times 4^4}$ as a single power of 4.

7. Express $\dfrac{7^6 \times 7^8}{7^9}$ as a single power of 7.

8. Express $\dfrac{10^7 \times 10^9}{10^4}$ as a single power of 10.

Exercise 4

Simplify the following, leaving your answers in index form:

A 1. $n^4 \times n^2$

5. $4x \times 2x$

9. $\dfrac{6d^6}{3d^3}$

2. $h^5 \div h^2$

6. $4x \times 2x^2$

10. $2v^2 \times 4v^4$

3. $\dfrac{m^{10}}{m^5}$

7. $4x^3 \times 2x^2$

11. $10f \times 3f^7$

4. $4 \times 2x^2$

8. $\dfrac{4u^3}{2u}$

12. $12p^5 \div 4p$

B 1. $a^2c^4 \times a^3c^2$

5. $4p^3q^5 \times 3p^3$

2. $ef^3 \times e^2f^4$

6. $6l^4m^6 \times l^5m^2$

3. $2n^3p \times 3n^4p^3$

7. $8t^6u \times 2t^6u$

4. $5gh \times 3g^2h^5$

8. $2d^2j \times 4dj^2$

C 1. $\dfrac{m^3 \times m^7}{m^4}$

5. $\dfrac{12n^8r^2}{6n^3r^2}$

2. $\dfrac{a^6 \times a^3}{a^5}$

6. $\dfrac{10e^4}{2e^4}$

3. $\dfrac{4c^3d^5}{2cd^2}$

7. $\dfrac{8h^5i^4}{4h^3i^2}$

4. $9t^4u^8 \div 3t^2u^2$

8. $18g^7k^5 \div 12g^3k^2$

Negative Indices

Exercise 5

Express each of the following as a single power, *then* find its value:

1. $\dfrac{2^4}{2^6}$

2. $\dfrac{3^5}{3^7}$

3. $\dfrac{10^7}{10^9}$

4. $5^4 \div 5^6$

5. $\dfrac{2^4 \times 2^2}{2^9}$

6. $\dfrac{7^7}{7^4 \times 7^5}$

7. $\dfrac{3^4 \times 3^6}{3^8 \times 3^5}$

8. $\dfrac{8^4 \times 8^2}{8^8}$

Exercise 6

Simplify the following by expressing each one as a single power:

1. $\dfrac{a^2}{a^5}$

2. $c^3 \div c^7$

3. $\dfrac{n^4 \times n^2}{n^9}$

4. $\dfrac{u^4}{u^6 \times u^3}$

5. $\dfrac{m \times m^7}{m^9}$

6. $\dfrac{t^4 \times t^7}{t^5 \times t^9}$

7. $\dfrac{z^6 \times z^3}{z^7 \times z^5}$

8. $\dfrac{v^6 - v}{v^{15}}$

Exercise 7

Find the value of:

1. 3^{-3}

2. 2^{-4}

3. 4^{-2}

4. 9^{-2}

5. 2^{-1}

6. 10^{-3}

7. 10^{-5}

8. 10^{-1}

9. 3^{-4}

10. 5^{-3}

11. 15^{-2}

12. 12^{-2}

Standard Form

Exercise 8

A Write in standard form:

1. 3840
2. 497
3. 74 600
4. 824 000
5. 1 900 000
6. 0.0046
7. 0.000 819
8. 0.007
9. 0.000 02
10. 0.012
11. 0.76
12. 716 000
13. 0.0716
14. 0.000 008
15. 8 000 000

B Write the numbers in standard form:

1. Salzburg, in Austria, is 1427 ft above sea level.

2. Madrid, in Spain, has, on average, 2843 h of sunshine each year.

3. (a) In 1976, there were 420 000 pieces of diamond jewellery sold in the UK, excluding diamond engagement rings.
   (b) In 1976, there were 6 227 000 pieces of diamond jewellery sold in the USA, excluding diamond engagement rings.

4. (a) The wavelength of orange light is 0.000 000 6 m.
   (b) The wavelength of blue light is 0.000 000 5 m.

5. The area of Australia is about:
   (a) 2 968 000 sq. miles   (b) 7 687 000 km^2

6. The World Trade Centre in New York has 110 storeys and is 381 m high.

7. Mars is almost 228 million kilometres from the Sun.

8. A balance, manufactured in West Germany, can weigh objects of up to 0.5 g to an accuracy of 0.000 000 01 g, which is considerably less than the weight of the ink in this full stop.

9. 1 cm is about 0.39 in.

10. The diameter of a haemoglobin molecule is 0.000 000 007 m.

Exercise 9

1. Write half a million in standard form.

2. Work out the following, writing each answer in standard form:
   (a) 460 000 + 27 000
   (b) 298 000 + $\frac{1}{4}$ of a million
   (c) 4 × (5.8 × 10^4)
   (d) (1.9 × 10^3) × 20
   (e) (6.4 × 10^8) ÷ 20
   (f) (4.25 × 10^{13}) × 316

3. An aircraft's speed of Mach* 3.0 is 3.185 35 × 10^3 km/h.
   Mach 6.0 is twice as fast. How fast is that?

* See the glossary, p. 469.

4. The speed of a radar signal is 3×10^8 m/s. How far does the signal travel in 4 s? (Give your answer in standard form.)

5. If 1 mm $= 3.94 \times 10^{-2}$ in, write, in standard form, the number of inches in 6 mm.

Roots

Exercise 10

A Find:
1. $\sqrt{16}$
2. $\sqrt{81}$
3. $\sqrt{100}$
4. $\sqrt{121}$
5. $\sqrt{144}$

B Estimate the following square roots by giving two numbers, to one significant figure, between which the square roots lie:

e.g. $\sqrt{620}$ lies between 20 and 30.

1. $\sqrt{80}$
2. $\sqrt{40}$
3. $\sqrt{300}$
4. $\sqrt{7000}$
5. $\sqrt{88}$
6. $\sqrt{140}$
7. $\sqrt{6.9}$
8. $\sqrt{327}$
9. $\sqrt{29.6}$
10. $\sqrt{5}$
11. $\sqrt{0.05}$
12. $\sqrt{0.5}$

C Answer the following using a calculator. Give each answer correct to three significant figures.

1. $\sqrt{29}$
2. $\sqrt{67}$
3. $\sqrt{200}$
4. $\sqrt{384}$
5. $\sqrt{9216}$
6. $\sqrt{73\,000}$
7. $\sqrt{15.7}$
8. $\sqrt{38.6}$
9. $\sqrt{0.475}$
10. $\sqrt{0.186}$
11. $\sqrt{0.0086}$
12. $\sqrt{0.0431}$

The units digit of 7^3 is 3. ($7 \times 7 = \underline{49}$ $7 \times 9 = \underline{63}$)

The units digit of 43^3 is 7. ($3 \times 3 = \underline{9}$ $3 \times 9 = \underline{27}$)

$7^3 = 7 \times 7 \times 7 = 343$ (The *cube* of 7 is 343.)

Since $343 = 7^3$

$\sqrt[3]{343} = 7$ (The *cube root* of 343 is 7.)

Exercise 11

A Find the units digit for the following cubes:

1. 4^3 **2.** 9^3 **3.** 6^3 **4.** 8^3 **5.** 2^3

B Find the following:

1. the cube root of 27
2. $\sqrt[3]{8}$
3. $\sqrt[3]{125}$
4. the cube root of 1
5. the cube root of 216
6. $\sqrt[3]{512}$
7. the cube root of 1000
8. $\sqrt[3]{729}$

Revision Exercises I to VIII

Revision Exercise I

1. List the set of factors of 30.

2. List the set of multiples of 3 that lie between 25 and 35.

3. List the set of prime numbers that are less than 25.

4. The Venn diagram shows how many fish (set *F*) and how many bags of chips (set *C*) were eaten by some people (no one ate more than one of each):
   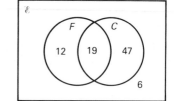
   (*a*) How many had only chips?
   (*b*) How many had fish and chips?
   (*c*) How many did not have fish?

5. Copy the Venn diagram. Complete it to show the number of people who had a ruler or a set square, given that: 26 people had both a ruler and a set square; 3 people had a set square but no ruler; 5 did not have a ruler and 47 had either a ruler or a set square or both.

   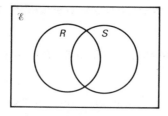

   (*a*) How many had a ruler but no set square?
   (*b*) How many did not have a ruler or a set square?
   (*c*) How many had a set square?

Revision Exercise II

1. A calculator's display shows: $\boxed{2.5638}$
   Write this number correct to:
   (a) three decimal places,
   (b) three significant figures,
   (c) one decimal place.

2. A box weighed 24.85 kg. Write its mass correct to the nearest kilogram.

3. The mountain that Samantha climbed was 23 482 ft high. Write its height correct to:
   (a) the nearest hundred feet,
   (b) the nearest thousand feet.

4. There were $3\,\ell$ of water in the bucket correct to the nearest litre. Write down the lowest and highest possible amounts of water in the bucket.

5. The number of people at a match was 26 000 correct to the nearest 1000. Write down the lowest and highest possible attendance.

6. A rectangular patio measures 6 m by 4 m, both measurements being correct to the nearest metre:
   (a) Write down the limits between which the length lies.
   (b) Write down the limits between which the breadth lies.
   (c) Calculate the minimum perimeter of the patio.
   (d) Calculate the maximum perimeter of the patio.
   (e) Calculate the minimum area of the patio.
   (f) Calculate the maximum area of the patio.

7. A pack of 6 packet of crisps cost £0.98. Find the cost of one packet of crisps.

8. Halim saved £8.85 per month for 8 months. *Estimate* the total amount saved.

9. Write the units digit of the answer to the calculation 238×49.

10. Choose the correct answer to 7.8×3.2:
    A. 25.24   B. 24.96   C. 252.4   D. 249.6

1. Consider the numbers 3, 4, 8, 9, 15, 19, 24:
  (*a*) Which of the numbers are prime?
  (*b*) Which of the numbers are multiples of 3?
  (*c*) Which of the numbers are factors of 36?
  (*d*) Which three numbers in the list total 28?
  (*e*) 19 + $\boxed{?}$ = a multiple of 9. Find the missing number from the given list of numbers.

2. Write down all the odd numbers that are factors of 45.

3. What is the smallest number that should be added to 157 to make it a multiple of 8?

4. Write the number 60 as a product of prime factors.

5. Write three multiples of 5 that are also multiples of 4.

6. Consider the numbers:
      4, 7, 10, 12, 18, 24, 31, 35, 40
  (*a*) Find numbers *a* and *b* in the list such that $a = 5b$.
  (*b*) Find numbers *c*, *d* and *e* in the list such that $c(d - e) = 32$.

7. Explain how to check whether or not a number is exactly divisible by 9.

8. List the common factors of 24 and 28.

9. List the common multiples of 10 and 12 as far as 120.

10. Copy the following number line:

On your number line mark and label:
  (*a*) the whole numbers 1 and 5,
  (*b*) the integers ⁻2 and 3,
  (*c*) the rational numbers $\frac{1}{2}$, $^-3\frac{1}{2}$, ⁻4.5,
  (*d*) the irrational numbers $^+\sqrt{7}$, $^-\sqrt{3}$.

11. A share was priced at 403 p on Monday. The daily changes throughout the week were $^-8$, $^+3$, $^-5$, $^+1$, $^+2$. What was the price of the share after these changes?

12. Is it true that $^-1.7 > {}^-2.1$?

13. Write the first six terms of the sequence that obeys the rule 'Multiply by 5 then add 3'. Using the numbers $\{1, 2, 3, 4, 5, 6\}$.

Revision Exercise IV

1. Total the following sums of money:
£1.64 + £0.23 + 67 p + 67 p + £0.19 + £0.19 + 84 p + 76 p

2. Work out: $7 + 2 \times 8$

3. Insert brackets to make the statement correct:
$$12 - 3 \times 8 - 6 = 18$$

4. Teresa had a $\frac{7}{16}$ in spanner. Write the size as a decimal of an inch.

5. There were 16 faulty parts out of a batch of 400. What percentage were faulty?

6. In a socket set there were:
18 metric sockets, 10 to 32 mm;
15AF sockets, $\frac{3}{8}$ to $1\frac{1}{4}$ in;
and 9 Whitworth sockets, $\frac{1}{8}$ to $\frac{5}{8}$ in:

SOCKET SET

(a) If the 9 Whitworth sockets increased in intervals of one-sixteenth of an inch and if four of the sockets were $\frac{1}{8}$ in, $\frac{5}{8}$ in, $\frac{1}{4}$ in and $\frac{7}{16}$ in, list all 9 sockets in order of size from smallest to largest.

(b) If the 15AF sockets also increase in intervals of one-sixteenth of an inch, list all 15 sockets in order of size from smallest to largest.

7. (*a*) There were 15 packets of stamps with 20 stamps in each packet. How many stamps were there altogether?

(*b*) If the stamps in part (*a*) were put into packets of 25, how many packets would there be?

8. Work out $\dfrac{43 \times 81}{47 - 33}$ giving your answer correct to one decimal place.

9. (*a*) Find the exact value of $\dfrac{6.3 \times 2.9}{4.8}$.

(*b*) Write the answer to part (*a*) correct to two significant figures.

10. Work out:

(*a*) $2\dfrac{1}{6} + 4\dfrac{7}{8}$ (*c*) $5\dfrac{5}{6} \times 1\dfrac{4}{5}$

(*b*) $5\dfrac{1}{6} - 3\dfrac{1}{2}$ (*d*) $1\dfrac{1}{8} \div 1\dfrac{1}{2}$

11. $1\dfrac{3}{10} \times 4\dfrac{3}{4}$ can be worked out on a calculator by pressing the keys $\boxed{\text{AC}}\ \boxed{1}\ \boxed{\cdot}\ \boxed{3}\ \boxed{\times}\ \boxed{4}\ \boxed{\cdot}\ \boxed{7}\ \boxed{5}\ \boxed{=}$.

(*a*) Show which keys to press to work out $1\dfrac{4}{5} \times 2\dfrac{1}{2}$.

(*b*) Find the answer to $1\dfrac{4}{5} \times 2\dfrac{1}{2}$.

12. Work out $9\dfrac{1}{4} - 3\dfrac{3}{4} \times 1\dfrac{1}{6}$.

13. Pam had £5.60 to spend. She spent $\frac{1}{4}$ of the money in one shop then $\frac{2}{3}$ of the remainder in another. If she spent a further 84 p, how much did she have left?

14. If Marie drank $1\frac{1}{4}\ \ell$ of orange juice each week, how much would she drink in (*a*) 8 weeks? (*b*) 6 weeks?

15. Find the remainder when:

(*a*) 841 is divided by 9, (*b*) 690 is divided by 45.

16. Work out:

(*a*) $3 + {}^{-}5$ (*c*) ${}^{-}9 \times {}^{-}3$

(*b*) ${}^{-}5 - 2$ (*d*) ${}^{-}6 \div 2$

1. (a) Measure angle ABD.
   (b) If ∠BCD = 55°, calculate the size of angle BDC.

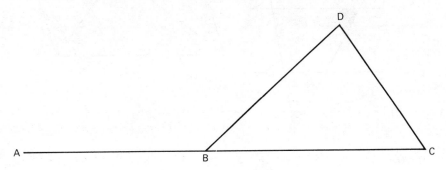

2. Calculate the size of each labelled angle:

(a)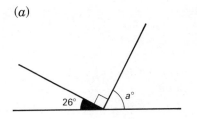

(b)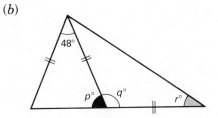

3. The diagram shows a tea
   trolley. Calculate the angle
   marked.

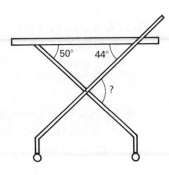

4. Calculate the angles labelled with letters:

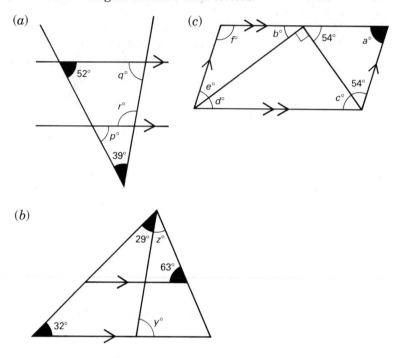

(a)

52° q°

r°

p°

39°

(b)

29° z°

63°

32°

y°

(c)

f°

b°

54°

a°

e°

d°

54°

c°

5. Three angles of a quadrilateral measure 124°, 58° and 107°. Calculate the size of the fourth angle.

6. (a) Calculate the size of an interior angle of a regular pentagon.
(b) Calculate the size of an interior angle of a regular 10-sided polygon.
(c) Will a 10-sided regular polygon and two regular pentagons fit together at a point without overlapping and without leaving any gaps?
(d) Will 10-sided regular polygons tessellate with regular pentagons?
(e) Check your answer to part (d) by trying to tessellate some cut-out 10-sided regular polygons and regular pentagons. Do they tessellate?

7. The diagram shows a tangent to a circle, centre O. Calculate the value of x.

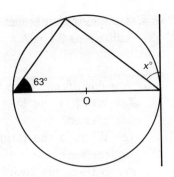

8. In the given circle, centre O, calculate the values of a and b.

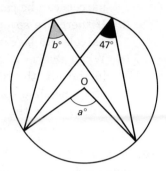

Revision Exercise VI

1. How many millimetres are there in 8.15 m?

2. To hang a picture, two eyelets are fixed on the back. The eyelets are placed 240 mm apart, as shown. The picture measures 40 cm by 25 cm. How far will the eyelets be from the upright edges of the picture?

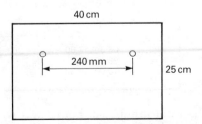

3. If a dress is made from 2.32 m of material, what is the total length needed to make 5 of the dresses?

4. How many suits can be made from 100 yd of material if each suit needs $3\frac{1}{2}$ yd?

5. A goods lift carries a maximum load of 120 kg:
  (*a*) What is the largest number of 4 kg parcels that can be carried?
  (*b*) What is the largest number of 9 kg parcels that can be carried?
  (*c*) If there are twenty 4 kg parcels in the lift, how many 9 kg parcels can be carried with them?
  (*d*) If there are seven 9 kg parcels in the lift, how many 4 kg parcels can be carried with them?
  (*e*) When twelve 9 kg parcels and three 4 kg parcels are put in the lift, the maximum load of 120 kg is reached. Find other possible combinations of 9 kg and 4 kg parcels that will also use the maximum load of 120 kg.

6. A lorry driver made two deliveries to a building site. He delivered $6\frac{1}{2}$ t of sand on his first delivery and $5\frac{3}{4}$ t on his second. Calculate the total mass of sand delivered by the lorry driver.

7. Nerys drank $\frac{1}{2}$ pt of water each morning. After how many mornings would she have drunk 2 gal? (8 pt = 1 gal)

8. The opening times of a garden centre are shown.

GARDEN CENTRE

OPENING TIMES:

Mon–Fri 08.30–17.00
Sat 08.30–16.00
Sun 10.00–16.30

  (*a*) Find the total number of hours in a week that the garden centre is open.
  (*b*) Write Sunday's closing time using the 12-hour clock notation.

9. If 18 May is a Friday, write the dates of all the Tuesdays in May.

10. Edith's d.o.b. (date of birth) is 30–10–79. How old will she be on 12 April 2021?

Revision Exercise VII ━━━━━━━━━━━━━━━━━━ **M**

1. Copy the correct sentence:
   A. The temperature was minus 3 degrees Centigrade.
   B. The temperature was minus 3 degrees Celsius.
   C. The temperature was negative 3 degrees Celsius.
   D. The temperature was negative 3 degrees Centigrade.

2. (*a*) Write the reading shown on the following meters:

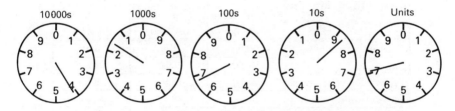

   (*b*) If 1028 further units were used, write down the new meter reading.
   (*c*) Show the new meter reading on a set of dials.

3. An electricity meter showed the reading 12 693 in February and 13 371 in May:
   (*a*) How many units of electricity were used during that quarter?
   (*b*) If electricity cost 5.7 p per unit plus a quarterly charge of £6.60, find the total cost of electricity used during the given quarter.

4. The table on the next page shows what a pint of milk provides:

	Pasteurised 3.8% fat	Homogenised 3.8% fat	Channel Islands 4.8% fat
Calories (energy)	380	380	445
Fat	22.2 g	22.2 g	28.1 g
Protein	19.3 g	19.3 g	21.1 g
Carbohydrate (lactose)	27.5 g	27.5 g	27.5 g
Calcium	702 mg	702 mg	702 mg

What a pint of milk provides

	Semi-skimmed 1.8% fat	Skimmed 0.1% fat	Sterilised 3.8% fat
Calories (energy)	280	195	380
Fat	10.5 g	0.6 g	22.2 g
Protein	19.5 g	19.9 g	19.3 g
Carbohydrate (lactose)	28.4 g	29.3 g	27.5 g
Calcium	729 mg	761 mg	702 mg

(a) Which sort of milk contains the most fat?
(b) Which sort of milk contains the least fat?
(c) How many grams of protein does 1 pt of sterilised milk contain?
(d) How many grams of carbohydrate are there in 1 gal of semi-skimmed milk? (8 pt = 1 gal)
(e) Which sort of milk contains the most calcium?
(f) Which type of milk would you choose to drink? Give a reason for your choice.

5. Part of a timetable is shown:

15 01	15 31	15 40	Brighton	16 44	17 14	17 43
15 04	15 34	15 43	Preston Park	16 41	17 11	17 40
15 12	15 42	15 51	Hassocks	16 34	17 04	17 33
15 15	15 45	15 56	Burgess Hill	16 30	17 00	17 29
15 17	15 47	15 58	Wivelsfield	16 28	16 58	17 27
15 22	15 52	16 07f	Haywards Heath	16 24	16 54	17 23
15 28	15 58	16 12	Balcombe	16 18	—	17 17
15 35	16 04	16 20	Three Bridges	16 12	16 44	17 11
15 39	16 09	16 24	Gatwick Airport	16 07	16 39	17 06

f arrives 5 min earlier

Answer the following questions using the given timetable:

(a) At what time does the 15.42 from Hassocks arrive at Three Bridges?

(b) At what time does the 16.18 from Balcombe arrive at Preston Park?

(c) The 16.54 from Haywards Heath was quarter of an hour late in arriving at Brighton. At what time did it arrive at Brighton?

(d) I need to be at Gatwick Airport before four o'clock, which train must I catch from Burgess Hill?

(e) Which of the given trains is the fastest in travelling from Gatwick Airport to Brighton?

6. Using the tables given in Exercise 9 on p. 84, find the total cost for 2 adults together with their 9-year-old daughter to stay at the Hotel Miami for 7 nights. They flew from Luton and set off on the 1 June. (Include the holiday insurance in the total cost.)

Revision Exercise VIII

1. Find the value of: (a) 9^2 (b) 0.2^2

2. Find the value of: (a) 2^6 (b) 4^3

3. Find the value of: (a) 4×3^2 (b) $2^5 - 2^3$

4. Use a calculator to find 2.98^2 correct to four significant figures.

5. If $y = x^2 - 4$, find y when $x = 7$.

6. Find the value of: (a) $(-3)^2$ (b) $(^-10)^4$

7. Find the value of $4m^2$ when $m = {}^-2$.

8. Express $\dfrac{6^3 \times 6^7}{6^5}$ as a single power of 6.

9. Simplify the following, leaving your answers in index form:

(a) $3x^2 \times 2x^4$ (b) $\dfrac{15t^5}{3t^2}$ (c) $\dfrac{n^8 \times n^7}{n^9}$

10. Simplify, leaving answers in index form:

(a) $6v^3t^2 \times 2vt^4$ (b) $\dfrac{18h^7d^9}{6h^4d^7}$

11. Express $\dfrac{3^4}{3^7}$ as a single power of 3, then find its value.

12. Express $\dfrac{2^7 \times 2^9}{2^{20}}$ as a single power of 2, then find its value.

13. Simplify $\dfrac{u^5 \times u^3}{u^4 \times u^7}$ by expressing it as a single power of u.

14. Find the value of: (a) 2^{-3} (b) 5^{-2}

15. (a) Work out $\frac{1}{2}$ million + 84 thousand.
(b) Write the answer to part (a) in standard form.

16. In 1976, 432 000 lb of gold was made into jewellery in the UK. Write the number in standard form.

17. The mass of one atom of oxygen is about 0.000 000 000 000 000 000 000 026 6 g. Write this mass in standard form.

18. The mass of one atom of hydrogen is about 1.66×10^{-24} g. Find the mass of two atoms of hydrogen. Give the answer in standard form.

19. Using a calculator, find $\sqrt{4826}$ correct to three significant figures.

20. The cube root of 64 is:
  A. 2   B. $21\frac{1}{3}$ C. 4   D. 8   E. $\frac{1}{4}$

9 Finance and Percentages

1. Deborah is paid £3.40 per hour for the first 38 h worked in a week. Overtime is paid at time and a half.

(a) How much will she earn for 38 h work?

(b) How much will she earn for 1 h overtime?

(c) How much will she earn for 7 h overtime?

(d) She worked 45 h in one week. How much did she earn?

(e) If during one week she earned £159.80, for how many hours did she work?

2. Rodney is paid £4.20 an hour. If he works from 08.15 to 18.00 and has a 45 min lunch break during which he is not paid:

(a) How many hours does he work?

(b) How much does he earn for a day's work?

3. Mr Parry earns £9800 per year.

Mr Locke earns £173 per week.

Mrs Jameson earns £795 per month.

(a) How much does Mrs Jameson earn in a year?

(b) How much does Mr Locke earn in a year, if he is paid for 52 weeks' work?

(c) Who earns the most?

(d) If Mr Parry gets a 5% salary increase, what will his new salary be?

4. Warwick earned £490 per month. If he got a 6.5% pay rise, calculate his new monthly earnings.

5. Mrs Ardener earned £7035 per year. How much is that per month?

6. Mr Alexander earned £154 per week gross. Deductions totalled £47.60. Calculate his net weekly wage.

7. Mrs Earnshaw earned £4.90 per hour for a basic working week of 40 h. Overtime was paid at time and a half rate. Her National Insurance came to £22.93, while her tax was £65.84. Copy and complete the following pay slip for a week in which Mrs Earnshaw worked 48 h.

Name	Basic wage	Over-time	Gross pay	National Insurance	Income tax	Net pay
Mrs Earnshaw						

Exercise 2   Spending Money   M

1. Adrienne spent £17.95 at one shop and £14.56 at another. If she set off with £40, find out how much money she had left.

2. Terry bought 7 pencils for £1. He used a calculator to find the cost of 1 pencil. The display showed:

$$0.1428571$$

What was the cost of 1 pencil correct to the nearest penny?

3. At a microwave centre, model 238A cost £320 plus VAT, while model 319B cost £290 plus VAT. If VAT is 15%:
   (a) Find the price of model 238A including VAT.
   (b) Find the price of model 319B including VAT.
   (c) How much cheaper is the actual selling price of model 319B than model 238A?
   (d) Find the discount off model 238A, if there is 15% off the actual selling price.
   (e) Find the total hire-purchase price of model 319B, if it is sold on the following terms:
         Deposit of £60
         12 monthly payments of £26

4. A bookshop held a sale. Mrs Read sent for some postal bargains. Copy and complete the invoice.

BARGAIN BOOKS							
Qty	Book number				Title	£	p
1	T	3	1	2	*The Good Road Guide*	7	50
1	T	3	2	6	*Where to Stay*	4	99
1	P	2	9	1	*Photography: A Traveller's Guide*	11	95
					Order Value		
					Less 20% discount		
					Sub-total		
					Add postage	2	15
					Total cost		

5. A newspaper advertisement costs £1.10 per line per day. Find the cost of the ad shown if it is placed for 3 days.

For sale : 3-piece suite in green velour. 3-seater settee and recliner chair. Excellent condition. £150 o.n.o. Tel. (0243) 64215 after 6 p.m.

6. Mr and Mrs Lowe's water services charge for a year was £139.80:
   (a) If the amount was paid in two equal instalments, how much would each instalment be?
   (b) If they saved monthly to pay the £139.80, how much should they have saved each month?
   (c) If they saved weekly to pay the £139.80, how much should they have saved each week?

Exercise 3 Arithmetical Examples of Pricing

A Find the cost of:

1. 2 jars of coffee at £3.64 each,

2. a 14 lb turkey at 70 p per pound,

3. 1.8 m of elastic at 10 p per metre,

4. a 21 cm zip at 2 p per cm,

5. 5 gal of petrol at £1.73 per gallon,

6. 40 ℓ of petrol at 37.8 p per litre,

7. 220 therms of gas at 38 p per therm,

8. 4 batteries at £1.49 each.

B Find the total cost of materials shown below that are needed to make some curtains:

3.6 m curtain material at £4.35 per metre   = £ ?
3.6 m curtain lining at £1.65 per metre   = £ ?
2.5 m rufflette tape at 70 p per metre   = £ ?
1 reel of thread at 35 p each   = £ ?
2 packs of curtain hooks at 50 p per pack   = £ ?

Exercise 4 Best Buys

1. Sheen shampoo is sold in three different-sized bottles. Which is the best buy? (Show how you obtained your answer.)

150 mℓ SHAMPOO   200 mℓ SHAMPOO   250 mℓ SHAMPOO

53 p   69 p   84 p

2. Two different sizes of jars of jam are sold: a 12 oz jar for 49 p and a 1 lb jar (that is, 16 oz) for 57 p. Which is the better buy?

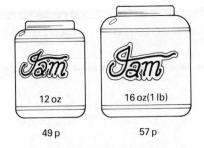

12 oz   16 oz (1 lb)

49 p   57 p

3. A 340 g jar of jam costs 46 p, while a 454 g jar costs 59 p. Which is the better buy?

4. A 725 mℓ bottle of orange costs 79 p while a 1.25 ℓ bottle costs £1.39. Which is the better value?

5. A 185 g tin of tuna costs 54 p, while a 213 g tin costs 63 p. Which is the better buy?

Percentages

Exercise 5 Percentage of a Quantity

1. Find 10% of £289.

2. Find 40% of £8.50.

3. Find 75% of £52.

4. Find 8% of £92.

5. Find 13% of £45.

6. Find 7.3% of £70.

7. Find $5\frac{3}{4}$% of £120.

8. Find 11.26% of £5 correct to the nearest penny.

9. Find 6.19% of £18.30 correct to the nearest penny.

10. Find $9\frac{3}{8}$% of £250 correct to the nearest penny.

Exercise 6   Expression of One Quantity as a Percentage of Another

A **1.** Express £6 as a percentage of £30.

2. Express £15 as a percentage of £20.

3. Express £2.16 as a percentage of £7.20.

4. Express 12 kg as a percentage of 80 kg.

5. Express 1.25 ℓ as a percentage of 2 ℓ.

6. Express 1.8 kg as a percentage of 4.5 kg.

B **1.** There were 12 boys and 18 girls in a class:
(*a*) What percentage of the class were boys?
(*b*) What percentage of the class were girls?

2. In a survey about building societies, 378 people out of 864 people questioned had some money in a building society account:
(*a*) What percentage of those questioned had money in a building society account?
(*b*) Write the answer to part (*a*) correct to the nearest 1%.

3. A cinema can seat 1250 people. What percentage of the seats were filled when 850 people were at the cinema?

4. Mrs Todd paid £45.15 for a jacket in a sale. If the normal price of the jacket was £52.50:
(*a*) What was the discount?
(*b*) What was the percentage discount?

Percentage Change

Exercise 7

1. A typewriter cost £215 plus 15% VAT:
(*a*) How much was the VAT?
(*b*) What was the price inclusive of VAT?

2. A holiday cost £385. If there was an 8% surcharge on top of this price, how much would the surcharge be?

3. Mr Usher normally paid £2.25 per day in bus fares. If his fare increased by 8%, calculate the daily increase in cost.

4. A car costing £8500 lost 20% of its value during the first year:
   (a) What is the car's value after one year?
   (b) After 18 months, the car owner sold the car at 13% less than the one-year-old price. Calculate the selling price.

5. A house valued at £29 500, appreciated in value by 7% over the year. Calculate the new valuation of the house.

6. Mrs Webster earned £125 per week. If she was given a 6.4% pay rise, calculate her new weekly earnings.

7. There was a 15% child reduction on a holiday price of £290. What is the cost after such a reduction?

8. A firm employing 285 people increased its work force by 13%. How many more people now work for the firm?

Exercise 8   Calculating the Percentage Change

1. A shopkeeper bought an article for £24 then sold it for £30. Calculate the percentage profit.

2. A shopkeeper bought an article for £35 then sold it for £47.60. Calculate the percentage profit.

3. A car was bought for £7950, then sold for £4929 one year later:
   (a) What was the selling price?
   (b) Calculate the percentage depreciation.

4. The price of a carton of milk price increased from 35 p to 37 p. Calculate the percentage increase, giving the answer correct to one decimal place.

5. Mrs Yeoman's train fare was £9.25. The following week, the fare had increased to £9.85.
   (a) By how much had the fare increased?
   (b) Calculate the percentage increase correct to one decimal place.

6. In a sale, a price was reduced from £7.95 to £6.36. What was the percentage reduction?

7. A stadium that used to seat 56 000 people now seats 63 000 people. Calculate the percentage change in the seating.

8. 24 m^2 of Mr Timpson's garden is used for growing vegetables. If this area is increased to 33 m^2, find the percentage increase in area used.

Finding the New Quantity

% increase
If a quantity is increased by 15%:

New Quantity = 100% of original + 15% of original
                    quantity   quantity
                = 115% of original quantity
                = 1.15 × original quantity

% decrease
If a quantity is decreased by 15%:

New quantity = 100% of original − 15% of original
                    quantity   quantity
                = 85% of original quantity
                = 0.85 × original quantity

Exercise 9

1. A clock cost £17.80 plus 15% VAT. Calculate the cost including VAT.

2. (*a*) Mr Armer earned £8950 p.a. If he got a 5% pay rise, calculate his new annual salary.
(*b*) Mrs Birchall earned £10 640 p.a. If she got a 5.3% pay rise, calculate her new annual salary.

3. Find the cost of a holiday that originally cost £329, if a 5% surcharge has been added.

4. Tyres costing £186 are sold at 30% discount:
(*a*) Calculate the discount price.
(*b*) If VAT at 15% needs to be added to the discount price, find the price inclusive of VAT.

5. A finance company charges a flat rate of 13.5% interest on loans made for one year. Calculate the total repayable on the following loans.

(*a*) £100   (*b*) £750   (*c*) £2280   (*d*) £1054

6. A piece of material of length 3.4 m shrank by 5% while being washed. Calculate the new length.

Appreciation and Depreciation

Certain items, such as houses, antiques or certain other valuables appreciate in value (that is, increase in value) as time passes. If something increases in value by the same percentage each year, a calculator can be used to work out its new value.

e.g. 1   An antique chest is valued at £450. Its value increases by 8% each year for 3 years. Find its value after 3 years.

Value after 1 year   = 108% of original value

= 1.08 × £450

= £486

Value after 2 years = 108% of 1st-year value

= 1.08 × £486

= £524.88

Value after 3 years = 1.08 × £524.88

= £566.8704

= £566.87   correct to the nearest penny

The above can be worked out on a calculator by first clearing the memory and the display, then by keying in:

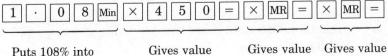

Puts 108% into   Gives value   Gives value   Gives value
the memory   after 1 year   after 2 years after 3 years

e.g. 2   A car valued at £8460 depreciates by 18% each year for 3 years. Find its value after 3 years.

Value after 1 year $= 82\%$ of £8460

$= 0.82 \times £8460$

$= £6937.20$

Value after 2 years $= 0.82 \times £6937.20$

$= £5688.50$ (£5688.504)

Value after 3 years $= 0.82 \times £5688.504$

$= \underline{£4664.57}$ (to nearest penny)

Exercise 10

A For each question, find the value after 3 years of the given amount of money if it *appreciates* at the given rate:

1. £260 at 5% p.a.   **3.** £1800 at $12\frac{1}{2}\%$ p.a.

2. £870 at 15% p.a.   **4.** £2995 at $7\frac{3}{4}\%$ p.a.

B For each question, find the value after 3 years of the given amount of money if it *depreciates* at the given rate:

1. £500 at 3% p.a.   **3.** £12 600 at 23% p.a.

2. £2000 at 12% p.a.   **4.** £765 at $8\frac{1}{4}\%$ p.a.

C **1.** Rory's motor bike cost £1250. If its value depreciated by 16% each year, find how much it was worth after 3 years.

2. Mrs Judson bought a house for £32 000. Its value increased by 8% each year. Find its value after 2 years.

3. A car, costing £8950 new, depreciated in value at a rate of 21% p.a. Find its value after:
(*a*) 2 years,   (*b*) 3 years.

4. Mr Oxley's stamp collection was valued at £4130. If its value increased by 14% p.a. find its value after:

(a) 2 years,   (b) 3 years.

Exercise 11   Profit and Loss

1. A shopkeeper bought an article for £23.75, then sold it for £29.49. How much profit was made?

2. A guitar was bought for £85, then sold to make 15% profit. What was the selling price?

3. A house was bought for £36 000, then sold for £45 000:
   (a) Calculate the profit.
   (b) Express the profit as a percentage of the buying price.

4. Jack bought a record for £5.50, then sold it for £3.85:
   (a) How much did he lose on the sale?
   (b) Express the loss as a percentage of the buying price.

5. A shopkeeper bought 20 articles at £12.50 each. 15 articles were then sold at £18 each, while the rest were sold at £15 each.
   (a) How much altogether did the shopkeeper pay for the articles?
   (b) What were the total takings from the sale of the articles?
   (c) What was the percentage profit on the total sales?

Finding the Price before a Percentage Increase

If an article is sold at a profit of 20%, then:

$$SP = 120\% \text{ of } CP \quad (CP = \text{cost price} \quad SP = \text{selling price})$$

$$SP = 1.2 \times CP$$

$$1.2 \times CP = SP$$

so $\quad CP = \dfrac{SP}{1.2}$

e.g. A television set was sold for £345, the profit from the sale being 20%. Find the cost price.

$$SP = 1.2 \times CP$$

$$1.2 \times CP = SP$$

$$CP = \frac{SP}{1.2}$$

$$CP = £\frac{345}{1.2}$$

so   Cost price = <u>£287.50</u>

e.g. A push-chair was sold for £49.45, at a discount of 14% in a sale. What was its normal price?

$$\text{Sale price} = 86\% \text{ of normal price}$$

$$\text{Sale price} = 0.86 \times \text{normal price}$$

so $$\text{Normal price} = \frac{\text{sale price}}{0.86}$$

$$= £\frac{49.45}{0.86}$$

so   Normal price = <u>£57.50</u>

Exercise 12

A For each question, the price inclusive of VAT at 15% is given. Find the price before VAT.

1. £23   **2.** £989   **3.** £48.30   **4.** £287.50   **5.** £86.25

B 1. A gold necklace appreciated in value by 8%. If it is now worth £324, what was it worth before the increase?

2. An antique table is now worth £232, after having appreciated in value by 16%. What was it worth before?

3. A camera was sold for £245, at a discount of $12\frac{1}{2}\%$. What was its price before discount?

4. A second-hand TV was bought for £97.50, being a 70% reduction on its price when new. What was its price when new?

10 Shapes and Symmetry

Plane and Solid Shapes

Exercise 1

1. Part of a cuboid is shown:
   (a) Copy and complete the diagram.
   (b) How many edges has a cuboid?
   (c) How many faces has a cuboid?
   (d) How many vertices has a cuboid?

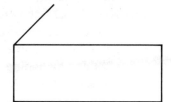

2. A sketch of a tetrahedron is shown:
   (a) How many faces has the tetrahedron?
   (b) How many edges has it?
   (c) How many vertices has it?

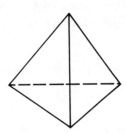

3. A sketch of a triangular-based prism is shown:
   (a) How many faces has the prism?
   (b) How many edges has it?
   (c) How many vertices has it?

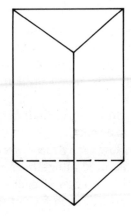

4. The diagram shows the tetrahedron of question 2 fitting exactly on top of the trianglar-based prism of question 3 to make a new solid. The hidden edges have not been shown.

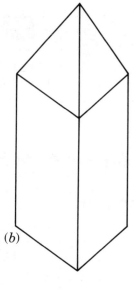

    (*a*) How many faces has the new solid?

    (*b*) How many edges has the new solid?

    (*c*) How many vertices has the new solid?

    (*d*) Explain why the answers for parts (*a*), (*b*) and (*c*) of this question are not the same as the answers obtained by adding the answers for the separate solids in questions 2 and 3.

5. (*a*) Draw a sketch of a square-based pyramid:

    (*b*) How many faces has it got?

    (*c*) How many edges has it got?

    (*d*) How many vertices has it got?

6. (*a*) Sketch a cylinder.

    (*b*) How many faces has it got?

Exercise 2

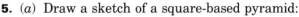

1. A 3 × 3 × 3 cube has been made from small cubes. The whole of the outside of the large cube has been painted grey.

    (*a*) How many small cubes are there?

    (*b*) How many faces were painted altogether?

    (*c*) If the edge of each small cube measures 2 cm, what is the area of each face of each small cube?

(d) What is the total area that has been painted? Give your answer in square centimetres.
(e) How many cubes had three faces painted grey?
(f) How many cubes had two faces painted grey?
(g) How many cubes had one face painted grey?
(h) How many cubes had no faces painted grey?

2. The given shape has been made from cubes. The whole of the outside of the shape has been painted white.

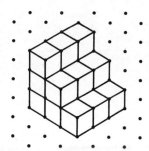

(a) How many small cubes are there?
(b) How many faces were painted altogether?
(c) If the edge of each small cube measures 20 cm, what is the area of each face of each small cube?
(d) What is the total area that has been painted? Give your answer in square centimetres.
(e) Write the answer to part (d) in square metres.
(f) How many cubes had one face painted white?
(g) How many cubes had two faces painted white?
(h) How many cubes had three faces painted white?
(i) How many cubes had four faces painted white?

3. In each of the following solids some cubes may be hidden. For each solid, find both the minimum and the maximum number of cubes there could be.

(a)　　　　　　　　　　　(b)

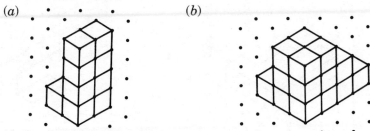

121

The diagrams show how a solid can be made from two other solids, an S-shaped solid and an L-shaped solid:

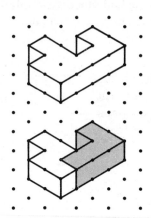

Copy each of the following solids. In each one, shade the L-shaped solid to show how the L- and S-shaped solids have been used.

1.

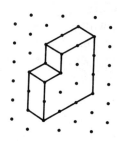

3.

2.

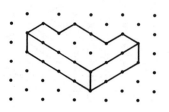

4.

Nets of Solids

Exercise 4

1. A net of a cube is shown. Draw two different nets of a cube.

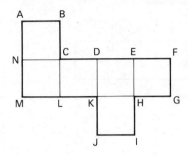

2. When the cube in question 1 is made, edge CD will meet with edge CB. Which edge meets with:
   (a) DE?   (b) MN?   (c) IJ?

3. When the net in question 1 is folded to make a cube, points B and D meet at the same vertex:
   (a) Which point meets with point E?
   (b) Which points meet with point I?

4. Draw two different arrangements of six squares that do *not* fold to make a cube.

5. The diagram shows part of the net of a cuboid that measures 3 cm by 2 cm by 1 cm. Make an accurate copy of the diagram and complete the net.

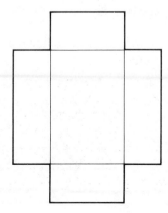

123

6. For each of the following diagrams, write whether it shows the net of a cuboid or not:

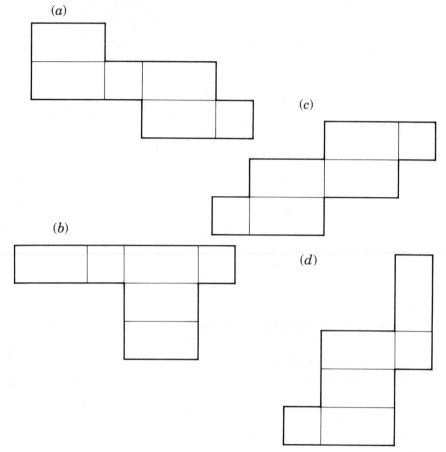

(a)

(c)

(b)

(d)

1. Which of the following are nets of a tetrahedron?

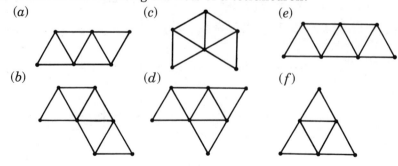

(a)   (c)   (e)

(b)   (d)   (f)

2. The given net can be folded to form a solid:
   (a) Name the solid.
   (b) Which letter will point F meet?
   (c) Which letters will point A meet?
   (d) Which edge will meet edge FG?

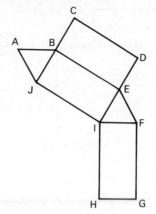

3. Here is a net of a triangular-based prism:
   (a) What sort of triangle forms the base?
   (b) How many edges does the solid have?
   (c) Which edge will meet edge IJ?
   (d) Which points will meet at C?

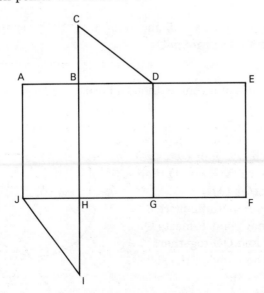

Exercise 6

1. A net of a cylinder is shown:

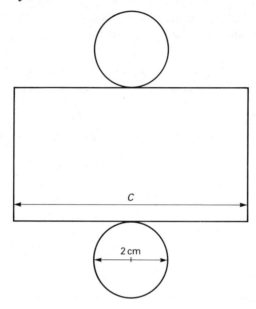

If the base has a diameter of 2 cm calculate the distance labelled *C* (use $\pi = 3.14$).

2. A cylinder has a base diameter of 3 cm. If the cylinder has no top, draw an accurate net.

3. Draw the net of a cone without a base.

4. On a piece of thin card, draw a circle (choose your own size). Draw two radii, P and Q then cut out sector POQ. Curve the remaining piece of card so that point P meets Q. Stick OP and OQ together. What is the name of the solid you have made?

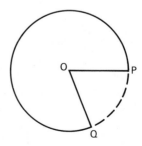

Exercise 7   Plane Shapes

A **1.** A regular octagon is shown:
 - (*a*) Find the size of angle AOB.
 - (*b*) Make an accurate drawing of a regular octagon. Choose your own size.

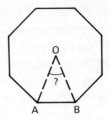

2. Draw a regular hexagon having sides measuring 4 cm.

3. Draw an equilateral triangle with sides measuring 5 cm.

4. (*a*) How many sides has the given polygon?
 (*b*) What is the name of the polygon?

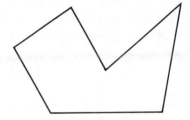

B **1.** Copy the trapezium. On your copy, mark the parallel sides.

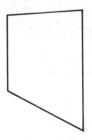

2. Which quadrilaterals have equal diagonals?

3. The opposite angles of a certain quadrilateral are equal, but are not right-angles. What sort of quadrilateral could it be?

4. Which quadrilaterals have two pairs of equal sides (all four are not equal)? Sketch and name each one.

Lines of Symmetry

Exercise 8

1. The diagram shows a design on the handles of some cutlery. The design has one line of bilateral symmetry. Design your own symmetrical pattern.

2. Half of a string of beads is shown below. Copy the beads given. Complete your copy so that the broken line is a line of symmetry.

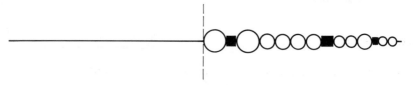

3. A car driver saw the following number plate in her mirror

   What is the registration number?

4. The given notice was put in a shop window. The diagram shows what the notice looked like from the back. What does the notice say?

   > Offers
   > Very good condition.
   > 3-piece suite for sale.

5. The following diagram shows part of the pattern on a wall tile:
   (a) Copy it.
   (b) Complete your copy of the tile so that it is symmetrical about broken lines AB and CD.
   (c) The completed tile has another sort of symmetry. Describe this other symmetry.

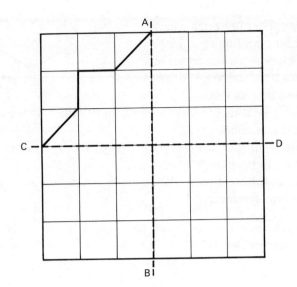

Exercise 9

1. (a) Draw a triangle having three lines of symmetry. Show all three lines of symmetry.
   (b) What sort of triangle has three lines of symmetry?
   (c) Describe fully another kind of symmetry this triangle has.

2. (a) How many lines of symmetry has a square?
   (b) What is the order of rotational symmetry of a square?

3. In each diagram below, part of a shape is shown. The broken lines are axes of symmetry. Name each complete shape.

   (a)   (b)

4. The two given lines are each
25 mm long and meet at 120°.
Make three separate copies of
the lines. On each copy, draw
one more line as follows.

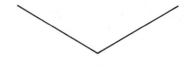

(a) The resulting figure should have line symmetry *and* rotational symmetry.

(b) The resulting figure should have line symmetry but *not* rotational symmetry.

(c) The resulting figure should have rotational symmetry but *not* line symmetry.

5. A triangle has one angle of 68° and another of 56°. Is the triangle symmetrical?

6. A quadrilateral has two angles each measuring 138° and two angles each measuring 42°. Investigate what types of quadrilateral it could be. For each type of quadrilateral found, describe its symmetry, if any.

Planes of Symmetry

Exercise 10

In each question, write whether or not the shaded part is a plane of symmetry for the solid shown:

1.

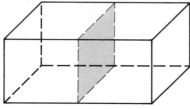

3.

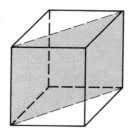

2.

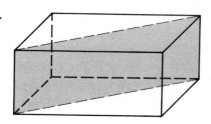

4.

5.

7.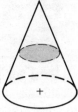

6.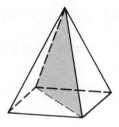

8.

Exercise 11

A For each solid, write the number of planes of symmetry it has:

1. A cuboid

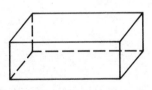

2. A triangular-based prism with equilateral triangles at each end

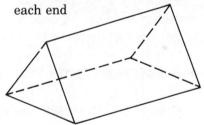

B A cone has an infinite number of planes of symmetry (three possible planes are shown below):

Name the solids in Exercise 10 which have an infinite number of planes of symmetry?

11 Brackets, Factorising and Formulae

Brackets

Exercise 1

A

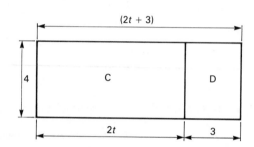

For the given diagram, copy and complete:

1. Area of rectangle C = $\boxed{?}$

2. Area of rectangle D = $\boxed{?}$

3. Area of large rectangle made up of C and D = $4\left(\boxed{?} + \boxed{?}\right)$

4. Area of large rectangle = area of C + area of D

so $\qquad 4\left(\boxed{?} + \boxed{?}\right) = \boxed{?} + \boxed{?}$

B

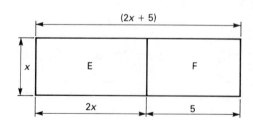

For the given diagram, copy and complete:

1. Area of rectangle E = $\boxed{?}$

2. Area of rectangle F = $\boxed{?}$

3. Area of large rectangle made up of E and F = $x\left(\boxed{?} + \boxed{?}\right)$

4.   Area of large rectangle   =   area of E   +   area of F

so $x\left(\boxed{?} + \boxed{?}\right)$ = $\boxed{?}$ + $\boxed{?}$

C Remove the brackets by multiplying out:

1. $2(x + 7)$	**4.** $6(4 - p)$	**7.** $2(5n - 4)$
2. $3(t + 3)$	**5.** $9(5 - g)$	**8.** $9(2y + 3)$
3. $5(c + 6)$	**6.** $2(3q + 6)$	**9.** $4(7 - 6v)$

D Remove the brackets by multiplying out:

1. $x(x + 3)$	**4.** $y(y - 6)$	**7.** $k(4k - 2)$
2. $x(x - 5)$	**5.** $y(9 - y)$	**8.** $t(6 - 2t)$
3. $y(2 + y)$	**6.** $h(2h + 5)$	**9.** $3a(2a + 4)$

E Remove the brackets by multiplying out:

1. $^-2(b - 9)$	**4.** $^-2s(2s + 7)$	**7.** $^-5g(5g + 2)$
2. $^-5(2 - d)$	**5.** $^-7f(1 - 7f)$	**8.** $^-6(8 - 2h)$
3. $^-4(8w - 9)$	**6.** $^-9(2u - 5)$	**9.** $^-2(3 - 4x)$

Exercise 2 Like Terms

Where possible, simplify the following:

1. $2d + 4d + 3d$	**9.** $x^2 + 3x - 2x + 1$
2. $9m + 4h + 5m + 2h$	**10.** $y^2 - 4y + 2y + 9$
3. $9c - 3c$	**11.** $g^2 - 5g - 3g + 6$
4. $8w - 3w + 7w - w$	**12.** $v^2 - v - v + 4$
5. $3x + 9 - 2x - 4 + 5x$	**13.** $9kl - 6kl$
6. $5e + 2f - 4e - 6f + e$	**14.** $4tu + 9ut$
7. $6w - 2z - 10w + z$	**15.** $7ab - 4ab - 8ba$
8. $^-q + 4j - 9q - 2j$	**16.** $4cd - 2d + 3dc - 3d$

Exercise 3

Remove the brackets and simplify:

1. $(a + 6) - 2$
2. $7 + (3n - 4)$
3. $8e + (5 - 3e)$
4. $7 + (6r - 1)$
5. $8b - (3b + 7)$
6. $6h - (1 - h)$

7. $(5v - 3) + (2v + 8)$
8. $(k - 7) + (12 - 3k)$
9. $(5p - 4) - (2p - 6)$
10. $(4l + 3m) - (2l + m)$
11. $(3y - q) - (y - 4q)$
12. $(9w + 3x) - (2w + 7x)$

Exercise 4

1. (a) What must be added to 5 to make 9?
   (b) What must be added to $(2x + 4)$ to make $(5x + 7)$?

2. What must be added to $(2t - 3)$ to make $(7t + 4)$?

3. (a) What is 4 less than 7?
   (b) What is $(t + 6)$ less than $(3t + 9)$?

4. What is $(2a - 3)$ less than $(4a + 2)$?

Exercise 5

Remove the brackets and simplify:

1. $19 + 4(u - 3)$
2. $3t + 2(t + 6)$
3. $7 + 5(3 - c)$
4. $2f + 6(4 - f)$
5. $9 + 4(2k - 2)$
6. $14 - 6(2 + r)$
7. $13s - 2(4s - 6)$
8. $20 - 4(4 - 3g)$

9. $(2x + 3y) + (3x + y)$
10. $(6h - 2z) - (h - 4z)$
11. $2(6e - 3) - 3(3e - 5)$
12. $7(3j + 2p) - 4(4j + 3p)$
13. $x(x + 6) - 2(x - 4)$
14. $y(y - 7) + 8(y - 5)$
15. $z(z - 4) + 6(z - 4)$
16. $d(d - 8) - 4(d - 8)$

Exercise 6

Multiply out and simplify your answers:

1. $(a + 3)(a + 6)$
2. $(h + 4)(h - 3)$
3. $(s - 2)(s + 7)$
4. $(g - 6)(g + 4)$
5. $(c - 7)(c + 1)$
6. $(w - 2)(w - 8)$

7. $(y + 2)(y - 3)$
8. $(e - 3)(e - 7)$
9. $(t + 7)(t + 4)$
10. $(v - 1)(v + 2)$
11. $(d + 3)(d - 7)$
12. $(x - 5)(x - 4)$

Factorising

Exercise 7

Factorise completely:

1. $5g + 20$
2. $4m - 8$
3. $24 - 18p$
4. $3a + 9b$
5. $4c - 8d$
6. $10x + 15y$
7. $18q - 12r$
8. $12 + 42i$
9. $16 - 18h$
10. $7l - 21$
11. $9 - 18f$
12. $25d + 5$

Exercise 8

Find the value of the following by factorising first:

1. $6 \times 48 - 6 \times 38$
2. $32 \times 7 + 7 \times 18$
3. $28 \times 73 - 63 \times 28$
4. $13 \times 156 + 13 \times 44$
5. $7 \times 28.4 - 7 \times 18.4$
6. $2.9 \times 36.1 - 26.1 \times 2.9$
7. $72.6 \times 6.29 + 72.6 \times 3.71$
8. $1.438 \times 31.8 + 1.438 \times 68.2$

Exercise 9

1. (a) Multiply out: $x(x + 4)$ (b) Factorise: $x^2 + 5x$

2. (a) Multiply out: $y(y - 3)$ (b) Factorise: $y^2 - 2y$

3. (a) Multiply out: $c(1 + c)$ (b) Factorise: $3c + c^2$

4. (a) Multiply out: $f(5 - f)$ (b) Factorise: $6f - f^2$

5. Factorise:
   (a) $x^2 + x$ (c) $8x - x^2$
   (b) $x^2 - 4x$ (d) $7x + x^2$

6. (a) Multiply out: $x(2x + 3)$ (b) Factorise: $2x^2 + 7x$

7. (a) Multiply out: $t(4t - 5)$ (b) Factorise: $3t^2 - 4t$

8. (a) Multiply out: $4v(2v - 4)$ (b) Factorise: $12v^2 - 10$

9. (a) Multiply out: $3d(2d + 3e)$ (b) Factorise: $8d^2 + 20de$

135

10. Factorise:
- (a) $3x^2 - 2x$
- (b) $5x^2 + 4x$
- (c) $x^2 + 7x$
- (d) $4x + x^2$
- (e) $2x^2 - 6x$
- (f) $3x^2 + 3x$
- (g) $6x^2 - 24xy$
- (h) $20xy + 16x^2$
- (i) $6x^2 - 15xy$

Using Formulae

Exercise 10

1. Given that:

Net pay = gross pay − deductions

Find the net pay when the gross pay = £189.40 and deductions = £63.50.

2. Chess players can be given a rating according to how good they are at chess. To change a rating in the ELO system to an English system rating, deduct 600 then divide by 8.

Find the English system ratings for players with the following ELO ratings.
- (a) 1560
- (b) 1400
- (c) 1320
- (d) 2040

3. On the back of a gas bill it states: 'To calculate the number of therms, multiply the volume of gas supplied (in hundreds of cubic feet) by the calorific value (in British Thermal Units per cubic foot) and divide by 1000'.

Calculate the number of therms if the calorific value is 1026 BTUs per cubic foot, and the volume of gas supplied in hundreds of cubic feet is:
- (a) 520
- (b) 200
- (c) 350
- (d) 475

4. The total cost of gas is given by the formula:

$$C = 8.20 + 0.38t$$

where £C is the cost when t therms of gas are used. Use the formula to find the cost of gas when the following number of therms are used.
- (a) 500
- (b) 350
- (c) 550

5. The formula $l = \sqrt{A}$ gives the length of a side of a face when its area, A is known. Find l when:
- (a) $A = 64$
- (b) $A = 6.25$

6. To hire a machine it costs £15 plus £4 per hour. Find the total cost of hiring the machine for:

(*a*) 4 h   (*b*) 6 h   (*c*) 7 h   (*d*) 15 h

7. If it costs £55 for the hire of the machine in question 6, for how many hours must it have been hired?

8. Use the formula $v = u + at$ to find v when

(*a*) $u = 40$, $a = 10$ and $t = 3$,

(*b*) $u = 50$, $a = {}^{-}10$ and $t = 6$.

9. Use $v = u + at$ to find:

(*a*) u when $v = 85$, $a = 10$ and $t = 2.5$,

(*b*) t when $u = 70$, $a = 10$ and $v = 90$.

Exercise 11

A Work out the exact value of the following:

1. $t^2 - 5$ when:

(*a*) $t = 6$ (*b*) $t = {}^{-}4$ (*c*) $t = 8.5$

2. $x^2 + 2x$ when:

(*a*) $x = 5$ (*b*) $x = {}^{-}5$ (*c*) $x = 1.6$

3. $n^2 - 4n + 6$ when:

(*a*) $n = 6$ (*b*) $n = {}^{-}2$ (*c*) $n = 8.7$

4. $u^2 + 4u - 7$ when:

(*a*) $u = 4$ (*b*) $u = {}^{-}8$ (*c*) $u = 2.9$

5. $\dfrac{a + 12}{a}$ when:

(*a*) $a = 5$ (*b*) $a = {}^{-}2$ (*c*) $a = 2.4$

6. $w + \dfrac{40.5}{w}$ when:

(*a*) $w = 9$ (*b*) $w = {}^{-}2$ (*c*) $w = 3.6$

7. $e - \dfrac{24}{e}$ when:

(*a*) $e = 8$ (*b*) $e = 9.6$ (*c*) $e = {}^{-}9.6$

8. $\dfrac{52.8}{k} - k$ when:

(*a*) $k = 0.8$ (*b*) $k = 1.2$ (*c*) $k = {}^{-}1.2$

B 1. If $s = ut^2$, find s when: (*a*) $t = 4$ and $u = 6$,
                                          (*b*) $t = 6$ and $u = 20$.

2. If $A = \pi r^2$, find A when $\pi = 3.14$ and $r = 2$.

3. If $S = 4\pi r^2$, find S when $\pi = 3.14$ and $r = 5$.

4. If $V = \frac{4}{3}\pi r^3$, find V when $\pi = 3.14$ and $r = 3$.

5. If $V = \pi r^2 h$, find V when $\pi = 3.14$, $r = 4$ and $h = 5$.

6. If $V = u^2 + 2as$, find V when $u = 20$, $a = 10$ and $s = 5$.

7. If $r = \sqrt{\dfrac{A}{12}}$, find r when: (*a*) $A = 108$,
                                          (*b*) $A = 27$.

8. If $t = \sqrt{\dfrac{s}{u}}$, find t when: (*a*) $s = 80$ and $u = 5$,
                                          (*b*) $s = 288$ and $u = 8$.

C 1. If $x * y = 4x - y$, find the value of:
   (*a*) $3 * 2$ (*b*) $7 * 3$ (*c*) $6.5 * 4$ (*d*) $9 * 9$

2. If $a * b = \dfrac{ab}{2}$, find the value of:
   (*a*) $3 * 6$ (*b*) $9 * 2$ (*c*) $20 * 5$ (*d*) $8 * 8$

3. If $l * b = 2(l + b)$, find the value of:
   (*a*) $6 * 2$ (*b*) $9 * 1$ (*c*) $8 * 7$ (*d*) $5 * 2.5$

4. If $m * n = \sqrt{mn}$, find the value of:
   (*a*) $4 * 4$ (*b*) $12 * 3$ (*c*) $20 * 5$ (*d*) $1.8 * 9.8$

Basic Arithmetical Processes Expressed Algebraically

Exercise 12

1. (*a*) What is the sum of 9 and 4?
    (*b*) What is the sum of a and b?

2. (*a*) What must be added to 6 to give 10?

(*b*) What must be added to *h* to give 10?

(*c*) What must be added to *h* to give *g*?

3. (*a*) Find the product of 3 and 7.

(*b*) Find the product of *x* and *y*.

4. (*a*) 18 sweets were shared equally between 2 people. How many did each receive?

(*b*) *n* sweets were shared equally between 2 people. How many did each receive?

5. (*a*) How many pence are there in £6?

(*b*) How many pence are there in £*m*?

6. (*a*) How many pounds are there in 800 pence?

(*b*) How many pounds are there in *z* pence?

7. (*a*) How much change will there be out of £5 when £3 is spent?

(*b*) How much change will there be out of £*t* when £*u* is spent?

(*c*) How much change will there be out of £5 when 45 p is spent?

(*d*) How much change will there be out of £*v* when *w* pence is spent?

8. (*a*) Dean has 10 p and Miles has four times as much:

(i) How much does Miles have?

(ii) What is the total amount?

(*b*) If Dean has *d* pence and Miles has four times as much:

(i) How much does Miles have?

(ii) What is the total amount?

9. Four girls each have £*e*. They give all their money to Constance who already has £8. How much, altogether, will Constance now have?

10. (*a*) A gas fire that is 3 ft wide is fixed in the centre of a wall that is 15 ft long. How much space is there to each side of the fire?

(*b*) A gas fire that is *f* ft wide is fixed in the centre of a wall that is *w* ft long. How much space is there to each side of the fire?

Exercise 13

Throughout this exercise, n is always a positive whole number:

1. (a) What is the next whole number bigger than 5?
(b) What is the next whole number bigger than n?

2. (a) What is the next even number bigger than 6?
(b) If n is even, what is the next even number bigger than n?

3. (a) Explain why $2n$ is always even.
(b) Explain why $2n + 1$ is always odd.
(c) What is the next highest even number after $2n$?
(d) What is the next highest odd number after $2n + 1$?

4. (a) What is special about n when $3n + 1$ is even?
(b) What is special about n when $3n + 2$ is even?

5. (a) Can $3n + 1$ ever be a multiple of 3?
(b) Can $3n + 2$ ever be a multiple of 3?
(c) Write down two consecutive numbers that are not multiples of 3. Add them. Note the answer.
(d) Repeat part (c) several times, then write what you notice about the answers obtained.
(e) $(3n + 1)$ and $(3n + 2)$ are consecutive numbers. Add them and simplify the answer.
(f) Factorise the answer to part (e).
(g) Explain why the sum of two consecutive numbers that are not multiples of 3 must be a multiple of 3.

6. Using the ideas of question 5, prove that the sum of two consecutive odd numbers must be a multiple of 4.

7. Write what you can discover about the sum of two consecutive even numbers.

8. (a) Find eight values of n such that $4n + 1$ always ends in 5.
(b) Write what you notice about the values of n found in part (a).

Construction of Formulae

Exercise 14

1. Olga had x pence. If she spent n pence and had l pence left, write a formula:
   (a) for l in terms of x and n,
   (b) for n in terms of x and l.

2. Three triangles are given below:

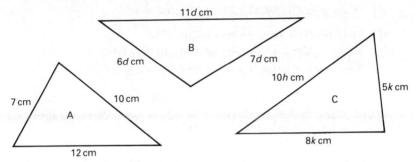

   (a) Calculate the perimeter of triangle A.
   (b) If triangle B has a perimeter of P cm, write P in terms of d. Simplify the answer.
   (c) If triangle C has a perimeter of P cm, write P in terms of h and k. Simplify the answer.

3. A rectangle is shown.
   Find its perimeter, P cm, in terms of x. Simplify the answer

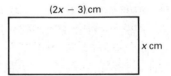

4. For the rectangle given in question 3:
   (a) If its area is A cm^2, find A in terms of x. (Multiply out the answer so that there are no brackets.)
   (b) If $x = 6$, calculate the area of the rectangle.

5. Clint, Davindar Singh and Davindar Kaur each had £10. Clint spent £x, Davindar Singh £y and Davindar Kaur £z.
   (a) How much money did each person have left?
   (b) If Davindar Kaur was given all the money that was left and she then had £L, write a formula giving L in terms of x, y and z.

A An engineer charged £15 for carrying out repairs in a home, plus a further £10 per hour:

1. (a) What was the total cost of 3 hours' work?
(b) What was the total cost of t hours' work?

2. If the visit still cost £15 but the hourly charge was £h per hour instead of £10 per hour:
(a) What was the total cost of 3 hours' work?
(b) What was the total cost of t hours' work?

3. If a visit cost £V plus £h per hour:
(a) What was the total cost of 3 hours' work?
(b) What was the total cost of t hours' work?

4. If an engineer charged £V for a visit plus £h per hour for t hours' work and the bill came to £T, write a formula giving T in terms of V, h and t.

B **1.** A salesperson was paid £w per week plus £s for each sale made. During a week in which n sales were made, the total earnings came to £E. Write a formula giving E in terms of w, s and n.

2. To hire a machine it costs £f plus £D per day. If a machine is hired for n days, write a formula for the total cost of hire, £C, in terms of f, D and n.

3. An electricity bill totalled £T. It was made up of a quarterly charge of £Q plus a charge of £u per unit, for the n units used. Write a formula giving T in terms of Q, u and n.

Transformation of Formulae

Exercise 16

1. If $F = ma$, find a in terms of F and m.

2. If $pV = K$, find V in terms of K and p.

3. Given that $\pi = \dfrac{C}{d}$, express:
(a) C in terms of π and d,   (b) d in terms of C and π.

4. If $R = r_1 + r_2$ express r_1 in terms of R and r_2.

5. If $P = 6l$, express l in terms of P.

6. $E = \dfrac{360}{n}$. Find n in terms of E.

7. If $I = \dfrac{s}{n}$:
  (a) Express s in terms of I and n.
  (b) Express n in terms of I and s.

8. $A = l^2$. Express l in terms of A.

Exercise 17

1. $A = \frac{1}{2}bh$. Express h in terms of A and b.

2. If $V = lbh$, express l in terms of V, b and h.

3. If $P = \dfrac{Wl}{4s}$:
  (a) Express l in terms of P, W and s.
  (b) Express W in terms of P, l and s.
  (c) Express s in terms of P, W and l.

4. $C = 2\pi r$. Rewrite the formula making r the subject.

5. $I = \dfrac{PRT}{100}$. Make T the subject of the formula.
  Find the value of T when $P = 400$, $R = 6$ and $I = 48$.

6. $V = \dfrac{Ah}{3}$. Express A in terms of V and h.
  Find the value of A when $V = 40$ and $h = 12$.

7. The formula $T = 60M + 27$ gives the time needed, T min, to roast a joint of beef having a mass of M kg. Rewrite the formula giving M in terms of T. Calculate M when $T = 117$.

8. $v = u + at$. Find u in terms of v, a and t. Calculate u when $v = 120$, $a = 32$ and $t = 3$.

9. $v = u + at$. Express t in terms of v, u and a. Calculate t when $v = 65$, $u = 45$ and $a = 5$.

10. $H = F + nc$ gives the hire charge £H of a piece of equipment when hired for n hours at £c per hour. £F is a fixed charge. Rearrange the formula to give n in terms of H, F and c. For how many hours has the equipment been hired if the total hire charge is £34, when the fixed charge is £12 and the hourly rate is £2 per hour?

12 Area and Volume

Miscellaneous Areas

Exercise 1

1. Passport photographs should be taken full face without a hat.
   The size should not be more than 63 mm by 50 mm ($2\frac{1}{2}$ in by 2 in) or less than 50 mm by 38 mm (2 in by $1\frac{1}{2}$ in).
   (a) Is the given photograph a suitable size to be used as a passport photograph?
   (b) Find the area of the given photograph.

   (c) What is the area of the largest possible passport photograph?
   (d) What is the area of the smallest possible passport photograph?

2. A rectangular piece of glass is cut to fit on the top of a bedside chest of drawers. If the glass measures 45 cm by 41 cm, calculate its area.

3. A carpet measuring 4.5 m by 3.67 m cost £99 to buy:
   (a) Calculate the area of the carpet.
   (b) Calculate the cost per square metre of the carpet.

4. A rectangular garden measures 12 m by 9.5 m:
   (a) Mrs Emmett wants to grass this piece of garden using lawn seed. If she uses 60 g of lawn seed per square metre, how many kilograms does she use altogether?
   (b) When she used some lawn fertiliser, she used 7.5 kg altogether. How many grams per square metre did she use? Give the answer correct to the nearest gram.

5. The diagram is of a front garden. It is rectangular. A concrete drive crosses the garden forming a lawn on one side and a triangular flower bed on the other.

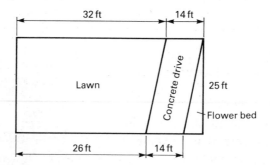

   (a) What shape is the lawn?
   (b) What shape is the drive?
   (c) Calculate the area of the drive.
   (d) Calculate the area of the lawn.
   (e) Calculate the area of the flower bed.

6. A square has sides measuring 29 mm. If all four sides are made three times as big to form a larger square:
   (a) How many times bigger is the area?
   (b) How many times bigger is the perimeter?

7. A rectangle measures 68 mm by 52 mm. If all four sides are made three times as big to form a larger rectangle:
   (a) How many times bigger is the area?
   (b) How many times bigger is the perimeter?

8. Mr Topping tiled his kitchen floor with 40 cm square carpet tiles. If the floor area measured 2.8 m by 2.4 m:
   (a) Calculate the total number of tiles used.
   (b) Calculate the total cost of the carpet tiles, if they cost £1.35 each.

146

1. The area of a square is $900\,\text{cm}^2$:
   (a) What is the length of one side of the square?
   (b) Calculate the perimeter of the square.

2. Building regulations stated that the glass area of an extension must be at least one tenth of the floor area. Mr Armitage built an extension with a floor measuring 3 m by 2.6 m.
   (a) Calculate the floor area.
   (b) What is the smallest allowable area of the glass?
   (c) The glass in a window is 1.4 m wide. If it is the smallest window that is allowed, give the dimensions of the piece of glass needed (to the nearest centimetre).
   (d) If the smallest square window allowed is to be fitted, what must the dimensions of its glass be (to the nearest centimetre)?

3. 15 cm square tiles were used to tile a rectangular piece of wall. 168 were needed. If there were at least 7 rows of tiles, give the dimensions of all possible sizes of wall that could have been tiled.

4. A triangular piece of cloth is shown. It has an area of $5.92\,\text{m}^2$. Other dimensions are as shown.
   Calculate the missing length that is marked.

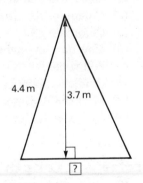

4.4 m   3.7 m

?

5. The given parallelogram has an area of $4032\,\text{mm}^2$.
   Calculate the length of its base.

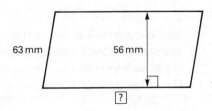

63 mm   56 mm

?

147

Circumference of a Circle

Exercise 3

1. Find the circumference of the given circle.
   Circumference = 3.14 × diameter

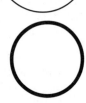

2. The edge of a circular plate is handpainted. The plate has a diameter of 17 cm, calculate the distance around the edge. (Take π to be 3.14.)

3. A metal band is fastened around a dustbin. Find the length of the metal band, if the diameter is 51 cm. (Take π to be 3.14.)

4. A bicycle wheel has a diameter of 27 in:
   (a) Calculate its circumference using $\pi = 3.14$. (Do not round the answer.)
   (b) How far, in inches, will the bike travel if the wheel turns 200 times?
   (c) Find the distance travelled in feet (12 in = 1 ft).
   (d) Find the distance travelled in yards (3 ft = 1 yd).
   (e) Give the distance travelled to the nearest hundred yards.

Exercise 4   Length of an Arc

A 1. The metal handle on a bucket is in the shape of a semi-circle. The distance between the ends of the handle is 25 cm. Calculate its length using $\pi = 3.14$.

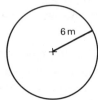

2. A cup hook is shaped as shown. The curved part is three-quarters of a circle of radius 8 mm. Calculate the length of the curved part. (Use $\pi = 3.142$.) Give your answer to the nearest millimetre.

3. A jar has a diameter of 58 mm. Find the length of a label that goes half-way around the jar. (Take π to be 3.1.)

B For each question, using $\pi = 3.14$, find the length of the arc:

1. radius = 4 cm   angle subtended = 90°

2. radius = 9 m   angle subtended = 45°

3. radius = 7.2 m   angle subtended = 135°

4. radius = 1.7 cm   angle subtended = 80°

Exercise 5

A The circumferences of several circles are given. Find: (a) the diameter, (b) the radius of each circle.

1. Circumference = 27 cm   Use $\pi = 3$.

2. Circumference = 8.34 m   Use $\pi = 3$.

3. Circumference = 125.6 cm   Use $\pi = 3.14$.

4. Circumference = 264 mm   Use $\pi = 3\frac{1}{7}$.

B **1.** A 1 ℓ cylindrical paint tin has a circumference of 345 mm. Find its diameter using $\pi = 3$.

149

2. A timer needs to be made to have a circumference of 210 mm. What should its diameter measure? Use $\pi = 3.14$ and give the answer to the nearest millimetre.

3. A metal rim of length 50 mm is fixed around a circular mirror. Find the diameter of the mirror to one decimal place, using $\pi = 3.14$.

Area of a Circle

Exercise 6

1. Calculate the area of the following circles:

(a)

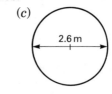

8 cm

(b)

7 m

(c)

2.6 m

(Use $\pi = 3.1$.)   (Use $\pi = 3\frac{1}{7}$.)   (Use $\pi = 3.142$.)

2. A children's paddling pool has a circular piece of PVC forming the base:

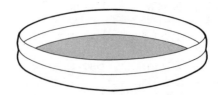

If this piece of PVC has a radius of 0.45 m, calculate its area to two decimal places $(\pi = 3.14)$.

3. A plastic tiddlywink has a diameter of 16 mm. Find the total area of plastic stamped out to make 500 of the tiddlywinks. (Take π to be 3.142.)

4. The velum on a banjo is circular and has a diameter of 10 cm.
Calculate its area using the value of π on your calculator (or 3.142). Give your answer correct to three significant figures.

Exercise 7   Area of a Sector

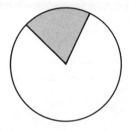

Calculate the area of each of the following sectors:

1. (a) radius = 7 cm, angle at centre = 90°, $\pi = \frac{22}{7}$,

 (b) radius = 7 cm, angle at centre = 45°, $\pi = \frac{22}{7}$,

 (c) radius = 7 cm, angle at centre = 270°, $\pi = \frac{22}{7}$,

2. radius = 35 cm, angle at centre = 60°, $\pi = 3\frac{1}{7}$,

3. radius = 10.5 cm, angle at centre = 120°, $\pi = 3\frac{1}{7}$,

4. radius = 10 m, angle at centre = 36°, $\pi = 3.14$,

5. radius = 1.2 cm, angle at centre = 30°, $\pi = 3.14$,

6. diameter = 1.8 cm, angle at centre = 150°, $\pi = 3.14$,

7. radius = 2.5 cm, angle at centre = 18°, $\pi = 3.14$,

8. diameter = 9.6 cm, angle at centre = 75°, $\pi = 3.14$.

Exercise 8   Areas of Borders and Composite Shapes

1. The diagram shows a bath mat with semi-circular ends. Calculate its area. (Use $\pi = 3.14$.)

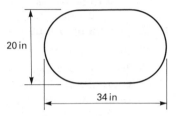

20 in

34 in

2. A plastic protractor is in the shape of a semi-circle with a rectangle at the bottom:

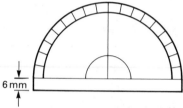

6 mm

The semi-circle has a radius of 46 mm and the rectangle is 6 mm wide. Calculate the area of the protractor. (Use $\pi = 3.14$.)

3. A path that is 1.2 m wide surrounds a lawn that measures 13 m by 7 m. Calculate the area of the path.

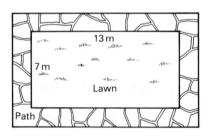

13 m

7 m

Lawn

Path

4. Calculate the shaded area shown in the diagram. (Take π to be 3.14.)

15 cm

15 cm

5. A tennis court is surrounded by wire netting. The side netting is 3.65 m (12 ft) from the outer sidelines, while the netting at each end is 5.48 m (18 ft) from the baselines.

(*a*) Calculate the total length of the netting:
    (i) in metres,   (ii) in feet.
(*b*) Calculate the total area enclosed by the netting:
    (i) in square metres,   (ii) in square feet.
(*c*) Calculate the actual doubles playing area (that is, the area enclosed by the baselines and the outer sidelines):
    (i) in square metres,   (ii) in square feet.

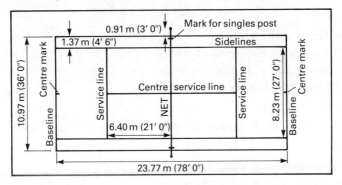

Surface Area and Volume

Exercise 9

1. A firm manufactured some gravy cubes. Each edge measured 2 cm. They sold them in thin cardboard boxes that measured 4 cm × 4 cm × 4 cm.

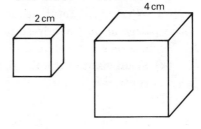

(*a*) How many gravy cubes would fit in each of these boxes?

(*b*) Shops bought these 4 cm × 4 cm × 4 cm boxes packed in larger boxes measuring 40 cm × 16 cm × 12 cm. How many 4 cm × 4 cm × 4 cm boxes fit inside these larger boxes?

(*c*) How many gravy cubes fit inside a 40 cm × 16 cm × 12 cm box?

(*d*) A box holds 24 gravy cubes. Two measurements of the cuboid-shaped box were 8 cm and 4 cm. What was the third measurement?

2. The diagram shows an open box (it has no lid):

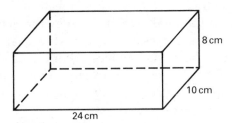

(a) Draw a sketch of a net of the box.

(b) Calculate the area of lining needed to cover the whole of the inside of the box exactly.

(c) Calculate the volume of the box.

3. A common brick measures 9 in by 4.5 in by 3 in. Calculate its volume.

4. Each edge of a cube measures 1 m. Its volume is 1 m^3.

(a) What is the length of each edge, in centimetres?

(b) How many cubic centimetres equal 1 m^3?

(c) What is the total surface area of the cube in square metres?

(d) What is the total surface area of the cube in square centimetres?

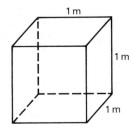

5. People who work in an office must have a minimum of 40 ft^2 each, but where ceilings are less than 10 ft high they need a minimum space of 400 ft^3 per person. Find the maximum number of people allowed to work in an office measuring:

(a) 30 ft by 25 ft by 11 ft,

(b) 20 ft by 18 ft by 9 ft.

6. What happens to the volume of a cuboid if its length, breadth and height are all doubled? (Try several cuboids. Calculate their volumes before and after the three dimensions are doubled.)

7. How much water, in litres, will the given tanks hold when full?

(a)

(b)

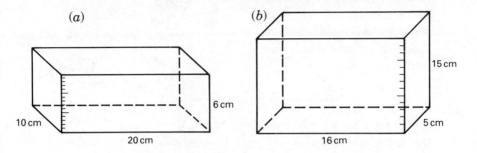

8. How far up the tanks in question 7 will the 1 ℓ mark be?
(Give each answer correct to the nearest centimetre.)

Miscellaneous Volumes and Surface Areas

> Curved surface area of a cylinder $= \pi dh$
>
> Total surface area of a cylinder $= \pi dh + 2\pi r^2$
>
> Volume of any prism $= Ah$
>
> (where A is the area of the base)

Exercise 10   Prisms

1. The triangular-based prism
shown has a base area of 7 cm².
Its height is 9 cm.
Calculate its volume.

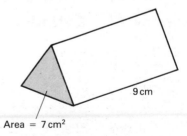

Area = 7 cm²

2. The diagram shows a wedge.
It is a triangular-based prism
where the base is a right-
angled triangle.
(a) Calculate the area of the base.
(b) Calculate the volume of the wedge.

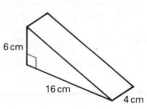

155

3. The diagram shows a chocolate called Tri-Choc and a box in which it is sold.
What is the largest number of chocolates that will fit in the box?

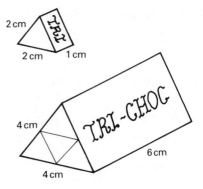

4. The diagram shows the uniform cross-section of a girder:
(*a*) Calculate the area of the cross-section.
(*b*) Calculate the volume of the girder if it is 4 m long.

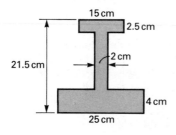 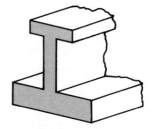

Exercise 11   Cylinders

A Find: (*a*) the volume, (*b*) the curved surface area of the following cylinders (where necessary, round answers to three significant figures).

	Radius	Height	π			Radius	Height	π
1.	4 cm	6 cm	3	**5.**	3 cm	4.5 cm	3.1
2.	5 m	8 m	3.14	**6.**	2.1 cm	1.7 cm	3.14
3.	2 m	7 m	3.14	**7.**	0.6 m	1.4 m	3.14
4.	6 cm	6 cm	3.14	**8.**	1.3 m	9 m	3.142

B Throughout this exercise, take π to be 3.14.

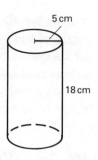

1. A can of lemonade is shown:
   (a) Calculate the volume of the can.
   (b) Write the number of litres of lemonade that are in the can when it is full.
   (c) Find the total surface area of the sealed can.

2. A metal rod in the shape of a solid cylinder is 8 cm long and has a base radius of 3 cm:
   (a) Calculate the volume of the metal rod.

   The metal rod is melted down to make some small solid cylinders, each with a base radius of 12 mm and each 20 mm in length:
   (b) Calculate the volume of one small cylinder.
   (c) Calculate the number of small cylinders that can be made from the original metal rod.

3. A solid wooden cylinder of length 16 cm and base radius 4 cm is cut exactly in half to form two cylinders. How much bigger is the total surface area of the two cylinders than the total surface area of the original cylinder?

4. A cylindrical steel shaft has a diameter of 72 mm and is 5 m long. Calculate its volume.

5. A cylindrical watering-can has a base diameter of 20 cm and a height of 30 cm. How many litres does it hold when full?

6. A cylindrical roller is 12 in wide and has a diameter of 8 in. Calculate:
   (a) its curved surface area,
   (b) its total surface area,
   (c) its volume.

7. A cylindrical measuring jug holds 1 ℓ of water when full:
   (a) Calculate its height if its base radius is 4 cm.
   (b) Calculate its height if its base radius is 5.8 cm.

8. A cylinder has a base area of $29\,\mathrm{cm}^2$ and a perpendicular height of $9\,\mathrm{cm}$. Calculate:
- (*a*) its volume,
- (*b*) the radius of its base,
- (*c*) its curved surface area,
- (*d*) its total surface area.

Exercise 12   Volume of a Composite Body

Calculate the volume of each given solid. Use $\pi = 3.14$.

1.

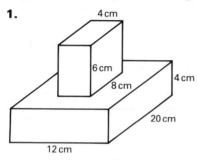

4 cm
6 cm
8 cm
4 cm
20 cm
12 cm

2.

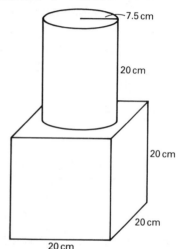

7.5 cm
20 cm
20 cm
20 cm
20 cm

Exercise 13   Estimating Volumes by Approximation to Simpler Bodies

1. Estimate the amount of wood in the trunk of the tree shown. The length of the trunk is $28\,\mathrm{m}$. Its diameter at the bottom is $3\,\mathrm{m}$ and at the top $1\,\mathrm{m}$. Assume the trunk to be a cylinder. Use a diameter of $2\,\mathrm{m}$ (the mean of $3\,\mathrm{m}$ and $1\,\mathrm{m}$). Take π to be 3.14.

Elm, Field
Ulmus procera

158

2. Estimate the amount of wood in the trunk of a tree, if its diameter at the bottom is 2 m and at the top, 0.8 m, and the length of the trunk is 21 m.

3. Estimate the volume of a bag of sugar. Assume the bag to be a cuboid and work with mean (average) sizes. The length varies from 150 to 180 mm, the width from 100 to 120 mm and the depth from 54 to 60 mm.

13 Constructions and Loci

Constructions

Exercise 1

1. Copy the given line AB and point P:

A   P   B

Using a protractor and a ruler draw an angle BPC equal to 54°.

2. Draw a straight line 65 mm long. Bisect it using a pair of compasses.

3. (*a*) Copy the given angle:

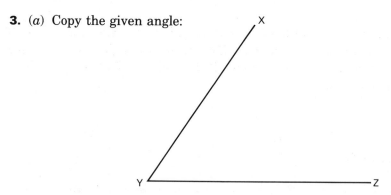

(*b*) Using only a ruler, pencil and a pair of compasses, bisect angle XYZ.

(*c*) Using only a ruler, pencil and a pair of compasses, bisect YZ.

(*d*) Label the point of intersection of the two constructed bisectors as Q. Measure YQ to the nearest millimetre.

4. Construct $\triangle$GHI where HI = 65 mm, $H\hat{I}G = 125°$ and $H\hat{G}I = 30°$. Measure GH to the nearest millimetre.

Exercise 2

1. Draw a straight line AB = 8 cm. Mark a point C on AB such that AC = 3 cm. At C, construct a perpendicular to AB using a ruler, pencil and pair of compasses only.

2. Copy the diagram. Using a pair of compasses, pencil and ruler only, construct a perpendicular from P to the line AB.

P
.

A ——————————————— B

3. Make another copy of the diagram for question 2. Using a set square, ruler and pencil only, draw a line PQ parallel to line AB.

4. Draw a straight line, ST, 83 mm in length. Using only a pair of compasses, ruler and pencil, construct an angle of 60° at S and 30° at T to form triangle RST. Measure RT to the nearest millimetre.

Exercise 3

Throughout this exercise, you may only use a protractor when instructed.

1. A rectangle has an area of 31.5 cm² and one of its sides measures 7 cm. Construct the rectangle and measure its diagonals to the nearest millimetre.

2. Construct a rhombus with sides measuring 42 mm, if one of its angles measures 56° (you may use a protractor). Measure its diagonals to the nearest millimetre.

3. Construct a parallelogram with sides measuring 66 mm and 45 mm, where an angle between the sides is 112° (use a protractor). Measure the diagonals to the nearest millimetre. By making suitable measurements and calculating, find the area of the parallelogram.

4. Construct a square with sides measuring 51 mm. Measure its diagonals to the nearest millimetre.

Exercise 4

1. Construct triangle PQR where QR = 80 mm, RP = 51 mm and QR̂P = 62°. By making suitable measurements, then calculating, find the area of triangle PQR.

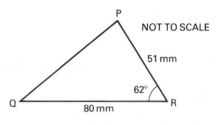

2. Construct an equilateral triangle with sides measuring 46 mm.

3. Construct an isosceles triangle with sides measuring 73 mm, 73 mm and 50 mm. Measure all three angles.

4. Construct a right-angled triangle with a side measuring 44 mm and an angle of 54°. How long is the hypotenuse?

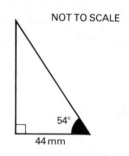

5. Construct △ABC where BC = 106 mm, ∠ABC = 52° and ∠ACB = 41°. Using a pair of compasses, bisect ∠ABC and bisect BC. Let the bisectors meet at P. Give the length of:
   (a) AB   (b) PB

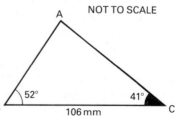

6. Construct quadrilateral PQRS such that SR = 80 mm, RŜP = 70° and SR̂Q = 63°. SP = 47 mm and RQ = 64 mm. Measure PQ giving its length to the nearest millimetre.

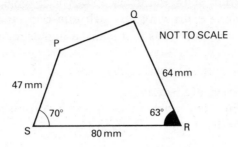

Loci

Exercise 5 Some Basic Loci

1. Mark a point X on your page. Draw the locus of a point which moves so that it is always 30 mm from point X.

2. Mark two points, A and B, on your page so that they are 65 mm apart. Draw the locus of a point which moves so that it is equidistant from points A and B.

3. Draw a line segment that is 40 mm in length. Draw the locus of a point that moves so that it is always 25 mm from the line segment.

4. Copy the two intersecting lines. On your copy, draw the locus of a point which moves so that it is always equidistant from the two lines.

163

In each question in this exercise there are some instructions that may or may not show the exact spot where some buried treasure is hidden. Make a drawing for each question, and show whether the given instruction leads to a point, a line or an area.

1.

A
•

B
•

The two trees are 8 m apart.
The treasure is 6 m from tree A and 5 m from tree B. Find two possible positions for the treasure.

2. AB and BC are hedgerows. The treasure is equidistant from positions A and B, as well as being equidistant from AB and BC. How far is the treasure from C?

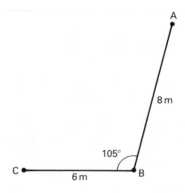

3. Three trees are positioned as shown. PQ = 16 m, PR = 14 m and QR = 12 m.

                                               P
                                             •

   (*a*) The treasure is equidistant from P and Q and exactly 6 m from R.

R •

   (*b*) The treasure is equidistant from P and Q and less than 6 m from R.

   (*c*) Explain the difference between the answers to parts (*a*) and (*b*).

                                      •
                                    Q

4. (*a*) The treasure is 4 m from a tree.

(*b*) The treasure is less than 4 m from a tree.

(*c*) Explain the difference between the answers to parts (*a*) and (*b*).

5. A circular pond has a diameter of 6 m.

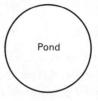

(*a*) The treasure is 2 m from the pond.

(*b*) The treasure is less than 2 m from the pond.

(*c*) Explain the difference between the answers to parts (*a*) and (*b*).

Exercise 7

M

1. Two radio stations R and S are 80 miles apart.

R
•

S
•

Broadcasts from R can be heard up to 60 miles away, while broadcasts from S can be heard up to a distance of 40 miles. Shade the area where both broadcasts can be heard.

2. Three radio stations are positioned as shown. T is 100 km from U and 160 km from V, while U is 120 km from V. Broadcasts from T can be heard up to 90 km away, from U up to 60 km away, and from V up to 100 km away. Shade where all three broadcasts can be heard.

T
•

• V

U
•

3. ABCD is a rectangular lawn measuring 40 ft by 25 ft.

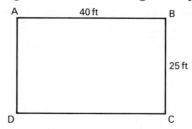

Richard watered the part of the lawn that was within 15 ft of edge CD, while his sister watered the part that was within 25 ft of edge BC. Show the areas watered and clearly mark the area watered by both.

4. Three goats are tethered in a rectangular field that measures 80 m by 60 m (shown by rectangle PQRS).

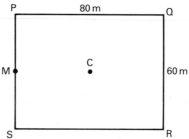

One goat is tethered at corner S on a 20 m rope; another is tethered at the mid-point, M, of edge PS, on a 15 m rope; while the third goat is tethered using a 10 m rope fastened to a post at the centre of the field, C.

(*a*) Make an accurate scale drawing of the field, and clearly show the areas where the goats are able to move.

(*b*) Shade and label any area where more than one goat can graze.

(*c*) Calculate the grazing area for each goat.

14 **Functions**

Exercise 1 M

Copy the following and fill in the missing values:

A 1.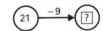

2.

3.

4. (14) — ×9.2 → (?)

5. (6.1) — −2.8 → (?)

6. (1.7) — ×6 → (?)

B 1.

2.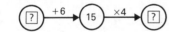

3.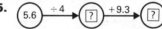

4. (?) — ×3 → (?) — +7 → (22)

5. (5.6) — ÷4 → (?) — +9.3 → (?)

6. (23) — ×1.6 → (?) — +4.7 → (?)

Exercise 2 M

Copy the following and fill in the missing values:

1. (*a*)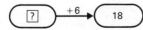

(*b*)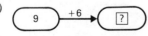

(*c*)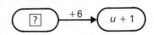

(*d*) ($y - 2$) — +6 → (?)

(*e*) (?) — +6 → (*t*)

(*f*) (?) — +6 → ($u + 1$)

167

2. (a) $4 \xrightarrow{\times 2} \boxed{?}$

(b) $\boxed{?} \xrightarrow{\times 2} 14$

(c) $a \xrightarrow{\times 2} \boxed{?}$

(d) $3c \xrightarrow{\times 2} \boxed{?}$

(e) $\boxed{?} \xrightarrow{\times 2} 8k$

(f) $\boxed{?} \xrightarrow{\times 2} m$

3. $\boxed{?} \xrightarrow{-11} w$

4. $\boxed{?} \xrightarrow{-8} g + 4$

5. $\frac{1}{3}d \xrightarrow{\times 3} \boxed{?}$

6. $\frac{1}{3}l \xrightarrow{\times 6} \boxed{?}$

7. $\boxed{?} \xrightarrow{+12} p + 6$

8. $12h \xrightarrow{\div 4} \boxed{?}$

Exercise 3  **M**

Copy the following and fill in the missing values:

1. (a) $5 \xrightarrow{\times 3} \boxed{?} \xrightarrow{-4} \boxed{?}$

(b) $\boxed{?} \xrightarrow{\times 3} 21 \xrightarrow{-4} \boxed{?}$

(c) $d \xrightarrow{\times 3} \boxed{?} \xrightarrow{-4} \boxed{?}$

2. (a) $\boxed{?} \xrightarrow{+7} 21 \xrightarrow{\times 2} \boxed{?}$

(b) $\boxed{?} \xrightarrow{+7} \boxed{?} \xrightarrow{\times 2} 26$

(c) $n \xrightarrow{+7} \boxed{?} \xrightarrow{\times 2} \boxed{?}$

3. $\boxed{?} \xrightarrow{+5} 17 \xrightarrow{-3} \boxed{?}$

4. $\boxed{?} \xrightarrow{+9} k \xrightarrow{-2} \boxed{?}$

5. $\boxed{?} \xrightarrow{+6} t + 6 \xrightarrow{\times 2} \boxed{?}$

6. $4.3 \xrightarrow{\times 7} \boxed{?} \xrightarrow{+1.6} \boxed{?}$

Exercise 4

Copy and complete the mapping diagrams:

1.

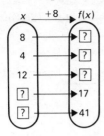

3.

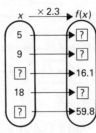

2.

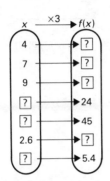

4.

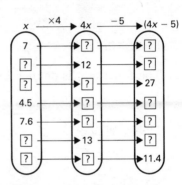

Exercise 5

1. The function f is defined by:

Find: (*a*) $f(9)$ (*b*) $f(64)$ (*c*) $f(3.5)$

2. The function f is defined by:

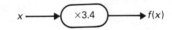

Find: (*a*) $f(6)$ (*b*) $f(200)$ (*c*) $f(8.1)$

3. The function f is defined by:

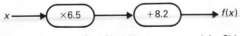

Find: (*a*) $f(2)$ (*b*) $f(100)$ (*c*) $f(4.6)$

4. The function f is defined by:

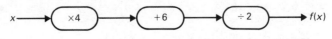

Find: (*a*) $f(8)$ (*b*) $f(125)$ (*c*) $f(2.7)$

5. The function f is defined by:

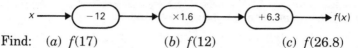

Find: (a) $f(17)$ (b) $f(12)$ (c) $f(26.8)$

6. The function f is defined by:

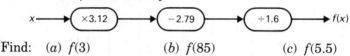

Find: (a) $f(3)$ (b) $f(85)$ (c) $f(5.5)$

7. The function f is defined by:

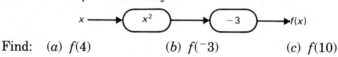

Find: (a) $f(4)$ (b) $f(^-3)$ (c) $f(10)$

8. The function f is defined by:

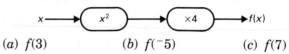

Find: (a) $f(3)$ (b) $f(^-5)$ (c) $f(7)$

Exercise 6

1. If $y = 3x + 6$, find the value of y when:
(a) $x = 4$ (b) $x = 0$ (c) $x = ^-4$ (d) $x = ^-2$

2. If $y = 8 - x$, find the value of y when:
(a) $x = 3$ (b) $x = 10$ (c) $x = ^-2$ (d) $x = ^-9$

3. If $y = 15 - 2x$, find the value of y when:
(a) $x = 4$ (b) $x = 10$ (c) $x = ^-4$ (d) $x = ^-10$

4. If $y = 2x^2$, find the value of y when:
(a) $x = 2$ (b) $x = 4$ (c) $x = ^-3$ (d) $x = ^-6$

5. If $y = x^2 - 2$, find the value of y when:
(a) $x = 6$ (b) $x = 4$ (c) $x = ^-9$ (d) $x = ^-1$

6. If $y = 2(x - 3)$, find the value of y when:
(a) $x = 8$ (b) $x = 0$ (c) $x = ^-2$ (d) $x = ^-5$

7. If $y = (2x + 4)/5$, find the value of y when:
   (a) $x = 8$ (b) $x = 4$ (c) $x = {}^-7$ (d) $x = {}^-2$

8. If $y = 3(x - 5)/2$, find the value of y when:
   (a) $x = 9$ (b) $x = 5$ (c) $x = {}^-3$ (d) $x = {}^-2$

Exercise 7

1. Given that $f(x) = 2x + 9$, find:
   (a) $f(2)$ (b) $f(10)$ (c) $f({}^-3)$ (d) $f({}^-7)$

2. If $g(x) = 15 - x$, find:
   (a) $g(6)$ (b) $g(15)$ (c) $g(19)$ (d) $g({}^-4)$

3. If $f(x) = 25 - 2x$, find:
   (a) $f(7)$ (b) $f(15)$ (c) $f(0)$ (d) $f({}^-6)$

4. If $f(x) \to 3x^2$, find:
   (a) $f(1)$ (b) $f(6)$ (c) $f({}^-2)$ (d) $f({}^-8)$

5. If $h(x) = x^2 + 11$, find:
   (a) $h(4)$ (b) $h({}^-4)$ (c) $h(7)$ (d) $h({}^-6)$

6. If $f(x) = 3(x - 5)$, find:
   (a) $f(8)$ (b) $f(2)$ (c) $f({}^-1)$ (d) $f({}^-7)$

7. If $f(x) = 2(x + 6)/5$, find:
   (a) $f(4)$ (b) $f(6)$ (c) $f({}^-1)$ (d) $f({}^-11)$

8. If $f(x) = \frac{5}{2}(x - 2)$, find:
   (a) $f(8)$ (b) $f(1)$ (c) $f(0)$ (d) $f({}^-4)$

Consider the expression $x^2 - 3x + 2$

In words it is:

| Square the value of x | | Take 3 lots of x | | Add 2 |

If $x = 4$, $x^2 - 3x + 2$

$\qquad = 4^2 - 3 \times 4 + 2$

$\qquad = 16 - 12 + 2$

$\qquad = \underline{\underline{6}}$

If your calculator sorts out the order of calculations for you, then

$\boxed{\text{AC}}\ \boxed{4}\ \boxed{x^2}\ \boxed{-}\ \boxed{3}\ \boxed{\times}\ \boxed{4}\ \boxed{+}\ \boxed{2}\ \boxed{=}$

should give the correct answer, 6.

If $x = {}^-5$ $x^2 - 3x + 2$

$$= ({}^-5)^2 - 3 \times {}^-5 + 2$$

$$= 25 + 15 + 2$$

$$= \underline{\underline{42}}$$

On a calculator,

$\boxed{\text{AC}}\ \boxed{5}\ \boxed{+/-}\ \boxed{x^2}\ \boxed{-}\ \boxed{3}\ \boxed{\times}\ \boxed{5}\ \boxed{+/-}\ \boxed{+}\ \boxed{2}\ \boxed{=}$

should give the correct answer, 42.

Exercise 8

A **1.** If $y = x^2 + 2x + 5$, find the value of y when:
     (a) $x = 3$ (b) $x = 5$ (c) $x = 0$ (d) $x = {}^-2$ (e) $x = {}^-7$

2. If $y = x^2 + 4x - 3$, find the value of y when:
     (a) $x = 4$ (b) $x = 1$ (c) $x = 0$ (d) $x = {}^-1$ (e) $x = {}^-6$

3. If $y = x^2 - 3x + 6$, find the value of y when:
     (a) $x = 7$ (b) $x = 2$ (c) $x = 1$ (d) $x = {}^-2$ (e) $x = {}^-5$

4. If $y = x^2 - 6x - 7$, find the value of y when:
     (a) $x = 7$ (b) $x = 2$ (c) $x = 9$ (d) $x = {}^-2$ (e) $x = {}^-1$

5. If $y = x^2 + 7x$, find the value of y when:
     (a) $x = 2$ (b) $x = 5$ (c) $x = 1$ (d) $x = {}^-1$ (e) $x = {}^-6$

B **1.** Find the value of y when $x = 7$, if:
     (a) $y = x^2 - 2x - 6$ (b) $y = (x + 2)(x - 4)$

2. Find the value of y when $x = 5$, if:
     (a) $y = x^2 - 8x + 15$ (b) $y = (x - 3)(x - 5)$

3. Find the value of y when $x = 0$, if:
     (a) $y = x^2 + 5x - 6$ (b) $y = (x - 1)(x + 6)$

C **1.** If $y = (x + 2)(x + 5)$, find y when:

    (a) $x = 2$ (b) $x = 5$ (c) $x = {}^-2$ (d) $x = {}^-5$ (e) $x = 0$

2. If $y = (x - 6)(x + 4)$, find y when:

    (a) $x = 8$ (b) $x = 4$ (c) $x = 0$ (d) $x = 6$ (e) $x = {}^-4$

3. If $y = (x - 6)(x - 4)$, find y when:

    (a) $x = 6$ (b) $x = 4$ (c) $x = 0$ (d) $x = {}^-2$ (e) $x = {}^-6$

Exercise 9

A **1.** If $f(x) = x^2 + 3x + 4$, find:

    (a) $f(2)$ (b) $f(5)$ (c) $f(0)$ (d) $f({}^-1)$ (e) $f({}^-5)$

2. If $f(x) = x^2 - 4x$, find:

    (a) $f(4)$ (b) $f(6)$ (c) $f(1)$ (d) $f({}^-2)$ (e) $f({}^-5)$

3. If $g(x) = x^2 + 2x - 10$, find:

    (a) $g(3)$ (b) $g(1)$ (c) $g(0)$ (d) $g({}^-1)$ (e) $g({}^-4)$

4. If $f(x) = x^2 - 7x - 4$, find:

    (a) $f(4)$ (b) $f(2)$ (c) $f(0)$ (d) $f({}^-1)$ (e) $f({}^-3)$

5. If $h(x) = x^2 - 6x + 15$, find:

    (a) $h(1)$ (b) $h(2)$ (c) $h(5)$ (d) $h({}^-2)$ (e) $h({}^-1)$

B **1.** Find $f(4)$ if:

    (a) $f(x) = x^2 + 6x + 5$ (b) $f(x) = (x + 1)(x + 5)$

2. Find $f(8)$ if:

    (a) $f(x) = x^2 - x - 12$ (b) $f(x) = (x + 3)(x - 4)$

3. Find $f(0)$ if:

    (a) $f(x) = x^2 - 7x + 10$ (b) $f(x) = (x - 2)(x - 5)$

4. Find $f({}^-2)$:

    (a) $f(x) = x^2 + 5x - 14$ (b) $f(x) = (x + 7)(x - 2)$

C **1.** If $f(x) = (x + 1)(x - 9)$, find:

    (a) $f(10)$ (b) $f(9)$ (c) $f(0)$ (d) $f({}^-1)$ (e) $f({}^-3)$

2. If $f(x) = (x - 4)(x - 2)$, find:

    (a) $f(0)$ (b) $f(8)$ (c) $f(4)$ (d) $f(2)$ (e) $f({}^-3)$

3. If $f(x) = (x - 1)(x + 2)$, find:

(a) $f(0)$ (b) $f(4)$ (c) $f(1)$ (d) $f(^-2)$ (e) $f(^-5)$

4. If $f(x) = (x + 4)(x + 4)$, find:

(a) $f(0)$ (b) $f(6)$ (c) $f(^-1)$ (d) $f(^-4)$ (e) $f(^-6)$

Exercise 10   M

Copy and complete the mapping diagrams:

1.

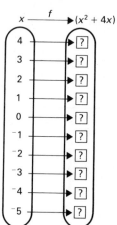

2.

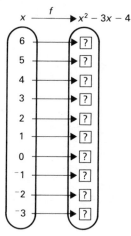

Exercise 11

1. If $y = \frac{6}{x}$, find the value of y when:

(a) $x = 2$ (b) $x = 3$ (c) $x = 1$ (d) $x = 8$ (e) $x = \frac{1}{2}$

2. If $y = ^-\frac{5}{x}$, find the value of y when:

(a) $x = 5$ (b) $x = ^-5$ (c) $x = 2$ (d) $x = \frac{1}{2}$ (e) $x = ^-\frac{1}{2}$

3. If $y = \frac{10}{x}$, find the value of y when:

(a) $x = ^-10$ (b) $x = 5$ (c) $x = ^-2$ (d) 1 (e) $x = \frac{1}{4}$

4. If $y = ^-\frac{12}{x}$, find the value of y when:

(a) $x = 6$ (b) $x = ^-4$ (c) $x = ^-3$ (d) $x = 2$ (e) $x = \frac{1}{3}$

174

Exercise 12

1. If $f(x) = \frac{2}{x}$, find:

    (*a*) $f(2)$ (*b*) $f(4)$ (*c*) $f(^-4)$ (*d*) $f(\frac{1}{4})$ (*e*) $f(^-\frac{1}{5})$

2. If $f(x) = ^-\frac{8}{x}$, find:

    (*a*) $f(4)$ (*b*) $f(^-8)$ (*c*) $f(^-2)$ (*d*) $f(\frac{1}{3})$ (*e*) $f(^-\frac{1}{2})$

3. If $f{:}x \rightarrow \frac{5}{x}$, find:

    (*a*) $f(1)$ (*b*) $f(^-1)$ (*c*) $f(^-5)$ (*d*) $f(2)$ (*e*) $f(\frac{1}{2})$

4. If $f{:}x \rightarrow ^-\frac{7}{x}$, find:

    (*a*) $f(7)$ (*b*) $f(^-1)$ (*c*) $f(2)$ (*d*) $f(^-4)$ (*e*) $f(\frac{1}{4})$

Exercise 13   M

A Copy and complete the mapping diagrams:

1.

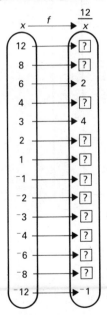

2.

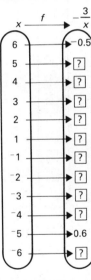

B Copy and complete the following tables:

1.

x	$^-24$	$^-12$	$^-8$	$^-6$	$^-4$	$^-3$	$^-2$		1	2	3		6	8	12	24
$y = \frac{24}{x}$		$^-2$					$^-24$			8	6	4				

175

2.

x	⁻18	⁻9	⁻6	⁻3	⁻1	1	3	6	9	18
$y = -\dfrac{9}{x}$										

Exercise 14 M

Copy and complete the following mapping diagrams. (Give one decimal place where necessary.)

1.

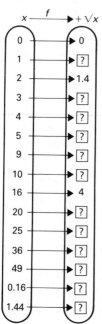

2.

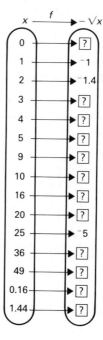

15 Banking, Interest and Loans

Banking

Exercise 1

A Mr Banks paid some money into his account at the Thrifty Bank. He used a paying-in slip.

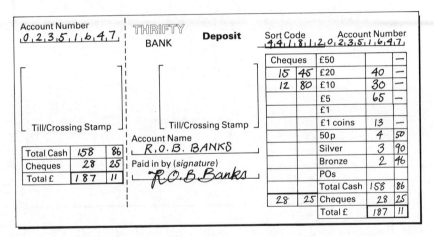

Account Number	0 2 3 5 1 6 4 7		

THRIFTY BANK **Deposit**

Till/Crossing Stamp

Account Name
R.O.B. BANKS

Paid in by (signature)
R.O.B. Banks

Sort Code 4 4 1 8 1 2	Account Number 0 2 3 5 1 6 4 7		
Cheques	£50	—	
15 45	£20	40	—
12 80	£10	30	—
	£5	65	—
	£1		
	£1 coins	13	—
	50p	4	50
	Silver	3	90
	Bronze	2	46
	POs		
	Total Cash	158	86
28 25	Cheques	28	25
	Total £	187	11

Total Cash	158	86
Cheques	28	25
Total £	187	11

Using the given paying-in slip, answer the following:

1. What was the total amount paid in?

2. What was the total cash payment?

3. How many £5 notes were paid in?

4. What was the total amount paid in in notes?

5. How many 50p pieces were paid in?

6. What was the total amount paid in in coins?

B You need a copy of a paying-in slip. Complete the paying-in slip with your own name and today's date. You can invent your own sort code and account number.

  1. Enter the following amounts of money on to the paying-in slip: two £20 notes, fourteen £5 notes, sixteen £1 coins, eleven 50 p pieces, £6.80 in silver, £3.74 in bronze, three cheques for £21.85, £6.72 and £13.69.

  2. Complete all necessary totals.

  3. Fill in the counterfoil*.

  4. Sign the paying-in slip if you have not already done so.

C

Mr Banks needed to pay his credit card balance of £142.56. He paid in two £20 notes, five £10 notes, eight £5 notes, six £1 coins, seven 50 p pieces, £2.80 in silver and 26 p in bronze.

Assume that you are Mr Banks. On a copy of the Bank Giro form, fill in the following particulars.

1. Sign the name R. O. B. Banks.

2. Fill in today's date.

3. Enter the amounts of money paid in in the correct places.

4. Find the total paid in and enter it on the form.

* See the glossary, p. 469.

A cheque is shown below. Note that the amount of money is written in both figures and words. However, the amount in figures is written with a dash rather than with a decimal point.

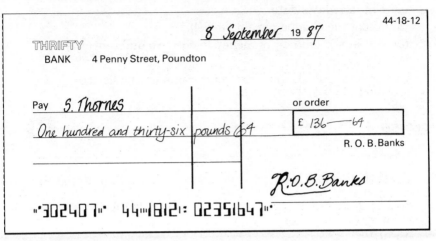

If the cheque is for a whole number of pounds the word 'only' is used to prevent people from putting extra figures after the word 'pounds'. For example £82 would be given as:

Eighty-two pounds only   £82————00

If the cheque is only in pence, for example, 75 p, you should write:

Seventy-five pence   £0————75

Exercise 2   **M**

A Write each amount of money in two different ways (in words and in figures) as on a cheque:

1. £3.45
2. £21.50
3. £29
4. £32.07
5. £493.30
6. £2500
7. £4.99
8. £187
9. £3462.49

B You need three copies of an unused cheque:

1. Complete one cheque by paying out £36.75 to anyone you wish.

2. Complete a second cheque by paying out £243 to somebody.

3. To withdraw money from your bank account, you need to use a cheque. Suppose you wish to withdraw £46.85. On a copy of an unused cheque:

(a) Fill in today's date.

(b) Make the cheque payable to self.*

(c) Fill in the amount of money in the two different ways.

(d) Sign your name.

(e) Endorse the cheque (sign your name on the back).

Exercise 3 M

THRIFTY BANK

BRANCH ADDRESS
4 Penny Street
Poundton

MR R. O. B. BANKS
6 YEW TREE CRESCENT
POUNDTON

				Account no.		Sheet no.
				1812 02351647		61
Date	*Code*		*Reference*	*Debit*	*Credit*	*Balance*
6 Oct 87				Brought forward		492.45
6 Oct 87	CHQ	302406		42.80		449.65
6 Oct 87	DD	HILTON LIFE		9.24		440.41
8 Oct 87	CHQ	302407		136.64		303.77
12 Oct 87	CHQ				220.00	523.77
13 Oct 87	CHQ	302410		215.79		307.98
15 Oct 87	CHQ	302409		15.99		291.99
16 Oct 87	DD	PROVIDENT INSURANCE		22.13		269.86
21 Oct 87	CHQ	302408		125.00		144.86
21 Oct 87	CHQ	302412		89.90		54.96
21 Oct 87	CHQ	302411		16.38		38.58
22 Oct 87	CSH				250.00	288.58
26 Oct 87	SO	NATIONAL B S		215.30		73.28
30 Oct 87	BGC	ACE PRODUCTS LTD			568.77	642.05
2 Nov 87	DD	BOROUGH COUNCIL		52.34		589.71
3 Nov 87	CHQ	302413		147.50		442.21

DR–Overdrawn Balance	SO–Standing Order	CSH–Cash
BGC–Bank Giro Credit	DD–Direct Debit	EUR–Eurocheque
	CHQ–Cheque(s)	COR–Correction

In the event of a query, please take this statement to your branch

---

* See the glossary, p. 470.

Mr Banks received a statement from his bank showing all his transactions for one month. A copy of one of his statements is shown.

Answer the following using the statement opposite:

1. What is the account number?

2. What was the balance in the account on 14 October 1987?

3. A cheque was paid out of the account on 8 October, 1987. How much was the cheque for?

4. What was the smallest amount paid out by cheque?

5. How much per month were Mr Banks' rates?

6. How much per month was Mr Banks' mortgage?

7. (a) How much was Mr Banks' monthly salary?
   (b) What was the name of the firm Mr Banks worked for?

8. Mr Banks paid two insurance policies. What did the two monthly premiums total?

9. Explain what CSH means in the code column.

10. Explain why the cheque numbers are not given in numerical order on the statement. (They were probably written in numerical order.)

11. What was the total amount of money paid out in cheques?

12. (a) What was the total amount paid into the account?
    (b) What was the total amount paid out of the account?
    (c) Why does the following calculation not give the balance:
         total paid in − total paid out?

13. For being overdrawn, some banks may charge for each debit over a whole quarter. Assuming that October to December is a quarter for the Thrifty Bank and that 27 p per debit is charged:
    (a) What would be the charge for October (sheet 61)?
    (b) If the charge for December was £2.97, how many debits must there have been?

181

Simple Interest

$$I = \frac{Prn}{100} \qquad A = P + I$$

I = the amount of *Interest* obtained,

P = the *Principal*, which is the amount of money that is saved,

r = the interest *rate*, i.e. the rate per cent per annum (or R),

n = the *number* of years the money is saved (T is sometimes used for *time* in years),

A = the amount of money received.

Exercise 4

A Find the simple interest on the following, giving your answers correct to the nearest penny:

1. £410 for 3 years at 8% p.a.
2. £800 for $2\frac{1}{2}$ years at 6% p.a.
3. £3400 for 3 years at 6.25% p.a.
4. £5140 for 4 years at $7\frac{3}{4}$% p.a.
5. £300 for 6 months at 5% p.a.
6. £780 for 9 months at 12% p.a.

B Calculate the amount received from the following investments (simple interest):

1. £920 for 2 years at 12% p.a.
2. £47 for 5 years at $6\frac{1}{2}$% p.a.
3. £176 for 10 months at 9% p.a.
4. £751 for $3\frac{1}{2}$ years at 8.16% p.a.

C 1. What sum of money will yield a simple interest of £84 at 6% p.a. for 5 years?

2. After how many years will £480 yield a simple interest of £144 at 10% p.a.?

3. At what rate per cent per annum simple interest will £75 amount to £111, after 6 years?

4. After how many years will £1200 amount to £1368 at 7% p.a. simple interest?

5. What sum of money will yield a simple interest of £1757.70 at 9.3% p.a. for $3\frac{1}{2}$ years?

Compound Interest

If £400 is invested at 5% p.a. *simple interest*:
the interest after 1 year = 5% of £400 = £20.

The interest for the second year is also £20.

Total interest after 2 years = <u>£40</u>

However, if £400 is invested at 5% p.a. *compound interest*

the interest after 1 year = 5% of £400 = £20 (as before)

but the second year's interest = 5% of £420 = £21 (more than before)

There is now £420 in the bank including the first year's interest

Total interest after 2 years = £20 + £21 = <u>£41</u>

For compound interest, the interest after one year is added to the original amount saved. In the following year, not only is interest earned on the amount of money that was saved but also on the interest that was added to the account. Each year, the amount of interest increases since interest is obtained on interest.

Hence, in the previous example the second year's interest was £21 (compound interest) but it would only have been £20 for simple interest.

The following example shows step-by-step calculations of interest for £5000 at 8% compound interest over 3 years:

Interest for first year = 8% of £5000 = £400
Amount after 1 year = £5000 + £400 = £5400

Interest for second year = 8% of £5400 = £432
Amount after 2 years = £5400 + £432 = £5832

Interest for third year = 8% of £5832 = £466.56
Amount after 3 years = £5832 + £466.56 = £6298.56

So interest = £6298.56 − £5000 = <u>£1298.56</u>

Exercise 5

For each of the following equations, find the compound interest giving answers correct to the nearest penny where necessary:

1. £200 for 2 years at 9% p.a.

2. £5000 for 3 years at 6% p.a.

3. £650 for 2 years at 4% p.a.

4. £400 for 2 years at $7\frac{1}{2}$ p.a.

5. £9000 for 3 years at 15% p.a.

6. £172 for 3 years at 8.2% p.a.

7. £3460 for 3 years at 6.75% p.a.

8. £5194 for 2 years at 5.48% p.a.

Compound Interest Tables

The calculation of compound interest is usually done with the help of a table. The following table shows the amounts obtained from an investment of £1, at varying rates of interest (from 4% to 10%) for 1 to 10 years.

Amount from £1 at:

No. of years	4%	$4\frac{1}{2}$%	5%	$5\frac{1}{2}$%	6%	$6\frac{1}{2}$%	7%	$7\frac{1}{2}$%	8%	9%	10%
1	1.0400	1.0450	1.0500	1.0550	1.0600	1.0650	1.0700	1.0750	1.0800	1.0900	1.1000
2	1.0816	1.0920	1.1025	1.1130	1.1236	1.1342	1.1449	1.1556	1.1664	1.1881	1.2100
3	1.1249	1.1412	1.1576	1.1742	1.1910	1.2079	1.2250	1.2423	1.2597	1.2950	1.3310
4	1.1699	1.1925	1.2155	1.2388	1.2625	1.2865	1.3108	1.3355	1.3605	1.4116	1.4641
5	1.2167	1.2462	1.2763	1.3070	1.3382	1.3701	1.4026	1.4356	1.4693	1.5386	1.6105
6	1.2653	1.3023	1.3401	1.3788	1.4185	1.4591	1.5007	1.5433	1.5869	1.6771	1.7716
7	1.3159	1.3609	1.4071	1.4547	1.5036	1.5540	1.6058	1.6590	1.7138	1.8280	1.9487
8	1.3686	1.4221	1.4775	1.5347	1.5938	1.6550	1.7182	1.7835	1.8509	1.9926	2.1436
9	1.4233	1.4861	1.5513	1.6191	1.6895	1.7626	1.8385	1.9172	1.9990	2.1719	2.3579
10	1.4802	1.5530	1.6289	1.7081	1.7908	1.8771	1.9672	2.0610	2.1589	2.3674	2.5937

e.g. Find, using the given table, the amount obtained from and the compound interest on £372 at 6% p.a. for 5 years.

From the table,
amount obtained from £1 at 6% for 5 years = £1.3382
so the amount obtained from £372 = £1.3382 × 372
= £497.82

(to nearest penny)

Interest = £497.81 − £372
= £125.81

Exercise 6

For each question, using the table opposite, find (*a*) the amount obtained from, and (*b*) the compound interest on the given sum of money, for the stated number of years at the given rate per cent per annum. Where necessary, give answers to the nearest penny.

1. £160 for 4 years at 8% p.a.
2. £745 for 7 years at 5% p.a.
3. £4160 for 10 years at 4% p.a.
4. £6482 for 8 years at 9% p.a.

5. £84 for 6 years at 10% p.a.
6. £398 for 9 years at $5\frac{1}{2}$% p.a.
7. £2791 for 5 years at $7\frac{1}{2}$% p.a.
8. £5608 for 7 years at 4.5% p.a.

Exercise 7   Simple and Compound Interest

Where necessary, give answers to the nearest penny:

1. Mrs Cleary wants to invest £2500 for 2 years:
   (*a*) Find the interest she would receive if she invested the money at 6% p.a. simple interest.
   (*b*) Find the interest she would receive if she invested the money at 5% p.a. compound interest.
   (*c*) Which of the above investments, (*a*) or (*b*) is better and by how much?

2. Which is the better investment of £3950 for 4 years and by how much:
   9% p.a. simple interest, or 8% p.a. compound interest?

3. Compare simple and compound interest on an investment of £1860 for 3 years at 7% p.a.

4. Find the difference between the simple and compound interest on an investment of £970 for 10 years at 6% p.a.

5. Find the difference between the simple and compound interest on an investment of £580 for 5 years at $6\frac{1}{2}$% p.a.

Savings and Interest

When you save money in a bank, building society or post office you will be paid interest. The interest payable is usually given as a percentage rate per annum.

With some accounts, the interest is not added to the account but is paid to the investor (possibly monthly); while with other accounts, the interest is paid into the account (often twice a year) and interest is obtained on the interest (as explained on p. 183 in the section on compound interest).

Building societies may quote their percentage rates of interest in different ways. For example, they may say:
'Interest is 10% net = 13.70% gross equivalent.'

The *net rate* is the rate at which you are paid interest. The *gross rate* is the rate you would have been paid at if the building society did not pay tax on the interest. The net is the gross after tax has been deducted.

e.g. Now consider an account where the interest rate is 10% p.a. net. If there is £100 in the account:
(*a*) Calculate the interest received after one month.
(*b*) Calculate how much there will be in the account after one year, if interest is added twice yearly.

(*a*) *To calculate the interest received after one month*:

Interest after one month $= \frac{1}{12}$ of (10% of £100)

$$= \underline{£0.83} \text{ (to the nearest penny)}$$

(b) *To calculate the amount in the account after one year:*

Interest for the first 6 months $= \frac{1}{2}$ of (10% of £100)

$= £5$

Amount now in the account $= £100 + £5 = £105$

Interest for the second 6 months $= \frac{1}{2}$ of (10% of £105)

$= £5.25$

Amount now in the account $= £105 + £5.25 = £110.25$

Amount in the account after one year $= \underline{£110.25}$

Note   If the building society paid interest yearly, the rate would need to be 10.25% p.a. for £100 to become £110.25. This rate is referred to as CAR (Compounded Annual Rate). Some societies state this rate per annum together with their ordinary rate.

Exercise 8

A The Poundton Building Society offer four different savings accounts:

> ### POUNDTON BUILDING SOCIETY
>
> *Regular Share Account*   5.00% net p.a.
>   (Interest is compounded every six months)
>
> *High Interest Account*   6.75% net p.a.
>   (Interest is compounded once a year.
>   Provided a balance of £500 is maintained, withdrawals can be made without loss of interest)
>
> *Extra Interest Account*   8.5% net p.a.
>   (Interest is compounded once a year.
>   Provided a balance of £10 000 is maintained, withdrawals can be made without a loss of interest)
>
> *Monthly Interest Account*   8.19% net (8.5% CAR)
>   (Interest can be paid monthly into any account or direct to your bank or home)

Ms Nicholls wanted to invest £800 for 3 years in one of the Poundton Building Society's accounts:

1. Calculate the total interest she would receive by investing in the Extra Interest Account.

2. Calculate the total interest she would receive from an Extra Interest Account, if she withdrew the interest each year.

3. Calculate the total interest she would receive from the High Interest Account.

4. (a) Calculate the monthly interest received from a Monthly Interest Account. (Use the net rate.)
   (b) Calculate the total interest over 3 years from a Monthly Interest Account.

5. For a Regular Share Account, calculate the total interest:
   (a) after 6 months,   (d) after 2 years,
   (b) after 1 year,   (e) after $2\frac{1}{2}$ years,
   (c) after 18 months,   (f) after 3 years.

B 1. Mr Emery invested £400 in a bank deposit account at a rate of 7% p.a. compounded annually. If he made no further deposits or withdrawals, calculate the total amount in his account:
   (a) after one year,   (b) after two years.

2. Mrs Harper invested £1600 for one year at 6.25% p.a. compounded half-yearly:
   (a) Calculate the total interest obtained.
   (b) Calculate the amount in the account after one year (to the nearest penny).

3. Georgina opened a bank account with £240. If the interest rate was 6.75% p.a. payable monthly, calculate the monthly interest.

Loans

Most people need to borrow money at some time in their lives. It may be a hire-purchase or credit sale agreement, where an item is paid for over a number of months; it may be a personal loan from a bank or from a moneylending company; it may be a mortgage to buy a house, to be paid back over a number of years; it may be borrowing by using a credit card or it may be an overdraft at a bank.

Whatever the type of loan, the money borrowed will have to be paid back together with an *interest charge* (the charge for borrowing the money). The interest is calculated from the amount of the loan and the interest rate at that time.

Interest rates vary and need to be examined carefully.

Look at the advert:

1 p per pound per week sounds cheap, but, the loan costs 52 p per year for each pound borrowed.

Q P Loans
£250–£200 000
(for any purpose)
Only 1 p per pound per week

That is an interest rate of 52% p.a., if the repayment is paid one year after borrowing the money. If the money is repaid weekly, the true interest rate is in fact 67.8% p.a.*

For example, if you borrowed £100 for one year the interest will be £52. This interest is calculated on the full amount borrowed. After almost a year's weekly repayments you will owe very little, but the interest payable is still based on the full amount and not on what is owed at the time.

An interest rate that takes repayments into consideration is the *annual percentage rate* (APR). It is referred to as the true interest rate, and should always be considered when comparing the costs of loans.

A credit card rate of 2% per month works out to be 26.8%* p.a. APR.

Exercise 9

1. A cooker cost £299.98 cash. It could be bought on HP for a deposit of £90 followed by 24 monthly payments of £12.60.
   (a) Calculate the total hire-purchase cost.
   (b) Calculate the amount saved by paying cash.

* See Appendix 2, p.468.

2.

Compact Disc Player
Laser Tracking

Cash price 10% discount

Normal price £279.50

Easy terms 25% deposit

+ 30 monthly payments
of £9.60

(a) Calculate the cash price of the CD player.
(b) Calculate the deposit when buying on easy terms.
(c) Calculate the total easy terms cost.
(d) Calculate the extra paid by buying on credit.

3. Mrs Lloyd's new carpet measured 4 m by 3.8 m.
It cost £10.75 per m².
(a) Calculate the area of the carpet.
(b) Calculate the cash price of the carpet.

If the carpet can be bought for a deposit of 10% followed by 18 payments of £9.75:
(c) Calculate the deposit.
(d) Calculate the total credit price.
(e) Calculate the amount saved by paying cash.

4. Mr Allinson obtained a personal loan from his bank to buy some bedroom furniture costing £540. He was charged a flat rate of 10% p.a. (the interest for each year was 10% of the amount of the loan). He borrowed the £540 over 3 years and repaid it by equal monthly repayments.
(a) Calculate the interest for 1 year.
(b) Calculate the interest for the 3 years.
(c) Calculate the total repayable.
(d) Calculate each monthly payment.

Exercise 10

A **1.** If monthly mortgage repayments were £8 per £1000 borrowed, find the monthly repayments on a £15 000 mortgage.

2. If monthly mortgage repayments were £7.95 per £1000 borrowed over 25 years, and if Mr and Mrs Isherwood borrowed £18 000, calculate:
(a) their monthly repayments,
(b) the total repayment in one year,
(c) the total repayment over the full 25-year term of the mortgage,
(d) the total amount of interest paid on the mortgage over the 25 years.

3. Dilys and Terence Caley wanted to buy a house costing £31 500. They needed an 80% mortgage. Repayments were going to cost £8.50 per month per £1000 borrowed over 20 years.
(a) Calculate the amount they needed to borrow.
(b) Calculate what their monthly repayments would be.
(c) Calculate what their yearly repayments would be.
(d) Calculate the total repayment over the full 20-year term of the mortgage.
(e) Calculate the total amount of interest paid on the mortgage over 20 years.

B On a credit card company's statement a minimum payment that must be made will be given. For this exercise, take the minimum payment to be £5 or 5% of the amount owed, whichever is the greater. The payment should be *rounded down* to the nearest pound. (Some companies do this while others round to the nearest pound.)

1. Mr J Fielding owed a credit card company £146.40. Find his minimum payment.

2. Mrs Gibbons owed a credit card company £79.98. Find her minimum payment.

3. Mrs Coggin owed a credit card company £238.79. Calculate her minimum payment.

4. Find the minimum payment to be paid by Mr Weir if he owes £183.51.

5. Mr Mills owed £359.84. He paid £79.84 of that amount to the credit card company.

(*a*) How much did he still owe?

(*b*) If he had to pay 2% interest for one month on the amount owed, calculate the interest payable.

6. Mrs Newsham owed a credit card company £643.71. She paid the minimum payment allowed.

(*a*) What was the minimum payment?

(*b*) If she had a credit limit of £950, what is the largest total she can now spend using that credit card?

C 1. Mrs Ferguson had an authorised overdraft of £146 (that is, her bank manager allowed the overdraft). She was charged 16% p.a. interest. Calculate the interest to the nearest penny if she had the overdraft:

(*a*) for exactly 1 month,

(*b*) for exactly 25 days (assume a 365-day year).

2. Mr Raines had an unauthorised overdraft of £98 (his bank manager had not been consulted). He was charged 24.5% p.a. interest. Calculate the interest to the nearest penny if he had the overdraft for:

(*a*) exactly 1 month,

(*b*) exactly 18 days (assume a 365-day year),

(*c*) exactly 41 days (assume a 365-day year).

16 Transformations

1. Copy the diagram.
   (a) Draw the result of translating the triangle 5 squares downwards.
   (b) Draw the image of triangle ABC after a reflection in line *m*.
   (c) Draw the image of triangle ABC after a rotation through a quarter turn anticlockwise about point P.

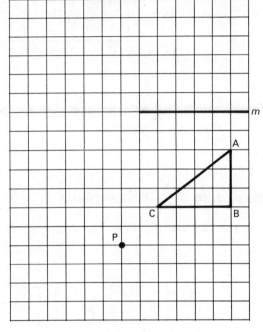

2. Copy the diagram. Draw the result of reflecting the triangle in line *m*.

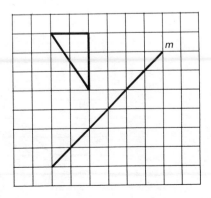

193

3. Copy the pair of axes and △PQR on to squared paper.

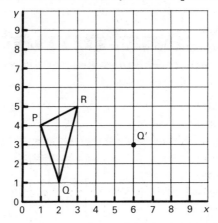

Mark the point Q′ (6, 3) which is the image of Q (2, 1) under a translation. Now mark P′ and R′, the images of P and R under the same translation.

Exercise 2   Reflections ═══════════════ **M**

1. (*a*) Copy the following diagram. Parallelogram A is the image of the shaded parallelogram after a reflection in the line $y = {}^-1$.

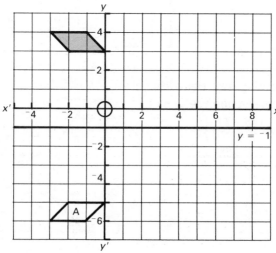

(b) Draw the line $x = 2$.

(c) Draw the image of the reflection of the shaded parallelogram in the line $x = 2$. Label it B.

(d) Draw the straight line $y = 3$.

(e) Draw the image of the reflection of the shaded parallelogram in the line $y = 3$. Label it C.

2. (a) Draw another pair of axes as in question 1, but only copy the shaded parallelogram.

(b) Draw the straight-line graph of $y = x$.

(c) Draw the reflection of the shaded parallelogram in the line $y = x$. Label the image P.

(d) Draw the image of the shaded parallelogram when it is reflected in the line $y = -x$. Label the image Q.

(e) Draw the reflection of P in the line $y = -x$.
Label the image R.

(f) Reflect R in $y = x$. Write what you notice.

3. (a) Make a copy of the two right-angled triangles.

(b) Find and draw the mirror line so that triangle B is the image of triangle A, under a reflection.

Rotations

Exercise 3   M

A Copy the diagrams. For each question, rotate line AB through 90° clockwise about point C. Label each image A′B′. Write what you notice about the direction of an image A′B′ when compared with the direction of its object.

1.
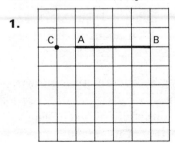

2.
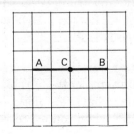

3.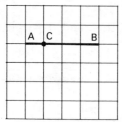

5.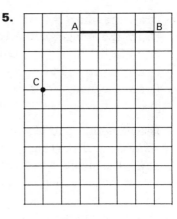

4.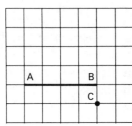

B 1. Copy the given triangle PQR. Rotate it clockwise through 90° about C. Label the image P'Q'R'. Compare the directions of the lines PQ and P'Q'; QR and Q'R'; PR and P'R'; then write what you notice.

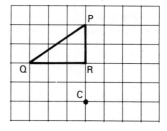

2. Draw any triangle on squared paper. Label it PQR.
Mark any point C. Rotate △PQR through 90° anticlockwise about C. Label the image P'Q'R'.
Compare the direction of each side of △PQR with the direction of its image. Write what you notice.

C 1. Draw any triangle on squared paper. Label it DEF. Mark any point C. Rotate △DEF through a half-turn about C. Label the image D'E'F'.

2. Repeat question 1 several times using a different triangle with a different centre of rotation each time.
Write what you notice about the direction of each side of △DEF when compared with the direction of its image.

A 1. The diagram shows a trapezium PQRS and its image P′Q′R′S′ after a rotation through 180° about point C.

(*a*) Copy the diagram.

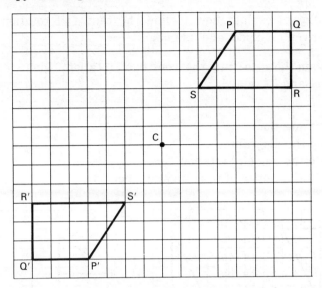

(*b*) Join each vertex to its image (P to P′, Q to Q′, etc.).

(*c*) Write what you notice.

2. Explain how to find the centre of rotation, when given an object and its image, from a 180° rotation.

B 1. (*a*) Copy the diagram showing △LMN and its image △L′M′N′ after a rotation through 90° clockwise about point C.

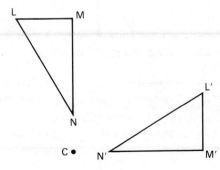

(*b*) Join L to its image L′ using a straight line. Bisect LL′ and draw the perpendicular bisector.

(*c*) Join MM′ and construct its perpendicular bisector.

(*d*) Join NN′ and construct its perpendicular bisector.

(*e*) Write what you notice about all three perpendicular bisectors.

(*f*) Try to explain how to find the centre of rotation, when given an object and its image.

2. Explain how to find the centre of rotation, when given an object and its image.

C For each question:

(*a*) Copy the diagram.

(*b*) State the angle of rotation.

(*c*) Mark the centre of rotation and label it C.

1.

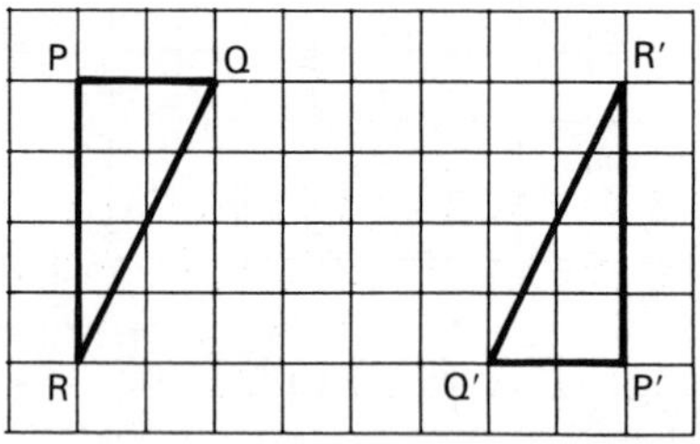

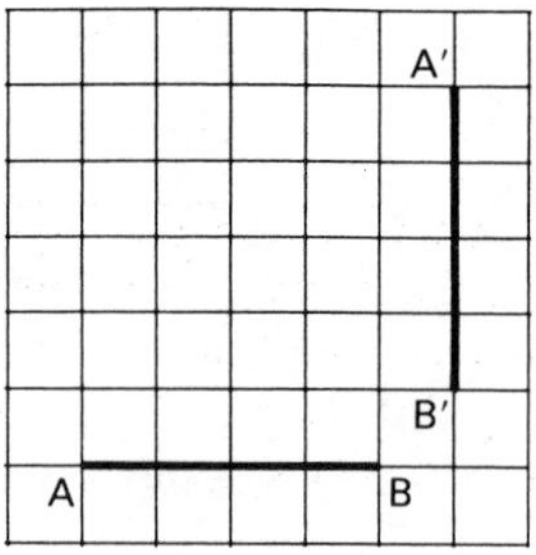

2.

3.

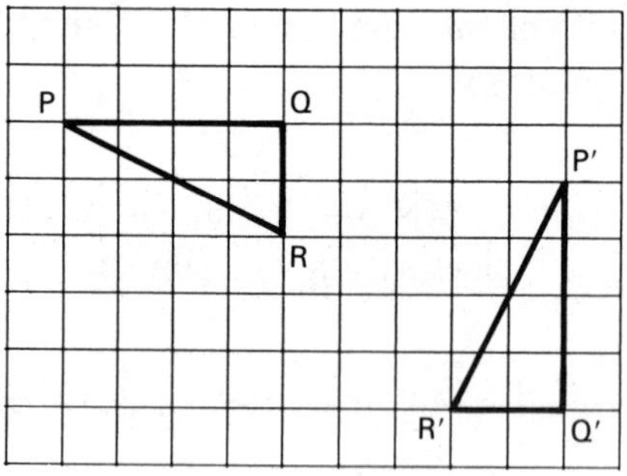

4.

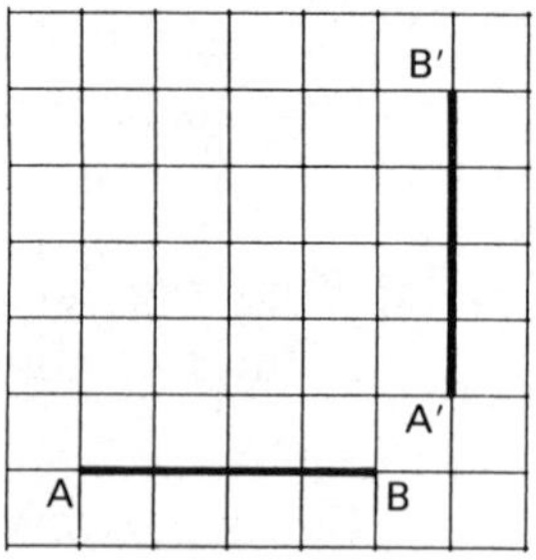

5.

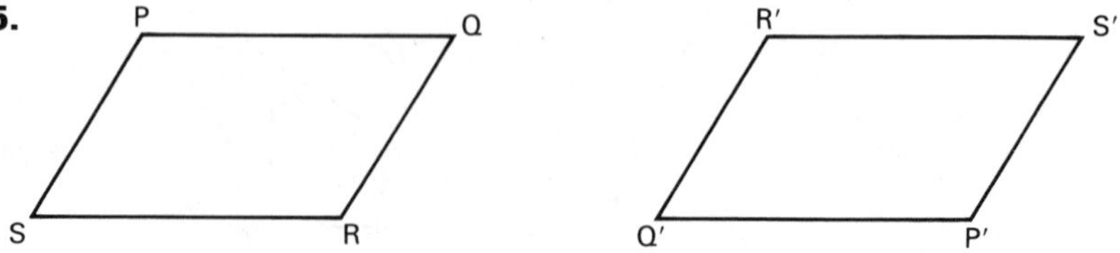

Enlargements

Exercise 5 Enlargements with Positive Integral Scale Factors

1. (a) On squared paper, draw an enlargement of the given shape so that every line becomes 3 times as big (the scale factor = 3).

   (b) By counting squares, find the area of the given shape.

   (c) By counting squares, find the area of the enlargement.

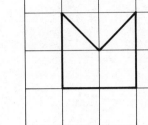

   (d) How many times as big as the original shape is the enlargement?

2. (a) Copy the following square and mark on your page, the position of C.

   (b) By drawing lines from C to pass through the corners of the square, draw an enlargement having a scale factor of 2.

   (c) By measuring, then calculating, find the area of the given square.

   (d) By measuring, then calculating, find the area of the enlargement.

   (e) How many times as big as the original square is the enlargement?

3. Repeat question 2, but use a scale factor of 3.

4. (*a*) Copy the following diagram. (It shows an enlargement of △PQR. P′Q′R′ is the image.)

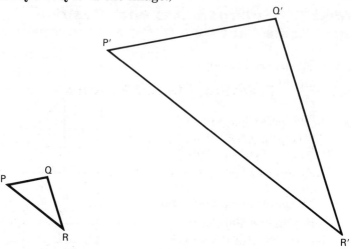

(*b*) By drawing straight lines through the vertices of the triangles, find the centre of the enlargement. Label it C.

(*c*) What is the scale factor of the enlargement?

(*d*) Using the same diagram, draw an enlargement of △PQR having a scale factor of 2. Use C as the centre of this new enlargement.

5. (*a*) Copy the following diagram. It shows an enlargement of quadrilateral JKLM.

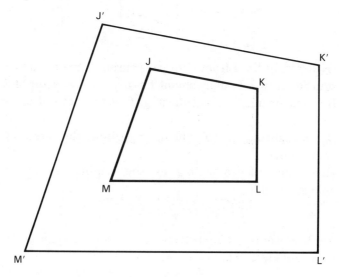

(b) By drawing straight lines through the vertices, find the centre of the enlargement. Label it C.

(c) On the same diagram, using C as the centre, enlarge JKLM using a scale factor of 3.

Exercise 6   Fractional Scale Factors ━━━━ M

e.g. In the given diagram, by drawing lines through the vertices, the centre of the enlargement is found to be (⁻6, ⁻2).

Since all the lengths on the image are $\frac{1}{3}$ of the lengths on the object, the scale factor = $\frac{1}{3}$.

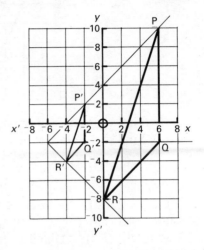

1. △P′Q′R′ is the image of △PQR:

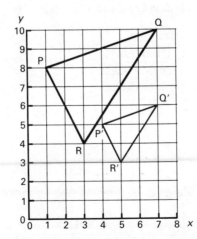

(a) Find the centre of enlargement.

(b) Find the scale factor.

201

2. △P'Q'R' is the image of △PQR:

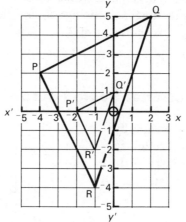

(a) Find the centre of enlargement.
(b) Find the scale factor.

3. Draw a pair of axes where the x-values range from $^-5$ to $^+5$ and the y-values range from $^-4$ to $^+4$.
Plot and join P ($^-5$, $^-3$), Q ($^-3$, $^-3$) and R (1, $^-3$), and also P' (0, 2), Q' (1, $^-1$) and R' (3, $^-1$).
If △P'Q'R' is the image of △PQR:
(a) Find the co-ordinates of the centre of the enlargement.
(b) Find the scale factor of the enlargement.

4. A sketch of a trapezium is given. Make an accurate scale drawing of it using a scale factor of $\frac{1}{5}$.

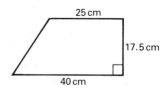

Negative Scale Factors

The first diagram opposite shows an enlargement of △PQR with scale factor 2, while the second diagram shows another enlargement of the same triangle PQR from the same centre C, but this time, with scale factor $^-2$.

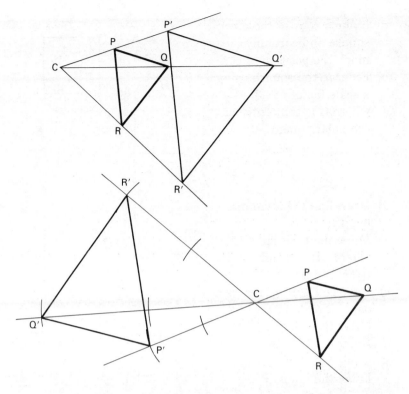

Note For a negative scale factor the lines from the centre that pass through the vertices are projected away from the object. The image is then on the opposite side of centre C to the object.

Exercise 7

1. (*a*) Construct △PQR where
PR = 40 mm,
PQ = 30 mm and
QR = 20 mm.
C is 20 mm from P and
35 mm from R.
Mark the position of C.

(*b*) Draw an enlargement of
△PQR with a scale factor
of ⁻2, where C is the
centre of enlargement.
Label the image P′Q′R′.

C
•

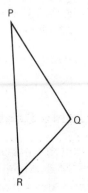

2. (*a*) Make a copy of the given square and carefully mark the position of C.

(*b*) Enlarge the square using a scale factor of $^-3$, where C is the centre of the enlargement.

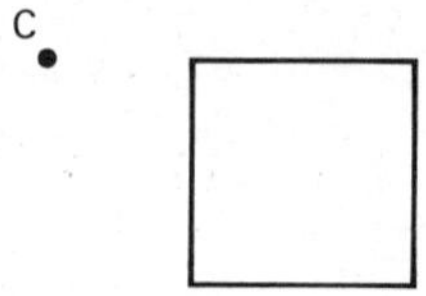

C

3. (*a*) Draw line PQ, 3 cm in length.

(*b*) Mark the position of C, where PC = 20 mm and QC = 25 mm.

(*c*) Enlarge PQ from centre C using a scale factor of 2. Label the image P′Q′.

(*d*) Enlarge PQ from centre C using a scale factor of $^-2$. Label the image P″Q″.

P

C

Q

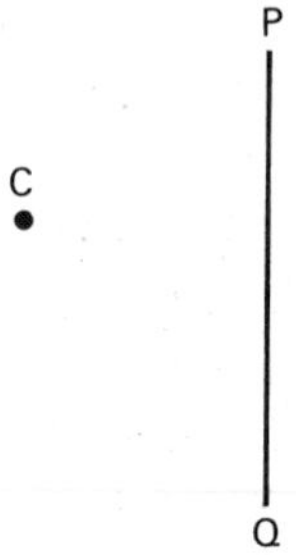

4. (*a*) Copy the two lines p and q.

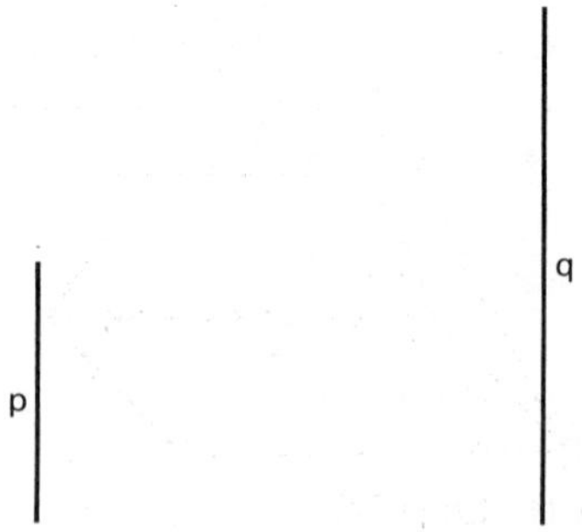

q

p

(*b*) If line p can be mapped onto line q by two different enlargements (that is, q is an enlargement of p), find, by drawing lines, the centre of each enlargement. Label these centres C and D.

Exercise 8   Enlargements of Three-Dimensional Shapes

1. The diagram shows a cuboid that measures 4 cm by 3 cm by 2 cm.

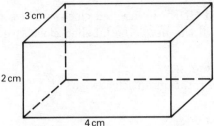

(a) Calculate its volume.

(b) Draw a sketch of a net of the cuboid.

(c) Calculate its surface area.

(d) Make an accurate drawing of an enlargement of the cuboid using a scale factor of 2.

(e) Calculate the volume of the enlarged cuboid.

(f) How many times as big as the given cuboid is the volume of the enlargement?

(g) Calculate the surface area of the enlarged cuboid.

(h) How many times as big as the surface area of the given cuboid is the surface area of the enlargement?

2. The diagram shows a solid with a square base:

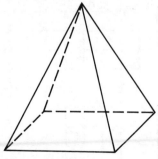

(a) Write the name of the solid.

(b) By taking measurements from the given drawing, draw an enlargement of this solid using a scale factor of 2.

(c) On card, draw a net of your enlargement. (Put flaps where necessary.)

(d) Cut out the net and make the solid.

Miscellaneous Transformations

1. Quadrilateral CDEF is labelled clockwise. Its image is labelled C′D′E′F′. Will the image be labelled clockwise or anticlockwise after:
   (a) a reflection?
   (b) a $\frac{3}{4}$ turn rotation anticlockwise?

2. (a) Describe fully the single transformation that maps trapezium:
   (i)   A onto B
   (ii)   A onto C
   (iii)   C onto D
   (iv)   A onto D
   (v)   A onto G
   (vi)   B onto G
   (vii)   C onto H
   (viii) H onto C

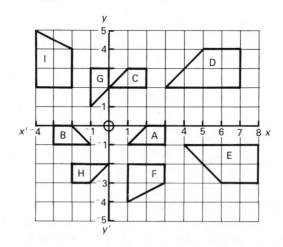

   (b) Which shape is congruent to shape D?
   (c) Which shapes are congruent to shape A?
   (d) Which shapes are similar to but not congruent to shape A?

3. (*a*) Draw a pair of axes as shown and copy triangle A.

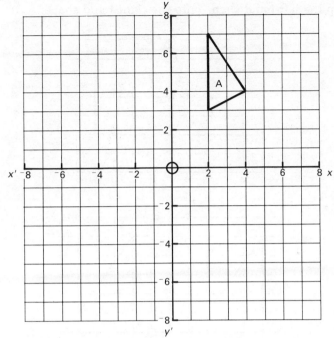

(*b*) If triangle A is reflected in the *x*-axis, draw its image and label it B.

(*c*) If triangle A is rotated through 180° about (0, 0), draw its image and label it C.

(*d*) If triangle A is rotated through a half-turn about the point (0, 5), draw its image and label it D.

(*e*) Describe fully the transformation that maps C onto B.

(*f*) Describe fully the transformation that maps C onto D.

4. The shaded trapezium, when rotated a half-turn about the mid-point of one of its parallel sides, gives a hexagon (when the object and image are looked at together).

What shape is obtained when the half-turn rotation is about the mid-point of a non-parallel side?

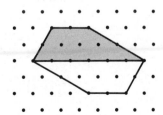

5. For each question, write all possible transformations that will map the left-hand shape onto the right-hand shape:

(a)

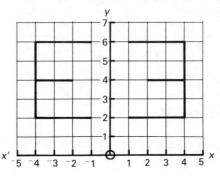

(b)

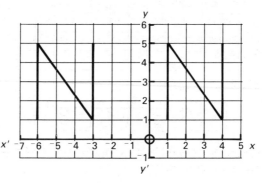

Revision Exercises IX to XVI

Revision Exercise IX ██████ **M**

1. Mrs Kendrick is paid £3.90 per hour for the first 36 h worked in a week. Overtime is paid at time and a third.
(*a*) How much will she earn for 1 h overtime?
(*b*) How much will she earn if she works 42 h in one week?
(*c*) If during one week she earned £187.20, for how many hours did she work?

2. Chloe's calculator showed

$$\boxed{\text{4.3773585}}$$

on its display, the answer being in pounds. Write the answer correct to the nearest penny.

3. A fridge-freezer costs £259.99 cash. It can be bought on easy terms for a deposit of £60 followed by 20 payments of £13.75. How much more is the hire-purchase price?

4. Mrs Miller bought some bed linen. Copy and complete the following invoice:

Quantity	Item		Unit price	£	p
2	Flat sheets		£11.99		
1	Fitted sheet	4 ft 6 in	£12.99		
1	Valance	4 ft 6 in	£14.99		
2 pairs	Pillowcases		£5.50 per pair		
			Total cost		

5. Which size is the best value?

75 g
£0.89

100 g
£1.25

200 g
£2.39

6. (*a*) Find 30% of £8.70.   (*b*) Find $12\frac{1}{2}$% of £51.20.

7. (*a*) Express £18 as a percentage of £60.
    (*b*) Express £1.30 as a percentage of £8.

8. Out of 840 pupils in a school, 65% are learning German. How many is that?

9. Mrs Tomlinson earned £96 per week, while Mrs Nelson earned £168 per week:
    (*a*) If they are both given a 5% pay increase, find their new weekly wages.
    (*b*) If instead of the percentage increase they both received a flat-rate increase of £6 per week, find both percentage increases.

10. The cash price of a car was £7830. It could be bought on hire-purchase for a deposit of 20% of the cash price followed by 36 payments of £237. Calculate:
    (*a*) the amount of the deposit,
    (*b*) the total amount paid for the car,
    (*c*) the extra paid on hire-purchase when compared with the cash price.

11. As a special offer, a 150 mℓ can of antiperspirant is sold containing an extra 30% free. How many millilitres does this larger can hold?

12. A car costing £7450 depreciated in value at a rate of 19% p.a. Find its value after:
    (*a*) 2 years,   (*b*) 3 years.

13. A briefcase was sold for £42, at a discount of 25%. What was its normal price?

1. (a) Draw a sketch of a triangular-based pyramid. (The base may be any type of triangle.)
   (b) How many faces does it have?
   (c) How many edges does it have?
   (d) How many vertices does it have?

2. The given shape has been made from cubes. The whole of the outside of the shape has been painted grey.

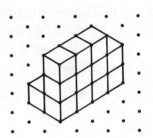

   (a) How many small cubes are there?
   (b) How many faces were painted altogether?
   (c) How many cubes had 5 faces painted grey?
   (d) How many cubes had 4 faces painted grey?
   (e) How many cubes had 3 faces painted grey?
   (f) How many cubes had 2 faces painted grey?

3. In the given solid, some cubes may be hidden. Find the minimum and maximum number of cubes there could be.

4. The diagram shows part of a net of a cuboid. Copy it. Complete your copy of the net.

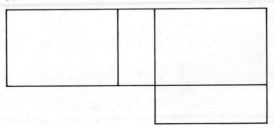

5. Here is a net of a solid:

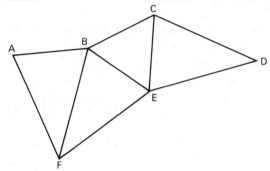

(a) Name the solid.
(b) Which edge will meet edge AF when the solid is made?

6. Sketch the net of a cylinder with a base and a top.

7. Part of a shape is shown. The broken lines are lines of symmetry.

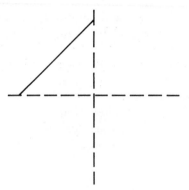

(a) Name the complete shape.
(b) The complete shape has bilateral symmetry. What other sort of symmetry does the shape have?

8. A symmetrical triangle has one angle measuring 50°. What sizes could the other two angles be? (Give all possible answers.)

9. For the given diagrams, is the shaded part a plane of symmetry?

(a)

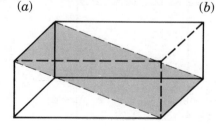

(b)

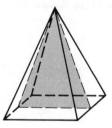

212

1. Remove the brackets by multiplying out:

    (a) $2(3y - 2)$ (b) $^-7(8 - x)$ (c) $(x - 3)$

2. Simplify:

    (a) $7c - 9c + 8c$ (c) $z^2 - 5z + 2z + 6$

    (b) $9j + 2k - 4j + 5k$ (d) $3vw - 2uv + 6wv + 7uv$

3. Which expression must be added to $(4m - 3n)$ to make $(7m + 2n)$:

    A. $3m + n$ D. $^-3m - 5n$

    B. $3m + 5n$ E. $3m - 5n$

    C. $11m + n$

4. Remove the brackets and simplify:

    (c) $2(p + 7) + 3(p - 5)$ (b) $8(x - 4) - 2(x - 9)$

5. Multiply out then simplify your answers:

    (a) $(y + 1)(y - 4)$ (b) $(x - 3)(x - 3)$

6. Find the value of $2.4 \times 3.8 + 2.4 \times 6.2$ by factorising first.

7. Factorise completely:

    (a) $15m - 6$ (c) $4e - 6e^2$

    (b) $3g^2 + 9g$ (d) $8x^2 + 20xy$

8. $d = 7w$

    (a) Find d when $w = 5$.

    (b) Rewrite the formula giving w in terms of d.

    (c) Find w when $d = 56$.

9. If $h = \dfrac{2A}{b}$:

    (a) Express A in terms of b and h.

    (b) Calculate A when $h = 9$ and $b = 14$.

    (c) Express b in terms of A and h.

    (d) Calculate b when $h = 4$ and $A = 14$.

10. If $A = \frac{1}{2}Dd$, express D in terms of A and d.

11. If $A = \pi dh$, express d in terms of π, h and A.

    Find d when $h = 5$, $A = 94.2$ and $\pi = 3.14$.

12. Work out the exact value of $x^2 - 3x + 5$ when:

(a) $x = 5$ (b) $x = {}^{-}4$ (c) $x = 10$ (d) $x = 2.6$

13. If $V = \frac{1}{3}\pi r^2 h$, calculate V when $\pi = 3.14$, $r = 7$ and $h = 12$.

14. If $m*n = 2m + n$, find the value of:

(a) $4*6$ (b) $6*4$ (c) $10*7$ (d) $18*3$

15. (a) Multiply 4 by 9.   (b) Multiply a by b.

16. (a) How many seconds are there in 4 min?

(b) How many seconds are there in t min?

17. Write a formula giving the total cost, £T, of n shirts costing £S each.

18. If I bought 7 pencils costing c pence each, what would be the change from £1?

Revision Exercise XII

1. A rectangular room measured 14 ft by 11 ft. It was carpeted using a single piece of carpet that was 12 ft wide. Each foot of its length cost £11.65 fitted. The underlay used was also sold in 12 ft widths and cost a further £4 per foot of its length.

(a) Calculate the area of the room.

(b) Calculate the area of the carpet purchased.

(c) Find the cost of the carpet.

(d) Find the cost of the underlay.

(e) Find the total cost of carpeting the room.

(f) Find the area of the waste carpet.

2. The radius of each curve of a running track is 35 m. The 'straights' measure 90 m.

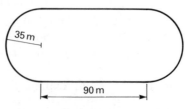

(a) Calculate the total distance around the track. (Use $\pi = 3\frac{1}{7}$.)

(b) Calculate the extra distance run on each lap by a runner who ran 1 m outside the line shown, all the way around.

3. Calculate the length of the arc of the given sector. Use $\pi = 3.142$. Give the answer to the nearest millimetre.

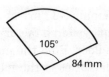

105°

84 mm

4. Calculate the area of the skin on one end of a drum, if it is circular and has a radius of 38 cm. (Use $\pi = 3.142$.)

5. Calculate the area of the given sector. (Use $\pi = 3.14$.)

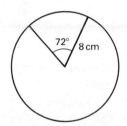

72°

8 cm

6. A circle of radius 3.2 cm is cut out of a rectangular piece of paper measuring 9.4 cm by 7.5 cm. Calculate the area of the remaining paper. (Use $\pi = 3.14$.)

7.

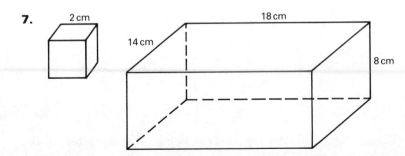

2 cm

18 cm

14 cm

8 cm

How many 2 cm cubes will fit exactly inside a box measuring 18 cm by 14 cm by 8 cm?

8. Normally, $11\,\text{m}^3$ of space must be allowed for every person employed in a factory, not counting space more than $4.2\,\text{m}$ from the floor. Find the maximum number of people allowed to work in factories of the following sizes:

(*a*) $15\,\text{m}$ by $12\,\text{m}$ by $4\,\text{m}$,

(*b*) $24\,\text{m}$ by $13.8\,\text{m}$ by $3.9\,\text{m}$.

9. The uniform cross-section of the given prism is a right-angled triangle. Calculate its volume.

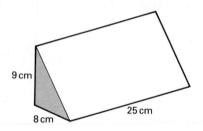

10. For the can shown, calculate:

(*a*) its volume,

(*b*) the number of millilitres of orange juice it will hold when full,

(*c*) its total surface area if it is a sealed can.

(Take π to be 3.14.)

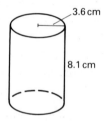

11. A glass tumbler is $13\,\text{cm}$ tall.

The diameter at the top is $7\,\text{cm}$, while the diameter at the bottom is $5\,\text{cm}$. Estimate the number of millilitres of water in the glass when it is full. (Assume the glass to be a cylinder and use an average (mean) radius.) Take π to be 3.14.

Revision Exercise XIII

1. Construct △ PQR such that QR = 100 mm, PQ = 62 mm and ∠ PQR = 70°. Using a pencil, ruler and a pair of compasses only, bisect ∠ RPQ and side PR. Label the point of intersection of the bisectors as point S.
   Measure: (a) PR   (b) PS

2. Draw a straight line, AB, 78 mm in length. By measuring, find the mid-point of AB and label it M. Using a pencil, ruler and pair of compasses, construct an angle BMC equal to 120°.

3. Construct △ LMN where LM = 58 mm, ∠ LMN = 127° (use a protractor) and MN = 55 mm. By taking suitable measurements, find the area of the triangle.

4. The sketch shows a rectangular lawn labelled ABCD. It is 16 m long and 14 m wide. A dog is tethered to a post at D on a 5 m rope. A lawn sprinkler is at S, the centre of the lawn. It has a 6 m spread in all directions. Make a scale drawing, then:

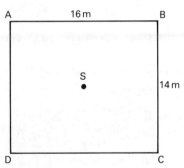

   (a) Show the area where the dog can move.
   (b) Show the area that can be sprinkled.
   (c) Shade the area where the dog could get wet.

Revision Exercise XIV

1. Copy the following and fill in the missing values:

   (a)

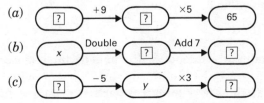

   (b)

   (c)

217

2. Copy and complete the mapping diagram:

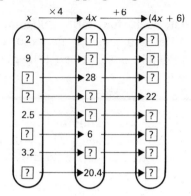

3. The function f is defined by:

Find: (*a*) $f(2)$ (*b*) $f(125)$ (*c*) $f(5.8)$

4. If $y = 3x - 8$, find the value of y when:
(*a*) $x = 7$ (*b*) $x = 0$ (*c*) $x = 2$ (*d*) $x = {}^-3$

5. If $f(x) = x^2 - 1$, find:
(*a*) $f(6)$ (*b*) $f(0)$ (*c*) $f({}^-5)$ (*d*) $f({}^-1)$

6. If $y = (3x - 2)/2$, find the value of y when:
(*a*) $x = 2$ (*b*) $x = 5$ (*c*) $x = 1$ (*d*) $x = {}^-4$

7. If $y = x^2 - 3x - 8$, find the value of y when:
(*a*) $x = 5$ (*b*) $x = 0$ (*c*) $x = 2$ (*d*) $x = {}^-3$

8. If $f(x) = x^2 + 4x - 6$, find:
(*a*) $f(3)$ (*b*) $f(1)$ (*c*) $f(0)$ (*d*) $f({}^-2)$

9. If $y = (x + 5)(x - 4)$, find the value of y when:
(*a*) $x = 6$ (*b*) $x = 4$ (*c*) $x = 0$ (*d*) $x = {}^-5$

10. If $y = \dfrac{9}{x}$, find the value of y when:
(*a*) $x = 9$ (*b*) $x = 2$ (*c*) $x = {}^-2$ (*d*) $x = \frac{1}{3}$

11. If $y = +\sqrt{x}$, find the value of y (to one decimal place if necessary) when:
(*a*) $x = 100$ (*b*) $x = 8$ (*c*) $x = 0.09$ (*d*) $x = 1.21$

1. (a) Enter the following amounts of money on to a paying-in slip:

> two £20 notes, one £10 note, nine £5 notes, twelve £1 coins, seventeen 50 p coins, £4.65 in silver and £2.84 in bronze

(b) Complete all the necessary totals.

(c) Fill in the counterfoil.

(d) Sign the paying-in slip if you have not already signed it.

2. Write the given amounts of money in two different ways (in words and figures) as on a cheque:

(a) £46.81　　(b) £75　　(c) £169.25　　(d) £1417.50

3. Complete an unused cheque by paying out £18.36 to anyone you wish.

4. Find the simple interest on £820 for 5 years at 7% p.a.

5. At what rate per cent per annum simple interest will £670 yield £402 interest after 5 years?

6. Using the compound interest table on p.184, find to the nearest penny: (a) the amount obtained from and (b) the compound interest on £693 for 6 years at 8% p.a.

7. Maxine Rayner invested £600 for 3 years in a building society account at 9% net p.a. Interest was calculated day by day, but only added to the account on 31 December each year.

(a) Calculate the interest when the money has been invested for exactly one year.

(b) Calculate the interest for the second year.

(c) Calculate the interest for the third year, giving your answer to the nearest penny.

(d) Work out the total interest obtained over 3 years.

8. A 200-piece tool kit cost £149.95 cash. It could be bought on HP for a 20% deposit followed by 12 equal monthly payments of £11.20.

(a) Calculate the deposit.

(b) Calculate the total HP price.

(c) Calculate the amount saved by paying cash.

9. Mr Broyd obtained a personal loan of £1800, repayable by equal monthly instalments over 3 years. He was charged a flat rate of 11% p.a.
   (a) What was the interest for 1 year?
   (b) What was the interest for 3 years?
   (c) Calculate each monthly repayment.

10. If mortgage repayments were £8.20 per month per £1000 borrowed over 25 years, find, for a £14 000 mortgage:
   (a) the monthly repayments,
   (b) the total repayment in one year,
   (c) the total repayment over the full 25-year term of the mortgage,
   (d) the total amount of interest paid on the mortgage over 25 years.

11. Mr Arjan owed a credit card company £176.41. He paid the minimum payment, which was either £5 or 5% of the amount owed, whichever was greater. The payment was rounded down to the nearest whole pound. How much did he pay?

Revision Exercise XVI ━━━━━━━━━━━━━━ $\boxed{M}$

1. (a) Draw a pair of axes as shown opposite. Copy kite ABCD and line $y = x$.
   (b) Reflect kite ABCD in $y = x$, draw the image and label it $A_1B_1C_1D_1$.
   (c) Rotate ABCD through 90° anticlockwise about $(0, 0)$. Label the image $A_2B_2C_2D_2$.
   (d) Describe a single transformation that will map kite $A_1B_1C_1D_1$ onto kite $A_2B_2C_2D_2$.
   (e) Rotate ABCD through half a turn about the point $(1, 0)$. Label the image $A_3B_3C_3D_3$.
   (f) Describe fully a single transformation that will map $A_3B_3C_3D_3$ onto $A_2B_2C_2D_2$.
   (g) Draw the graph of $x = {}^-2$, then reflect $A_3B_3C_3D_3$ in this line. Label the reflection $A_4B_4C_4D_4$.

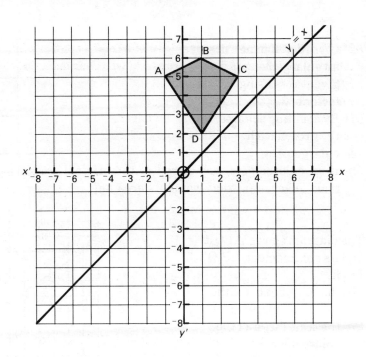

2. (a) Copy the diagram.
   (b) State the angle of rotation.
   (c) Mark the centre of rotation and label it C.

   (i)   (ii)

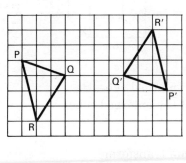   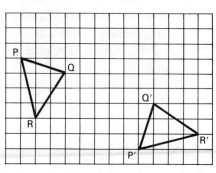

3. (a) A cross is shown on the next page.
      What is its area?
   (b) On squared paper, draw an enlargement of the given cross
      using a scale factor of 2.

(c) On squared paper, draw an enlargement of the given cross using a scale factor of 3.

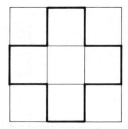

(d) By counting squares, find the area of each enlargement.

(e) If an enlargement was drawn of the original cross using a scale factor of 6, what would its area be?

4. The diagram shows △PQR and its enlargement △P'Q'R'. Find:

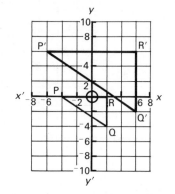

(a) the co-ordinates of the centre of enlargement,

(b) the scale factor of the enlargement.

5. The drawing shows a cube:

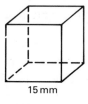

15 mm

(a) Calculate its volume.

(b) Calculate its surface area.

(c) Make an accurate drawing of an enlargement of the cube using a scale factor of 3.

(d) Calculate the volume of the enlarged cube.

(e) Calculate the surface area of the enlarged cube.

6. What possible transformations can transform

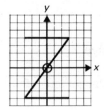 into 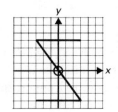 ?

17 Equations and Inequations

Equations

Exercise 1

Solve these simple equations:

1. $4x = 48$

2. $\dfrac{a}{5} = 6$

3. $k - 13 = 15$

4. $16 - t = 5$

5. $2p + 5 = 13$

6. $3m - 4 = 14$

7. $q + 8 = 3$

8. $4v + 10 = 2$

9. $2g - 15 = {}^{-}11$

10. $20 - 3y = 17$

11. $2f + 9 = 14$

12. $2 = 5l$

13. $8 - w = 14$

14. $8 - 2u = 14$

15. $\dfrac{x}{6} = 2\frac{1}{3}$

16. $6c - 8 = 1$

17. $13 + 3s = 40$

18. $42 = 7b - 14$

Exercise 2

Solve for x:

1. $5x - 8 = x + 12$

2. $4x = 21 - 3x$

3. $3 + 5x = 13 + 4x$

4. $18 - 2x = 4x - 12$

5. $5x + 1 = 2x - 5$

6. $6x + 9 = 63 - 3x$

7. $8x - 7 = 15 + 4x$

8. $6x + 30 = 6 - 2x$

9. $2x - 4 = 7x - 24$

10. $5x + 17 = 2x + 41$

11. $20 - 8x = 2 + x$

12. $28 - 5x = 5x$

Exercise 3

Solve the following equations:

1. $2(x - 3) = 10$

2. $4(x + 2) = 20$

3. $3(2x - 5) = 9$

4. $5(2x + 9) = 45$

5. $2(5x - 10) = 3x + 15$

6. $2(2x + 9) = 3(4x - 10)$

7. $16 + (3x - 1) = 2(5x - 3)$

8. $21 - (6x + 7) = 8(3 - 2x)$

9. $5 + 7(2x - 1) = 4(x + 7)$

10. $43 - 3(7 - x) = 4 - 3x$

11. $15 - 2x = 4 - 4(x - 4)$

12. $10x + 60 = 10 + 5(3 - x)$

Exercise 4

A Solve the following equations:

1. $\dfrac{m}{4} = \dfrac{1}{2}$

2. $\dfrac{x}{30} = \dfrac{1}{15}$

3. $\dfrac{y}{3} = \dfrac{1}{2}$

4. $\dfrac{a}{5} = \dfrac{1}{10}$

5. $\dfrac{p}{8} = \dfrac{1}{20}$

6. $\dfrac{e}{9} = \dfrac{1}{18}$

7. $\dfrac{b}{100} = \dfrac{3}{20}$

8. $\dfrac{u}{6} = \dfrac{4}{15}$

9. $\dfrac{t}{150} = \dfrac{7}{60}$

10. $\dfrac{2c}{9} = \dfrac{4}{3}$

11. $\dfrac{3f}{4} = \dfrac{9}{16}$

12. $\dfrac{8n}{3} = \dfrac{4}{15}$

B 1. $\dfrac{2}{a} = \dfrac{2}{3}$

2. $\dfrac{2}{c} = \dfrac{1}{4}$

3. $\dfrac{12}{x} = 4$

4. $\dfrac{2}{n} = 5$

5. $\dfrac{6}{q} = \dfrac{2}{5}$

6. $\dfrac{9}{z} = \dfrac{6}{5}$

7. $\dfrac{1}{f} = \dfrac{2}{3}$

8. $\dfrac{63}{d} = 18$

9. $\dfrac{5}{2k} = \dfrac{1}{3}$

10. $\dfrac{10}{3w} = \dfrac{5}{6}$

11. $\dfrac{1}{4h} = \dfrac{5}{8}$

12. $\dfrac{7}{6p} = \dfrac{35}{9}$

Exercise 5

Solve the following equations:

A **1.** (a) $\dfrac{X}{4} = 3$ (b) $\dfrac{(x+1)}{4} = 3$ (c) $\dfrac{x-2}{4} = 3$

2. (a) $\dfrac{X}{5} = 3$ (b) $\dfrac{(2x+1)}{5} = 3$ (c) $\dfrac{2x-3}{5} = 3$

3. (a) $\dfrac{X}{2} = 8$ (b) $(2x+1)/2 = 8$ (c) $\dfrac{2x-6}{2} = 8$

4. (a) $\dfrac{X}{3} = 4$ (b) $\tfrac{1}{3}(5x+7) = 4$ (c) $\dfrac{5x-8}{3} = 4$

5. (a) $\dfrac{X}{6} = 7$ (b) $(4x+2)/6 = 7$ (c) $\dfrac{4x+9}{6} = 7$

B **1.** $\dfrac{x-3}{2} = 1$ **3.** $\dfrac{3x+8}{5} = 7$ **5.** $(6x-20)/4 = 10$

2. $\dfrac{(4x-2)}{8} = 2$ **4.** $(5x-8)/3 = 9$ **6.** $\dfrac{(25-4x)}{9} = 5$

Exercise 6

1. (a) Simplify: $\dfrac{1}{2} + \dfrac{1}{3}$ (b) Solve: $\dfrac{x}{2} + \dfrac{x}{3} = 10$

2. (a) Simplify: $\dfrac{1}{2} - \dfrac{1}{4}$ (b) Solve: $\dfrac{x}{2} - \dfrac{x}{4} = 2$

3. (a) Simplify: $\dfrac{1}{3} + \dfrac{1}{5}$ (b) Solve: $\dfrac{x}{3} + \dfrac{x}{5} = 4$

4. (a) Simplify: $\dfrac{1}{3} - \dfrac{1}{5}$ (b) Solve: $\dfrac{x}{3} - \dfrac{x}{5} = \dfrac{2}{3}$

5. (a) Simplify: $\dfrac{1}{2} + \dfrac{2}{3}$ (b) Solve: $\dfrac{x}{2} + \dfrac{2x}{3} = 3\tfrac{1}{2}$

6. (a) Simplify: $\dfrac{3}{4} - \dfrac{2}{3}$ (b) Solve: $\dfrac{3x}{4} - \dfrac{2x}{3} = 1$

7. (a) Simplify: $\dfrac{3}{4} - \dfrac{3}{8}$ (b) Solve: $\dfrac{3x}{4} - \dfrac{3x}{8} = 6$

Exercise 7

Solve for x:

1. $\dfrac{x}{2} + \dfrac{(x-4)}{6} = 4$

2. $\dfrac{x}{2} - \dfrac{(x-4)}{6} = 3$

3. $\dfrac{3x+2}{4} - \dfrac{3x}{5} = 2$

4. $\dfrac{3x}{4} - \dfrac{x-4}{3} = 3$

5. $\dfrac{4x+6}{10} + \dfrac{2x}{5} = 3$

6. $\dfrac{(2x-5)}{2} - \dfrac{2x}{3} = 2$

7. $\dfrac{(x-5)}{6} + \dfrac{(x+10)}{4} = 5$

8. $\dfrac{3x-4}{8} - \dfrac{2x+1}{6} = 1$

Exercise 8

1. Evelyn had n pencils and bought 12 more. She then had 20 altogether. This is given by the equation:

$$n + 12 = 20$$

Solve the equation to find the value of n.

2. If I think of a number, double it then add fourteen, the answer is 20. What is the number?

3. When I add 3 to a number and then multiply the result by 2, the final answer is 16. What is the number?

4. The width of a rectangular garden is x m. Its length is 3 m longer than its width.

x m

  (a) Write an expression for the length in terms of x.
  (b) Write an expression for the perimeter in terms of x, writing the expression in its simplest terms.
  (c) If the perimeter of the garden is 34 m, write an equation in x, then solve it to find the value of x.
  (d) Give the dimensions of the garden.

5. Teri went shopping. She set off with £x. She spent £8 at one shop, £5 at another and had £7 left. Find the value of x.

6. Mrs Littler is 3 times as old as her daughter, Joy. Archy Littler is 6 years older than Joy. If Joy is y years old:
   (a) Write an expression for Archy's age.
   (b) Write an expression for Mrs Littler's age.
   (c) Write an equation showing that the sum of the three ages is 81 years.
   (d) Solve the equation formed in part (c) to find the value of y.
   (e) Write the ages of all three people.

7. Douglas, Humphrey and Sophie had saved some money. Douglas had saved £60 less than Sophie, while Humphrey had saved four times as much as Sophie.
   (a) If Sophie saved £n, express the amount each of the others had saved in terms of n.
   (b) If the savings of all three people totalled £1380, find out how much each person saved.

8. (a) A bus travelled 60 miles at an average speed of 30 m.p.h. How long did the journey take?
   (b) A bus travelled x miles at an average speed of 30 m.p.h. Write an expression in x for the length of time the journey took.
   (c) If a car travelled the same journey of x miles at an average speed of 40 m.p.h., write an expression in x for the length of time the journey took.
   (d) Write the answers to parts (b) and (c) in minutes (that is, change to minutes the times taken by the bus and the car).
   (e) If the car completed the journey 4 minutes faster than the bus, form an equation in x and solve it.
   (f) How long, in minutes, did each vehicle take to travel the journey of x miles (use the value of x found for answer (e)).

Quadratic Equations

Exercise 9

A Solve the following quadratic equations:

1. $x^2 = 25$
2. $x^2 = 64$
3. $x^2 = 169$
4. $2x^2 = 18$
5. $5x^2 = 80$
6. $3x^2 = 108$
7. $2x^2 = 162$
8. $4x^2 = 196$
9. $2x^2 = 242$

B **1.** $4x^2 = 9$ **4.** $4x^2 = 25$ **7.** $18x^2 = 32$

   2. $9x^2 = 25$ **5.** $4x^2 = 1$ **8.** $64x^2 = 9$

   3. $16x^2 = 9$ **6.** $4x^2 = 121$ **9.** $27x^2 = 12$

C **1.** $x^2 - 1 = 0$ **4.** $3x^2 - 27 = 0$ **7.** $4x^2 - 49 = 0$

   2. $x^2 - 36 = 0$ **5.** $3x^2 - 75 = 0$ **8.** $3x^2 - 300 = 0$

   3. $x^2 - 144 = 0$ **6.** $9x^2 - 4 = 0$ **9.** $18x^2 - 2 = 0$

Exercise 10

1. Each side of the square shown measures $2x$ cm. Its area is $36\,\text{cm}^2$. Calculate the value of x.

2x cm

36 cm²   2x cm

2. A square has an area of $144\,\text{cm}^2$. If each side measures $3x$ cm, find the value of x.

3. Using the formula, area of a circle, $A = 3r^2$, calculate r when the area is $147\,\text{cm}^2$.

4. Using the formula, area of a circle, $A = \pi r^2$, calculate r when $\pi = 3$ and the area is $243\,\text{mm}^2$.

5. The surface area of a sphere is given by the formula, $A = 4\pi r^2$. Calculate r when $\pi = 3$ and the surface area is $300\,\text{cm}^2$.

Inequations

If x is an integer:

$x > 5$ can be written as: $\{6, 7, 8, 9, \ldots\}$

$x < 2$ can be written as: $\{1, 0, {}^-1, {}^-2, \ldots\}$

or as: $\{\ldots, {}^-2, {}^-1, 0, 1\}$

228

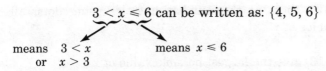

$3 < x \le 6$ can be written as: $\{4, 5, 6\}$

means $3 < x$ means $x \le 6$
or $x > 3$

$3 < x \le 6$ means x is bigger than 3 *and* x is less than or equal to 6.

$^-4 \le x \le 3$ means x is bigger than or equal to $^-4$ *and* x is less than or equal to 3.

So $^-4 \le x \le 3$ is the set $\{^-4, \, ^-3, \, ^-2, \, ^-1, \, 0, \, 1, \, 2, \, 3\}$.

Exercise 11

Throughout this exercise, n is a whole number and x is an integer. For each question, list the set of values of n or x.

1. $n < 8$
2. $n - 3 \le 8$
3. $x + 4 \ge 10$
4. $x - 8 < 4$
5. $3n \le 18$
6. $6x > 24$
7. $4n < 23$
8. $8x \ge 17$

9. $x + 3 < 6$
10. $2 \le n - 9$
11. $7 > n + 10$
12. $3 \ge x - 6$
13. $n + 2 \le 6$
14. $x - 1 \ge \, ^-4$
15. $5 < x + 9$
16. $n + 5 > 0$

17. $3 \le n < 10$
18. $4 < x \le 7$
19. $1 \le n \le 9$
20. $9 < n < 11$
21. $^-2 \le n \le 8$
22. $^-5 < x < 1$
23. $^-7 < x \le 0$
24. $^-9 \le x < \, ^-4$

Exercise 12   **M**

Throughout this exercise, take n to be a whole number and x to be an integer.

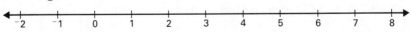

Make 5 copies of the above number line for use during this exercise.

1. If $n < 6$, show on the number line, by using dots, all possible values of n.

2. If $x + 4 \leqslant 3$, show in the number line, by using dots, all possible values of x.

3. If $x + 7 \leqslant 13$, give the largest possible value of x.

4. If $n - 2 > 3$, give the smallest possible value of n.

5. If $x - 8 < 7$, give the largest possible value of x.

6. If $x + 5 \geqslant 2$, show on the number line, by using dots, all possible values of x.

7. If $x + 6 > 4$, give the smallest possible value of x.

8. If $n + 6 > 4$, give the smallest possible value of n.

9. If $2n \geqslant 9$, give the smallest possible value of n.

10. If $5x < 24$, give the largest possible value of x.

11. If $3x < 21$, give the largest possible value of x.

12. If $2n - 3 > 5$, show on the number line, using dots, all possible values of n.

13. If $4x + 5 < 30$, give the largest possible value of x.

14. If $3n - 7 \leqslant 6$, give the largest possible value of n.

15. If $12 - n > 7$, give the largest possible value of n.

16. If $2 \geqslant 14 - x$, give the smallest possible value of x.

17. If $20 \leqslant 5n + 1$, give the smallest possible value of n.

18. If $7 \geqslant 2x - 7$, give the largest possible value of x.

19. If $2 + 3n \leqslant 17$, show on the number line, using dots, all possible values of n.

20. If $2x + 6 > 20$, give the smallest possible value of x.

$^-6 < n - 4 \leqslant 2$ can be written as two inequations:

as $\qquad ^-6 < n - 4 \quad$ *and* $\quad n - 4 \leqslant 2$

that is $\quad n - 4 > {}^-6 \quad$ *and* $\quad n - 4 \leqslant 2$

so $\qquad n > {}^-2 \quad$ *and* $\quad n \leqslant 6 \quad ({}^-2 < n \leqslant 6)$

and the solution set is $\{{}^-1, 0, 1, 2, 3, 4, 5, 6\}$.

Exercise 13

Throughout this exercise, take n to be a whole number and x an integer. For each question, list all possible values of n or x.

e.g. $\quad 4 < 3x - 5 \leqslant 12$

$$3x - 5 > 4 \qquad \text{and} \qquad 3x - 5 \leqslant 12$$

$$3x > 9 \qquad \text{and} \qquad 3x \leqslant 17$$

$$x > 3 \qquad \text{and} \qquad x \leqslant 5 \quad \text{(ignore the fraction)}$$

so x can have the values <u>4 or 5</u>

1. $7 \leqslant 2x + 5 < 19$

2. $1 \leqslant 2x - 3 \leqslant 7$

3. $10 < 3n + 4 \leqslant 30$

4. $3 < 5n - 7 < 25$

5. $2 \leqslant 3x + 8 < 40$

6. $6 < 4n - 2 < 12$

7. $2 < 6 - n \leqslant 5$

8. $0 \leqslant 15 - x \leqslant 10$

9. $^-5 \leqslant 2 - x < {}^-2$

10. $3 < 11 - n < 11$

11. $0 < 5x + 6 \leqslant 42$

12. $4 < 2x + 7 < 13$

13. $1 \leqslant 7n + 5 \leqslant 36$

14. $^-1 \leqslant 4x + 15 < 23$

15. $^-3 < 6n - 8 \leqslant 34$

16. $^-5 \leqslant 3x - 14 \leqslant 0$

18 Flow Charts

1. (*a*) Follow the instructions in the given flow chart.

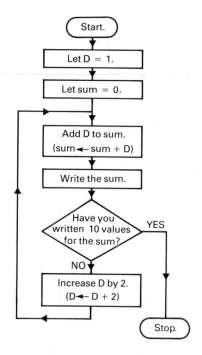

(*b*) What sort of numbers have you written?

(*c*) Draw a dot pattern to show the sixth number written.

2. The flow chart opposite can be used to find either the price inclusive of VAT from the pre-VAT price, or the pre-VAT price from the VAT inclusive price.

232

Use the flow chart to help you to complete the following table.
Let the VAT rate be 15%

	Price before VAT	Price including VAT
(a)	£120	
(b)	£2.80	
(c)		£16.10
(d)	£2060	
(e)		£460
(f)		£6.67
(g)		£82.80
(h)	£0.60	

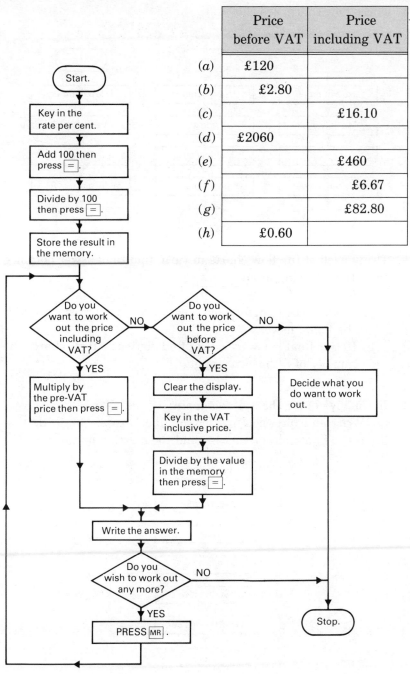

Start.

Key in the rate per cent.

Add 100 then press =.

Divide by 100 then press =.

Store the result in the memory.

Do you want to work out the price including VAT?

NO

Do you want to work out the price before VAT?

NO

Decide what you do want to work out.

YES

Multiply by the pre-VAT price then press =.

YES

Clear the display.

Key in the VAT inclusive price.

Divide by the value in the memory then press =.

Write the answer.

Do you wish to work out any more?

NO

YES

PRESS MR.

Stop.

233

1. Three flow charts are shown:

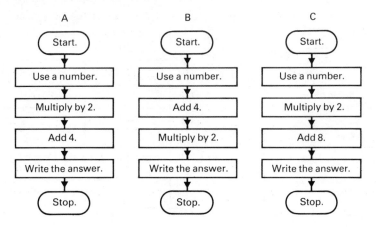

Using each of the flow charts in turn, find the answer obtained from the following input:

   (*a*) 6   (*b*) 3   (*c*) 8   (*d*) 2.5   (*e*) $^-4$

   (*f*) If n is input find, for each flow chart, an expression in n for the final answer.

   (*g*) If the final answer is 18, find for each flow chart, the number of n that was input.

2. In the given flow chart, if x is input:

   (*a*) Write an expression in x for the final answer obtained.

   (*b*) If the final answer was 14, find the starting number, x.

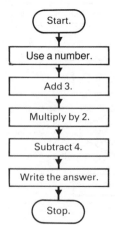

3. In the given flow chart, if p is input:

    (a) Write an expression in p for the final answer obtained.

    (b) If the final answer was 26, find the starting number, p.

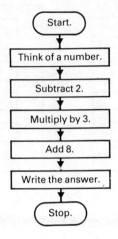

Start.

Think of a number.

Subtract 2.

Multiply by 3.

Add 8.

Write the answer.

Stop.

4. In the given flow chart if y is input:

    (a) Write an expression in y for the final answer obtained. (Simplify the expression.)

    (b) If the final answer was 20, find the starting number, y.

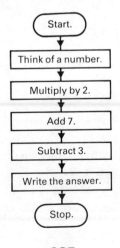

Start.

Think of a number.

Multiply by 2.

Add 7.

Subtract 3.

Write the answer.

Stop.

5. (*a*) Carry out the instructions in the given flow charts:

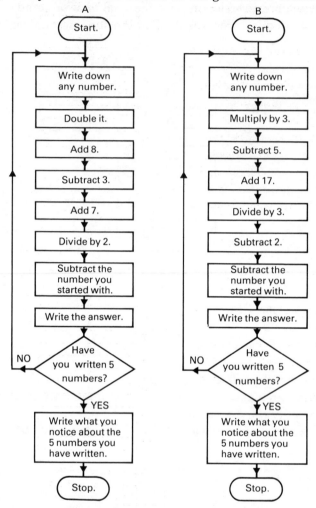

(*b*) Carry out the instructions in the flow charts above, but use the letter *n* as input.

Exercise 3

The flow chart opposite, when completed, should give instructions on how to change a tyre on a car.

There are 13 empty boxes, labelled 1 to 13.

The contents of those boxes are listed opposite and are labelled from A to M.

List the numbers from 1 to 13 and next to each number, write the appropriate letter.

A   Jack up the car until the wheel is clear of the ground.
B   Prise off the hub cover.
C   Is the ground soft?
D   Remove the wheel.
E   Tighten the wheel nuts.
F   See the car handbook.
G   Put on the spare wheel.
H   Put something solid (a brick or piece of wood) under the jack.
I   Slacken the wheel nuts about one turn.
J   Lower the car on to the wheel.
K   Totally remove the wheel nuts.
L   Replace the wheel nuts (bevelled side inward).
M   Insert jack into jacking up point.

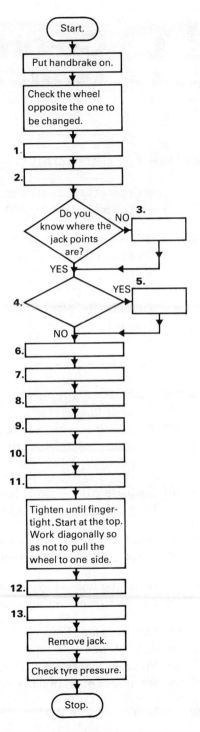

237

19 Co-ordinates and Graphs

Exercise 1   Cartesian Co-ordinates

1. Draw a pair of axes as shown:
   $^-8 \leqslant x \leqslant 8$ and $^-10 \leqslant y \leqslant 10$

2. (a) A is the point $(^-6, 2)$.
   What are the co-ordinates
   of B?
   (b) Copy points A and B,
   then plot the point C(4, 2).
   (c) Join A to B and B to C.

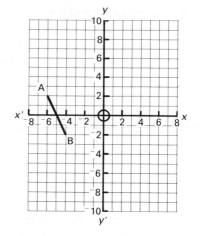

3. (a) If ABCD is a kite, find
   the co-ordinates of D.
   (b) If, instead of being a kite, ABCD is a rectangle, plot the point
   D and complete the rectangle, then write the
   co-ordinates of D.

4. (a) Measure AB.   (b) Measure BC.
   (c) Find the area of rectangle ABCD.

5. (a) What are the co-ordinates of the mid-point of AD?
   (b) What are the co-ordinates of the mid-point of CD?

6. (a) Draw the lines of symmetry for rectangle ABCD.
   (b) At what point do they cross?

7. (a) Plot the point P(4, $^-8$).
   (b) Join PB and PC.
   (c) Measure length PB.
   (d) What sort of triangle is △PBC?

8. (a) Measure angle BPC.   (b) Calculate angle PBC.

Gradient

Exercise 2

A Find the gradient of the line segments given:

1.

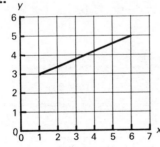

3.

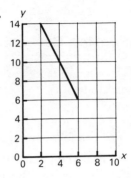

2.

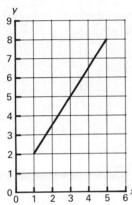

4.

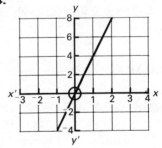

B Find the gradient of the line segments joining the given pairs of points:

1. $(3, 1)\ (7, 9)$

4. $(^-15, ^-2\frac{1}{2})\ (^-8, 1)$

2. $(7, 11)\ (13, 15)$

5. $(^-2, 8)\ (^-5, 17)$

3. $(^-2, 6)\ (^-1, 11)$

6. $(^-1, ^-3)\ (1, 2)$

239

Exercise 3

Draw a pair of axes as shown:
($^-10 \leqslant x \leqslant 10$ and $^-8 \leqslant y \leqslant 8$)

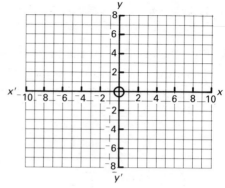

Answer the following questions using the one pair of axes.

1. (*a*) Plot the point A(6, 2).

    (*b*) Draw a line through (6, 2) with gradient 2.

2. (*a*) Plot the point B($^-6$, $^-2$).

    (*b*) Draw a line through ($^-6$, $^-2$) with gradient 3.

3. Draw a line through C(0, 2) with gradient $\frac{1}{2}$.

4. Draw a line through D($^-4$, 4) with gradient $^-1.5$.

Linear Graphs

Exercise 4

The equations of several graphs are given. For each one, write its gradient.

1. $y = 3x$

2. $y = 2x + 6$

3. $y = x + 7$

4. $y = 3 - 2x$

5. $y = {}^-6x + 1$

6. $3y = 12x + 6$

7. $y = \frac{1}{2}x - 9$

8. $3y = 2x + 12$

9. $x + y = 2$

10. $x + 2y = 6$

11. $2x - y = 10$

12. $3x - 4y = 3$

240

Exercise 5

1. Sketch the graphs of $y = {}^-5$ and $x = 4$. What are the co-ordinates of the point of intersection of the two graphs?

2. Draw a pair of axes where the x-values range from $^-2$ to 6 and the y-values from $^-4$ to 14. (Use a scale of 1 cm to 1 unit on both axes.)
   (a) Plot the graph of $x + y = 4$.
   (b) Plot the graph of $y = 2x + 1$.
   (c) Write the co-ordinates of the point of intersection of the two graphs.

3. The graph of the line with equation $4x + 3y = 36$ cuts the x-axis at X and the y-axis at Y:
   (a) Find the co-ordinates of X.
   (b) Find the co-ordinates of Y.
   (c) Calculate the length of XY.

4. The diagram shows a sketch of the graph of $3x + 2y = 12$ and of $y = {}^-3$.
   Calculate the co-ordinates of:
   (a) P
   (b) Q
   (c) R

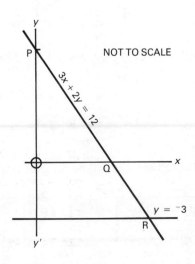

5. Draw a pair of axes as shown.
Using the one pair of axes:

(a) Draw the graph of $y = \frac{7}{10}x$.

(b) Draw the graph of $y = \frac{2}{5}x$.

(c) Draw the graph of $y = \frac{5}{4}x$.

(d) Which of the three graphs
is the steepest and why?

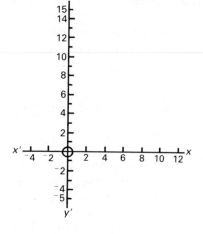

Exercise 6

1. A cylindrical water tank has a height of 80 cm. The number of
litres of water in the tank is given by the formula $N = \frac{6d}{5}$,
where d cm is the depth of the water.

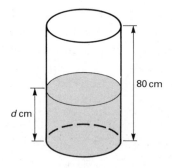

(a) Copy and complete the following table using the formula.

Depth of water, d(cm)	0	20	30	60	70
Number of litres, N			36		

(b) Draw a pair of axes as shown. The depth of water should range from 0 to 80 cm while the number of litres should range from 0 to 100.

(c) Draw the graph of
$$N = \frac{6d}{5}.$$

(d) Using your graph, find the number of litres in the tank when it is full.

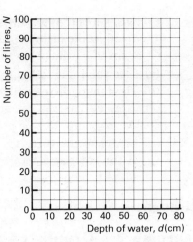

(e) Using your graph, find the depth of the water when the tank contains:
    (i) 60 ℓ (ii) 48 ℓ (iii) 12 ℓ (iv) 78 ℓ

2. A book club has a special sale. It charges £4 for each book sold, plus a £3 postal charge however many books are purchased.
If £C is the total charge when n books are sold:
(a) Copy and complete the following table of values.

Number of books sold, n	0	2	5	6	9
Total cost, £C	0		23		

(b) Using a scale of 2 cm to 1 book on the n-axis and 2 cm to £5 on the C-axis, draw a graph to show how C varies with n.
(c) Use your graph to find the number of books sold when the total cost was £35.
(d) Write a formula for C in terms of n.

3. A car set off on a journey with a full tank of petrol. Assuming the car uses petrol at a steady rate and has already used $n\,\ell$ of petrol, the car can travel a further s km before the petrol tank is empty. This is given by the formula $s = 700 - 14n$.
(a) Copy and complete the following table using the formula.

Number of litres used, n	0	10	20	30	40
Possible further distance, s km					

243

(b) Draw a pair of axes where the number of litres ranges from 0 to 50, while distance ranges from 0 to 800 km. (Use a scale of 2 cm to 5 ℓ and 1 cm to 50 km.)

(c) Use the table to help you to draw a graph of s against n.

(d) How many litres will a full tank hold?

(e) How far can the car go on a full tank of petrol?

(f) After using 18 ℓ of petrol, what distance will the car then be able to travel?

(g) If the car has a total range left of 210 km, how many litres must it have used?

Quadratic Graphs

Exercise 7   Graphs of the form $y = ax^2$

1. (a) Draw a pair of axes where the x-values range from $^-4$ to 4 and the y-values range from 0 to 80.

   (b) Draw the graph of $y = 4x^2$.

   (c) Using the same pair of axes, draw the graph of $y = 2x + 30$.

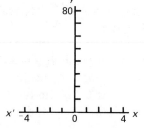

   (d) Write the co-ordinates of the points of intersection of the two graphs.

2. The area of a circle, $A = \pi r^2$. The area can be estimated using the formula $A = 3r^2$.

   (a) Copy and complete the table for $A = 3r^2$.

Radius, r(cm)	0	1	2	3	4	5	6	7	8
Area, A(cm^2)									

   (b) Draw a pair of axes as shown and draw the graph of $A = 3r^2$.

   (c) Using the graph, find the value of A when $r = 4.5$.

   (d) Using the graph, find the value of A when $r = 3.7$.

   (e) Using the graph, find the radius when the area is 72 cm^2.

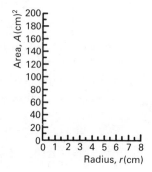

244

3. (a) Draw a pair of axes as shown.

(b) Plot the graph of $y = {}^-3x^2$.

(c) From the graph, find the value of y when $x = 1.3$.

(d) Using the same pair of axes, draw the line $y = {}^-12$.

(e) Write the co-ordinates of the points of intersection of the two graphs.

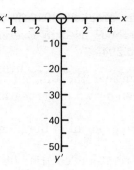

Exercise 8 Gradient of a Tangent to a Curved Graph

1. A graph of $y = 2x^2$ is given below.

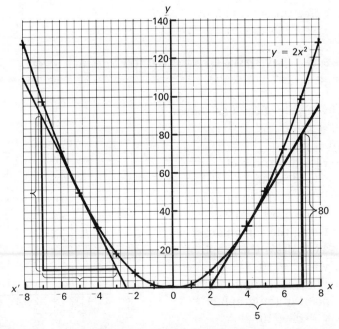

Two tangents have been drawn, one where $x = 4$ (it touches the curve at the points (4, 32)) and the other where $x = {}^-5$ (it touches the curve at the point (${}^-5$, 50)).

245

The gradient of each tangent can be estimated by using the methods used in Exercise 2, p. 239 (as explained in book 4G (pp. 294–6).

Consider the tangent at (4, 32). A right-angled triangle has been drawn underneath.

The gradient of the tangent $= \dfrac{\text{rise}}{\text{tread}} = \dfrac{80}{5} = \underline{\underline{16}}$

A right-angled triangle has been drawn under the tangent at ($^-$5, 50). Estimate the gradient of that tangent. (Remember, it slopes downwards.)

2. Using your graph of $y = 4x^2$ (drawn for Exercise 7, question 1, p. 244), estimate the gradient of the tangent at the point:
   (a) (2, 16)   (b) ($^-$3, 36)

3. Using your graph of $y = {^-}3x^2$ (drawn for Exercise 7, question 3, p. 245), estimate the gradient of the tangent at the point:
   (a) ($^-$2, $^-$12)   (b) (3, $^-$27)

Exercise 9   Graphs of the Form $y = x^2 + c$ and $y = c - x^2$ 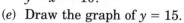 M

1. Draw a pair of axes as shown:
   ($^-8 \leqslant x \leqslant 8$ and
   $^-10 \leqslant y \leqslant 90$)
   (a) Plot the graph of
       $y = x^2 + 20$.
   (b) What is the minimum
       value of $x^2 + 20$?
   (c) Using the same pair of
       axes, draw the graph of
       $y = x^2 - 10$.
   (d) What is the minimum
       point of the graph of
       $y = x^2 - 10$?

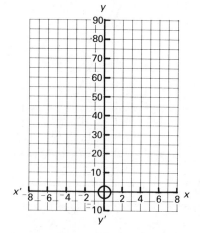

   (e) Draw the graph of $y = 15$.
   (f) Write the points of intersection of the graphs of $y = 15$ and
       $y = x^2 - 10$.

246

2. Draw a pair of axes where the x-values range from ⁻8 to 8 and the y-values from ⁻50 to 30. ($⁻8 \leqslant x \leqslant 8$ and $⁻50 \leqslant y \leqslant 30$) Use a scale of 1 cm to 1 unit on the x-axis and 1 cm to 5 units on the y-axis.

(a) Copy and complete the following table for the equation $y = 16 - x^2$.

x	⁻8	⁻7	⁻6	⁻5	⁻4	⁻3	⁻2	⁻1	0	1	2	3	4	5	6	7	8
x^2	64	49	36		16					1			16				
$-x^2$	⁻64	⁻49	⁻36		⁻16					⁻1			⁻16				
16	16	16	16		16					16			16				
$y = 16 - x^2$	⁻48	⁻33		⁻9			12			15							

(b) Draw the graph of $y = 16 - x^2$.

(c) Where does the graph cross the x-axis?

(d) What is the maximum value of $16 - x^2$?

(e) Estimate from your graph:
   (i) the value of y when $x = ⁻4.5$,
   (ii) the values of x, to one decimal place, when $y = 10$.

3. (a) Draw another pair of axes as for question 2.

(b) Draw up a table for $y = 30 - x^2$ (x should range from ⁻8 to 8 as in question 2).

(c) Draw the graph of $y = 30 - x^2$.

(d) Estimate, to one decimal place:
   (i) the values of x at the points where the graph crosses the x-axis,
   (ii) the values of x when $y = 15$.

Solution of an Equation using a Graph

Reminder: To use a graph to solve an equation such as $2x + 3 = 7$, draw the graph of $y = 2x + 3$ and of $y = 7$.

The point of intersection of the two graphs gives the solution to the equation.

The same method can also be used for harder equations. For example to solve $x^2 - 6 = 19$, draw the graphs:

$$y = x^2 - 6 \quad \text{and} \quad y = 19$$

Exercise 10

Use graphs to solve the following equations:

1. $3x - 5 = 13$

(Use a pair of axes where x ranges from 0 to 8 and y from $^-5$ to 20.)

2. $x^2 - 10 = 15$

(Use a pair of axes where x ranges from $^-7$ to $^+7$ and y from $^-10$ to $^+40$.)

3. $x^2 + 10 = 40$

Give the answers to one decimal place. (Use a pair of axes where the x-values range from $^-8$ to $^+8$ and the y-values from 0 to 80.)

Exercise 11   Graphs of the form $y = x^2 + bx + c$ ▮M▮

1. (*a*) Copy and complete the following table for the equation $y = x^2 - 4x$.

x	$^-5$	$^-4$	$^-3$	$^-2$	$^-1$	0	1	2	3	4	5	6	7	8	9
x^2			9					4						64	
^-4x	20		12							$^-16$				$^-32$	
$y = x^2 - 4x$			21								5			32	

(*b*) Draw a pair of axes where the x-values range from $^-5$ to 9 (use a scale of 1 cm to 1 unit) and the y-values range from $^-5$ to 45 (use a scale of 2 cm to 5 units).

(*c*) Using the table to help you, draw the graph of $y = x^2 - 4x$.

(*d*) What is the minimum point for the graph?

(*e*) At which points does the graph cross the x-axis?

(*f*) Using the graph, find the value of y when $x = ^-4.4$.

(*g*) Using the graph, find the values of x when $y = 20$.

(*h*) Draw a tangent to the curve at the point (5, 5), then find its gradient.

2. (*a*) Copy and complete the following table for the equation $y = x^2 + 2x - 8$.

	x	$^-5$	$^-4$	$^-3$	$^-2$	$^-1$	0	1	2	3	
+	x^2	25			4					9	+
+	$+2x$		$^-8$					2		6	+
+	$^-8$	$^-8$	$^-8$		$^-8$	$^-8$				$^-8$	+
	$y = x^2 + 2x - 8$									7	

(*b*) Draw a pair of axes where the x-values range from $^-5$ to 3 (Use a scale of 2 cm to 1 unit.) and the y-values range from $^-10$ to 8. (Use a scale of 1 cm to 1 unit.)

(*c*) Draw the graph of $y = x^2 + 2x - 8$ using the table to help you.

(*d*) What is the minimum point for this graph?

(*e*) At which points does the graph cross the x-axis?

(*f*) At which point does the graph cross the y-axis?

(*g*) Draw the line of symmetry for the graph.

(*h*) What is the equation of the line of symmetry?

3. (*a*) Copy and complete the following table for the equation $y = x^2 - 3x + 5$.

	x	$^-3$	$^-2$	$^-1$	0	1	2	3	4	5	6	7	8	9	10	11	$1\frac{1}{2}$	
+	x^2		4								36					121		+
+	^-3x	9							$^-12$									+
+	$^+5$	5	5		5		5				5		5	5			5	+
	$y = x^2 - 3x + 5$																	

(Note the extra column in the table, where $x = 1\frac{1}{2}$. You will see that the extra column is necessary when you try to draw a graph.)

(*b*) Draw a pair of axes where the x-values range from $^-3$ to 11 (Use a scale of 1 cm to 1 unit.) and the y-values range from 0 to 100. (Use a scale of 1 cm to 5 units.)

(*c*) Using the table to help you, draw the graph of $y = x^2 - 3x + 5$.

(*d*) From the graph, find the minimum value of $x^2 - 3x + 5$.

(*e*) By drawing a straight line, use the graph to solve the equation $x^2 - 3x + 5 = 15$.

4. (*a*) Copy and complete the table on the next page for the equation $y = x^2 - x - 8$.
(You will need to work out an extra column.)

x	$^-4$	$^-3$	$^-2$	$^-1$	0	1	2	3	4	
+ x^2	16		4					9		+
+ $-x$	4		2				$^-2$			+
+ -8	$^-8$	$^-8$	$^-8$		$^-8$			$^-8$	$^-8$	+
+ $y = x^2 - x - 8$			$^-2$							

(b) Draw a pair of axes. The x-values should range from $^-4$ to 4 (use a scale of 2 cm to 1 unit). The y-values should range from $^-10$ to 15 (use a scale of 4 cm to 5 units).

(c) Draw the graph of $y = x^2 - x - 8$.

(d) Write the co-ordinates of the minimum point of the graph of $y = x^2 - x - 8$.

(e) Write the y-value where the graph crosses the y-axis.

(f) Write the x-values of the points where the graph crosses the x-axis.

(g) Draw a tangent to the curve at the point where $x = {}^-2$, and estimate its gradient.

(h) By drawing a straight line, use your graph to estimate the solutions of the equation $x^2 - x - 8 = 2$.

5. (a) Copy the part of the graph of $y = x^2 - 4x - 12$ as given below.

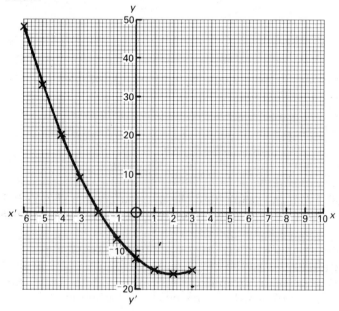

(b) Complete your copy of the graph of $y = x^2 - 4x - 12$ without doing any calculations.

Exercise 12   Graphs of the form $y = (x + a)^2$ and $y = (x + a)(x + b)$ **M**

A 1. (a) Copy and complete the table for the equation $y = (x + 3)^2$.

x	-8	-7	-6	-5	-4	-3	-2	-1	0	1	2	3	4	5	6	7
$x + 3$	-5			-2			1			4			7			
$y = (x + 3)^2$	25						1						49			

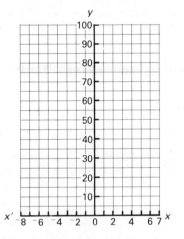

(b) Draw a pair of axes as shown.

(c) Using the table, draw the graph of $y = (x + 3)^2$.

(d) Where does the curve meet the y-axis?

(e) By drawing a tangent, estimate the gradient of the graph at the point $(^-2, 1)$.

2. (a) Copy and complete the table for the equation $y = (x - 4)^2$.

x	-6	-5	-4	-3	-2	-1	0	1	2	3	4	5	6	7	8	9	10
$x - 4$				-7					-2				2				
$y = (x - 4)^2$				49					4				4				

(b) Draw a pair of axes where the x-values range from $^-6$ to 10 (use a scale of 1 cm to 1 unit) and the y-values range from 0 to 100 (use a scale of 1 cm to 5 units).

(c) Using the table, draw the graph of $y = (x - 4)^2$.

(d) Where does the graph meet the y-axis?

(e) Use your graph to find the values of x for which $(x - 4)^2 = 20$.

1. (*a*) Copy and complete the following table for the equation $y = (x + 7)(x - 3)$.

x	-10	-9	-8	-7	-6	-5	-4	-3	-2	-1	0	1	2	3	4	5	6
$(x + 7)$		-2				2										12	
$(x - 3)$		-12				-8										2	
$y = (x + 7)(x - 3)$		24				-16										24	

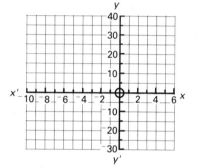

(*b*) Draw a pair of axes as shown, then, using the table, draw the graph of $y = (x + 7)(x - 3)$.

(*c*) Where does the graph cross the *y*-axis?

(*d*) Where does the graph cross the *x*-axis?

(*e*) Use your graph to find the values of *x* for which $(x + 7)(x - 3) = 10$.

2. (*a*) Draw up a table for the equation $y = (x - 8)(x - 1)$. *x* should range from ⁻5 to 10.

(*b*) Draw a pair of axes where the *x*-values range from ⁻5 to ⁺10 (use a scale of 1 cm to 1 unit) and where the *y*-values range from ⁻15 to ⁺80 (use a scale of 1 cm to 5 units).

(*c*) Draw the graph of $y = (x - 8)(x - 1)$.

(*d*) Where does the graph cross the *x*-axis?

(*e*) Where does the graph cross the *y*-axis?

(*f*) Use your graph to find the values of *x* for which $(x - 8)(x - 1) = ⁻5$.

(*g*) What is the minimum value of $(x - 8)(x - 1)$?

Graphs of $y = \dfrac{a}{x}$ $(x \neq 0)$

Consider the equation $y = \dfrac{a}{x}$ where a is not zero.

This can be rewritten as $xy = a$.

x can not be zero since $0 \times y = 0$ which means $a = 0$, but we have already stated that a is not zero.

1. (a) Copy and complete the following table for the equation $y = \frac{8}{x}$. (Where necessary, give the y-values correct to one decimal place.)

x	$\frac{1}{2}$	1	2	3	4	5	6	7	8	10	12	16
$y = \dfrac{8}{x}$	16	8					1.3				0.7	

(b) Draw a pair of axes where x and y both range from 0 to 16 (use a scale of 1 cm to 1 unit) then draw the graph of $y = \frac{8}{x}$ for values of x from $x = \frac{1}{2}$ to $x = 16$ (that is, $\frac{1}{2} \leqslant x \leqslant 16$).

(c) Using the same pair of axes and by drawing a suitable straight line, estimate a solution to the equation $\frac{8}{x} = 2.5$.

2. Ohm's law gives a relationship between current, I amperes, potential difference, V volts and resistance, R ohms. It is shown by the formula $I = \frac{V}{R}$.

(a) Copy and complete the following table when the voltage is 12 V, and therefore $I = \frac{12}{R}$.

R	0.75	1	2	3	4	6	8	10	12	15	16
$I = \dfrac{12}{R}$		12			3						0.75

(b) Draw a pair of axes where both the I and R axes are labelled from 0 to 16. (Use a scale of 1 cm to 1 Ω on the resistance axis and 1 cm to 1 A on the current axis.) Now draw a graph of $I = \frac{12}{R}$ for $0.75 \leqslant R \leqslant 16$.

(c) From the graph, estimate the current for a resistance of 5 Ω.

(d) From the graph, estimate the resistance for a current of 10 A.

3. (a) Copy and complete the table on the next page for the equation $y = \frac{4}{x}$ ($^-8 \leqslant x \leqslant {}^+8$, $x \neq 0$).

x	-8	-6	-4	-2	-1	$-\frac{1}{2}$	$\frac{1}{2}$	1	2	4	6	8
$y = \dfrac{4}{x}$	-0.5			-2			8		2			

(b) Draw a pair of axes where both the x- and y-values range from -8 to $+8$ (use a scale of 1 cm to 1 unit).

(c) Draw the graph of $y = \frac{4}{x}$ ($-8 \leqslant x \leqslant +8$, $x \neq 0$).

(d) Draw two lines of symmetry on your graph.

(e) Write the equations of the two lines of symmetry.

Exercise 14 Graph of $y = \sqrt{x}$

1. Copy and complete the following table for $y = \sqrt{x}$. (Where necessary, write the y-values correct to one decimal place.)

x	0	1	2	4	9	12	16	20	25	30	36	49
$y = \sqrt{x}$	0				3			4.5				

2. Draw a pair of axes as shown, then draw the graph of $y = \sqrt{x}$ for values of x from $x = 0$ to $x = 49$.

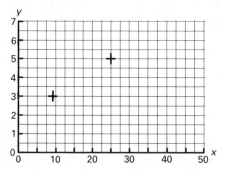

3. Using your graph, estimate a solution to the equation $\sqrt{x} = 5.3$.

20 Graphing Inequalities

Recognition of Regions Created by Lines $y = x$, $y = a$, $x = b$

Exercise 1

1. Sebastian worked for a greengrocer. He was allowed to eat as many apples as he wished, but was told not to eat more than 5 oranges.

   (a) Draw a pair of axes as shown.

   (b) Three points have been marked. Each shows what Sebastian is allowed to eat. A shows 2 oranges and 6 apples, B shows 4 oranges and 1 apple while C shows 5 apples and 4 oranges. On your pair of axes, mark all the points that show what Sebastian is allowed to eat.

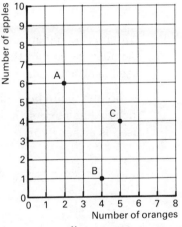

2. The graph of $y = 3$ is shown. At each cross on the line, $y = 3$. The points above the line $y = 3$ show the inequality $y > 3$. What inequality describes the circled points underneath the line $y = 3$?

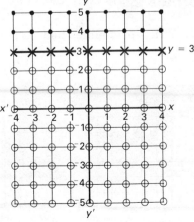

255

Two graphs are shown below. The shaded region in the first diagram shows the inequality $y \leqslant 2$, while the shaded region in the second diagram shows the inequality $y < 2$.

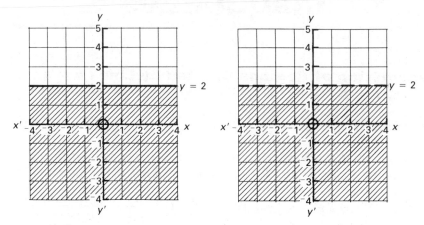

Note An unbroken boundary line means that the boundary is included as part of the shaded region, so the inequality sign used is either $\leqslant$ or $\geqslant$.

A broken boundary line means that the boundary is not included as part of the shaded region, so the inequality sign used is either $<$ or $>$.

Exercise 2

1. Write inequalities to describe the shaded regions:

(a)　　　　　　　(b)　　　　　　　(c)

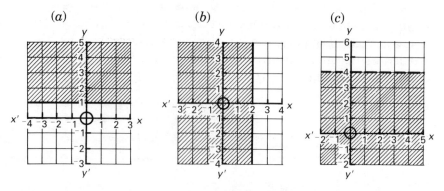

2. Write inequalities to describe the unshaded regions:

(a)

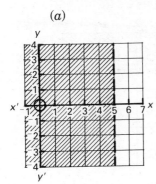

(b)

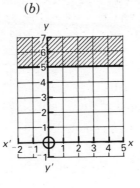

(c)

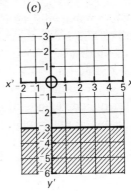

3. For each part of this question, draw a pair of axes as shown. Shade the regions described by the following inequalities.

(a) $x < 6$

(b) $y > 3$

(c) $x \leqslant 7$

(d) $y \leqslant {}^{-}1$

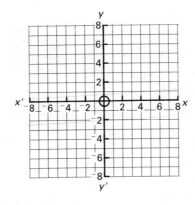

4. For each part of this question, draw a pair of axes as for question 3. Leave unshaded the regions described by the following inequalities. (Shade the rest of each diagram.)

(a) $y < 6$

(b) $x > 4$

(c) $y \leqslant 0$

(d) $x \geqslant {}^{-}2$

5. Using another pair of axes as for question 3:

(a) Draw the graph of $y = x$.

(b) Shade the region shown by the inequality $y \leqslant x$.

257

Exercise 3

A The unshaded area in the diagram is described by the inequalities:

$y < 3$ and $x \geqslant -2$

Use inequalities to describe the unshaded regions in each of the following diagrams.

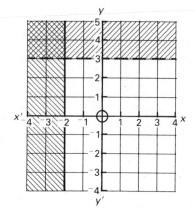

1.

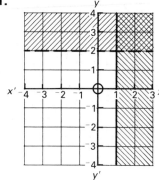

3.

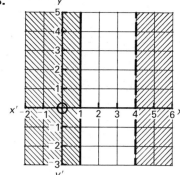

2.

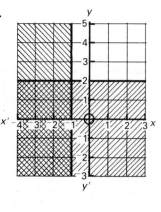

4.

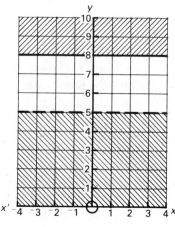

5.

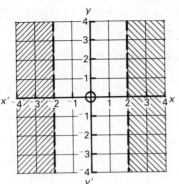

6.

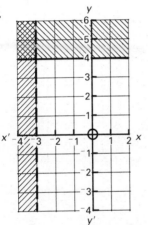

7.

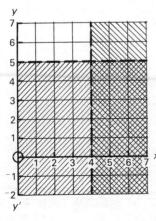

8.

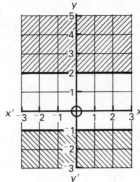

9.

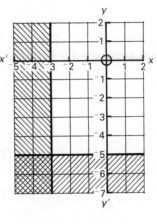

10.

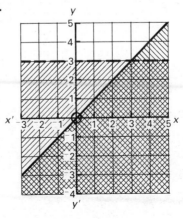

11.

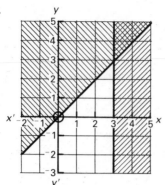

12.

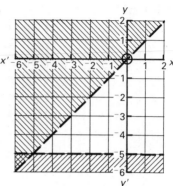

B For each question, draw a pair of axes as shown. Shade the part of the diagram that is not described by the given inequalities.

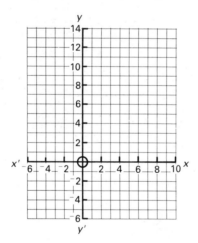

1. $x \geqslant {}^-4$ and $x < 6$

2. $y \geqslant 3$ and $y \leqslant 12$

3. $x \leqslant 4$ and $y \leqslant 7$

4. $x < 7$ and $y > {}^-3$

5. $x \geqslant 2$ and $y < 8$

6. $x > {}^-1$ and $y \geqslant {}^-4$

7. $y \geqslant x$ and $y \leqslant 9$

8. $y < x$ and $x \leqslant 8$

9. $y \leqslant x$ and $y < {}^-2$

10. $y > x$ and $x \geqslant {}^-3$

Exercise 4

A In the following questions, the unshaded regions can be described by three inequalities. For each diagram, write the three inequalities that describe the unshaded region.

1.

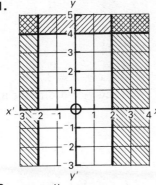

3.

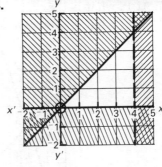

2.

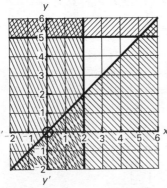

4.

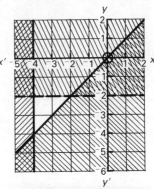

B In the given diagram, 13 regions have been labelled. Region A can be described by two inequalities, $x \leq 0$ and $y \geq 0$. Write inequalities to describe each of the other regions in turn.

Note Some regions need two inequalities to describe them, some need three, while one region needs four.

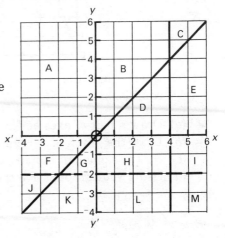

261

21 Simultaneous Equations

Exercise 1

1. The diagram shows the graphs of $y = 3x$ and $x + y = 8$.
The two graphs intersect at point P. The x- and y-co-ordinates at P give the solution of the equations:

$$y = 3x$$

$$x + y = 8$$

(a) At P, what is the value of x?
(b) At P, what is the value of y?

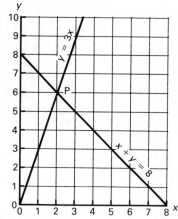

(c) Check that the x- and y-values found satisfy the two equations.

2. (a) Draw a pair of axes as for question 1.
(b) Draw the graph of $x + y = 6$.
(c) On the same pair of axes, draw the graph of $y = x + 2$.
(d) Using your graph, solve the simultaneous equations:

$$x + y = 6$$

$$y = x + 2$$

3. (*a*) Draw a pair of axes as shown:
(0 ≤ x ≤ 8 and
0 ≤ y ≤ 20)

(*b*) By drawing two straight lines, solve simultaneously the equations:

$$y = x + 8$$

$$y = 2x + 3$$

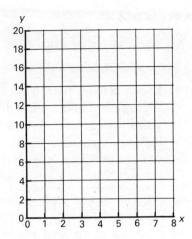

4. (*a*) Draw a pair of axes as shown:
(0 ≤ x ≤ 10 and
⁻6 ≤ y ≤ 10)

(*b*) By drawing two straight lines, solve simultaneously the equations:

$$x + y = 9$$

$$x - y = 5$$

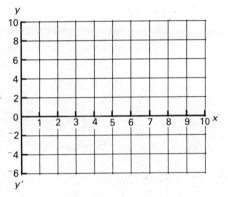

5. Draw a pair of axes as shown:
(⁻3 ≤ x ≤ 5 and ⁻5 ≤ y ≤ 5)
and then by drawing two graphs, solve the simultaneous equations:

$$3x + 4y = 12$$

$$9x + 2y = {}^-9$$

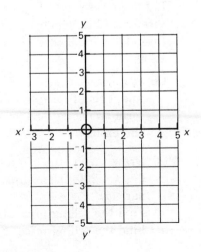

263

Exercise 2

For each problem write two equations. Solve them simultaneously using graphs.

1. Eileen is older than Nathan. The sum of their ages is 40 years, while the difference between their ages is 10 years. Let Eileen be y years old and Nathan x years old.

   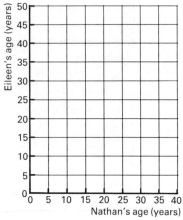

   (a) The sum of their ages can be written as $x + y = 40$. Copy the pair of axes and draw the graph.

   (b) The difference between their ages can be written as $y - x = 10$ (or $y = x + 10$). Using the same pair of axes, draw the graph.

   (c) Using your graphs, find Eileen's age.

   (d) Using your graphs, find Nathan's age.

2. A shop sells two sizes of suitcases (the two prices depend on the sizes of the cases).
   If 2 large cases and 1 small case cost £141, while 1 large case and 4 small cases cost £200:

   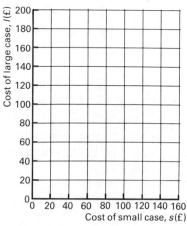

   (a) Let a large case cost £l and a small case £s, and form two equations for the problem.

   (b) Draw a pair of axes as shown $(0 \leqslant s \leqslant 160$ and $0 \leqslant l \leqslant 200)$, then draw graphs of the equations formed in part (a).

   (c) Find the selling price of a small suitcase.

   (d) Find the selling price of a large suitcase.

264

3. In a league, a new points system was used. A team that won 8 games and drew 4 got 36 points, while a team that won 2 games and drew 8 got 16 points.

(a) If a team got w points for a win and d points for a draw, form two equations for the problem.

(b) Draw a pair of axes then draw graphs of the equations formed in part (a).

(c) How many points are there for a win?

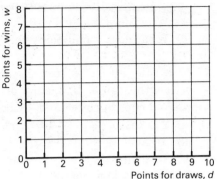

4. A jug and two glasses together hold 1.6 ℓ. The jug holds 0.7 ℓ more than each glass.
Draw a pair of axes as shown. Form two equations for the problem then by drawing graphs, find:

(a) the amount a jug holds in litres,

(b) the amount each glass holds in millilitres.

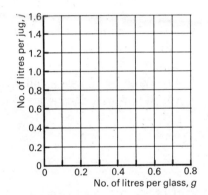

Exercise 3

A Solve the following simultaneous equations:

1. $4x + y = 16$
   $x + y = 7$

2. $x - 2y = 0$
   $x - y = 3$

3. $2x + y = 8$
   $2x + 3y = 14$

4. $x + 2y = 13$
   $x - y = 4$

5. $2x - 7y = 16$
   $2x + 3y = 16$

6. $3x + y = 10$
   $3x - 2y = {}^-2$

7. $4x - y = 5$
   $4x + y = 3$

8. $x + 3y = {}^-5$
   $x - 4y = 2$

9. $2x - 3y = 10$
   $x - 3y = 8$

265

B For each problem, write two equations. Solve them simultaneously.

1. A ball-point pen and 3 pencils cost 90 p, while a ball-point pen and 2 pencils (the same sort as before) cost 75 p:
   (*a*) What does a pencil cost?
   (*b*) What does a ball-point pen cost?

2. At a café, all cakes cost the same and all cups of coffee were priced the same. If 3 cups of coffee and 2 cakes cost £2.30, while 3 cups of coffee and 4 cakes cost £3.10, find the cost of:
   (*a*) 2 cakes,   (*b*) 1 cake,   (*c*) a cup of coffee.

3. 4 dance and 3 theatre tickets cost £59, while 4 dance and 2 theatre tickets cost £50:
   (*a*) What is the cost of a theatre ticket?
   (*b*) What is the cost of a dance ticket?

4. A tin of paint and 6 rolls of wallpaper cover an area of 65 m², while a tin of paint and 4 rolls of wallpaper cover an area of 54 m²:
   (*a*) What area does a roll of wallpaper cover?
   (*b*) What area does a tin of paint cover?

Exercise 4

A Solve the following simultaneous equations:

1. $2x + y = 20$
   $x + 2y = 16$

2. $x + 6y = 40$
   $3x + y = 18$

3. $3x + y = 15$
   $x - 3y = 15$

4. $4x + 3y = 18$
   $2x - y = 4$

5. $5x + 2y = 5$
   $x + y = 4$

6. $x + 3y = 24$
   $4x + y = 19$

7. $5x + 4y = 24$
   $3x - 2y = 10$

8. $2x - 3y = 6$
   $x - 2y = 5$

266

9. $2x + 9y = 16$
$6x - 5y = 16$

11. $3x + 8y = 30$
$4x + 5y = 23$

10. $2x + 5y = 25$
$3x - 2y = 9$

12. $3x + 7y = 7$
$5x - 2y = 39$

B For each problem write two equations. Solve them simultaneously.

1. There were two different prices of tickets for a concert.
3 expensive and 5 cheaper tickets cost £46, while 5 expensive and
3 cheaper tickets cost £50. Find the cost of each type of ticket.

2. If it takes 50 min to creosote 5 panels of fencing and to clean
2 windows, and 59 min to creosote 3 panels of fencing and to clean
7 windows (the panels take the same amount of time each and so
did the windows), find the time needed to:
(*a*) creosote one fence panel,
(*b*) clean one window.

3. 2 large packs and 5 small packs of screws contain 50 screws
altogether, while 3 large packs and 2 small packs contain a total
of 42 screws:
(*a*) How many screws does a large pack hold?
(*b*) How many screws does a small pack hold?

4. 8 Choco and 3 Caramella bars cost £2.88, while 5 Choco and 2
Caramella bars cost £1.84:
(*a*) Find the cost of a Choco bar.
(*b*) Find the cost of a Caramella bar.

5. 6 tins of soup and 2 tins of beans cost £2.50 altogether, while 4
tins of soup and 3 tins of beans cost £2.15. Find the cost of:
(*a*) A tin of soup, (*b*) a tin of beans.

22 Ratio and Proportion

Ratio

Exercise 1

1. The ingredients of a vegetarian risotto for 4 people are given:

> **Risotto (serves 4)**
> 6 oz butter or margarine
> 2 onions, sliced
> 1 clove garlic, crushed
> 12 oz brown rice
> salt and pepper
> 4 cups stock or water and vegetable stock cubes
> 8 oz button mushrooms, sliced
> 4 tablespoons grated Parmesan cheese

(a) Rewrite the list of ingredients showing the quantities needed to serve 10 people.

(b) When 6 onions are used, how many cups of stock should be used?

(c) When 9 oz of butter is used, how many ounces of mushrooms should be used?

(d) When 2 lb of mushrooms are used, how many pounds of brown rice should be used?

2. The following table shows the relationship between miles and kilometres.

No. of miles	5	10	15			30			45		55
No. of kilometres	8			32	40		56	64		80	

The ratio of the number of miles to the number of kilometres is always the same. Copy and complete the table.

3. An American recipe to make condensed milk uses $1\frac{1}{3}$ cups non-fat dry milk and $\frac{3}{4}$ cup sugar:
   (a) How much sugar needs to be mixed with $2\frac{2}{3}$ cups of dry milk?
   (b) When the sugar is mixed with the $2\frac{2}{3}$ cups of dry milk, how many cups of the mixture will there be?

4. A nurse diluted a drug with water in the ratio $1:8$:
   (a) If $60\,m\ell$ of the drug was used, how much water was used?
   (b) If $360\,m\ell$ of water was used, how many millilitres of the drug were used?
   (c) If $30\,m\ell$ of the drug was used, how much solution was made up altogether?
   (d) If $360\,m\ell$ of solution was made up altogether, how many millilitres of that solution was the drug?

5. A concrete mix suitable for house foundations and driveways uses cement, dry sand and coarse aggregate in the ratio $1:2:4$:
   (a) If $50\,kg$ of cement is used, how much dry sand and coarse aggregate is needed?
   (b) If $80\,kg$ of dry sand is used, how much cement and coarse aggregate is needed?

Exercise 2

Write the following ratios in their simplest terms:

1. $15:12$
2. $18:36$
3. $21:28$
4. $24:20$
5. $4\frac{1}{2}:2$
6. $1\frac{3}{4}:2\frac{1}{2}$
7. $2:1\frac{1}{3}$
8. $4:8:6$
9. $40:25:15$
10. $2:2\frac{1}{2}:3\frac{1}{2}$
11. $2\,cm$ to $8\,mm$
12. 3.75 to 2.25

Exercise 3 Proportional Division

A 1. Divide $15\,kg$ in the ratio $3:2$.
2. Divide £40 in the ratio $3:5$.
3. Divide £2.70 in the ratio $5:1$.
4. Divide £6.23 in the ratio $4:3$.
5. Divide $3.6\,lb$ in the ratio $5:7$.

B

1. £80 was shared between Dora and Cliff in the ratio 3:1. How much did each person receive?

2. £72 was shared between two people in the ratio 2:5. Calculate the larger share, correct to the nearest penny.

3. Some fifth year pupils collected £200 for charity. It was divided between Cancer Research and Oxfam in the ratio 5:3. How much was donated to Oxfam?

4. £744 was donated by a school to three charities: Children in Need, Heartbeat and Animal Care in the ratio 4:3:1. How much did each receive?

5. A sum of money is shared between two people in the ratio 3:4. If the smaller amount was £120, find the larger amount.

6. Brass is an alloy made up of copper (Cu) and zinc (Zn) in the ratio 3:2:
   (a) How heavy is brass containing 1.2 kg of copper?
   (b) What percentage of the alloy is zinc?

7. Pewter is an alloy made of tin (Sn), lead (Pb) and antimony (Sb) in the ratio 13:6:1:
   (a) What percentage is tin?
   (b) What is the mass of the lead in 5 g of pewter?

8. Some money was shared amongst Diane, Grahame and Alyn in the ratio 4:5:3. If Grahame received £60:
   (a) How much did Diane receive?
   (b) How much money was shared amongst them?

9. Mr England and Mrs Ireland started a business together. Mr England invested £40 000 while Mrs Ireland invested £60 000. They shared the profits in the same ratio as their investment. If the profits totalled £25 000, how much should Mrs Ireland receive?

10. Three people set up in business together and decided to share the profit in the ratio of their investments in the business. Mrs Rich invested £75 000, Mr Speakman £30 000 and Mr Vann £15 000.
    How much should each receive out of profits of £52 000?

Elementary Ideas and Applications of Direct and Inverse Proportion

Exercise 4   Direct Proportion

1. Bob walked at a steady 6 km per hour for 8 h. His distance travelled each hour can be shown in a table. A partly completed table is given below.

Time (h)	0	1	2	3	4	5	6	7	8
Distance (km)	0	6			24			42	

   (*a*) Copy and complete the given table.
   (*b*) Using the formula $s = 6t$, find s when t is:

      (i)   0   (iv) 3   (vii) 6
      (ii) 1   (v) 4   (viii) 7
      (iii) 2   (vi) 5   (ix) 8

   (*c*) Compare your answers to part (*b*) with the values in the table, and write what you notice.
   (*d*) Draw a pair of axes as shown.
   (*e*) Using the table in part (*a*), draw a graph to show the relationship between distance and time.

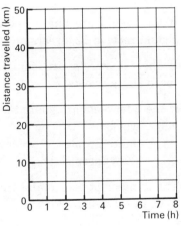

   Note   The table gives sets of numbers that are in *direct proportion*, and the graph shows this direct proportion. (As time gets bigger, so does the distance. As time gets smaller, the distance also gets smaller.)

2. 900 g of flour is used in making 4 cakes. How much flour is needed to make:

   (*a*) 8 of those cakes?   (*b*) 6 of those cakes?

271

3. Five bars of chocolate cost £1.85. What do eight of those chocolate bars cost?

4. A car used 20 ℓ of petrol in travelling 280 km. At the same rate of petrol consumption, how many litres will be used in travelling 350 km?

5. Mr Gardner used 5 kg of fertiliser on a 90 m² lawn. How much fertiliser would he need for a 126 m² lawn, if the fertiliser was spread at the same rate per square metre?

6. A carpet measuring 6 m by 3 m cost £117. What should the same sort of carpet cost if it measured 7 m by 4 m?

Inverse Proportion

If 60 sweets are shared equally amongst 5 people, each person should receive 12 sweets.

If the 60 sweets are shared by *more* people, each person will receive *less* sweets.

If the 60 sweets are shared by *less* people, each person will receive *more* sweets.

       more people ⟶ less sweets
       less people ⟶ more sweets

The number of people and the number of sweets obtained are said to be in *inverse proportion*.

The proportional relationship between the two quantities can be seen in the following table.

Number of people	1	2	3	4	5	6	10	12	15	20	30	60
Number of sweets	60	30	20	15	12	10	6	5	4	3	2	1

Note   If you double the number of people, they get half the number of sweets. Three times the number of people get one-third the number of sweets, and so on.

If making a quantity bigger, causes a second quantity to become smaller in the same ratio, the two quantities are in *inverse proportion*. Also, if making the first quantity smaller causes the second quantity to become bigger in the same ratio, the two quantities are in *inverse proportion*. We can also say that one quantity *varies inversely* as the other.

Exercise 5

1. (a) Draw a pair of axes as shown.
   (b) Using the table opposite, draw a graph to show the relationship between the number of people and the number of sweets.

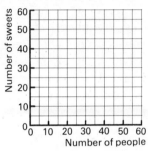

   (This shape of graph is the shape you will obtain for any two quantities that are in inverse proportion. Compare the graph with the answers drawn to Exercise 13, p. 253.)
   (c) If there were n people who received s sweets each, check that the formula $s = \frac{60}{n}$ gives the same values as in the table opposite.

2. Some sweets are shared equally amongst 4 people, and they get 3 sweets each. How many sweets would each get, if the same number of sweets as before are shared equally amongst:
   (a) 2 people?   (b) 3 people?

3. Sheila had a certain amount of money to spend on books. She worked out that she could afford to buy 5 books at £8 each. How many books could she afford:
   (a) at £4 each?   (b) at £5 each?

4. 3 people have enough food to last 12 days. For how many days will the same amount of food last 4 people?

5. Mr and Mrs Oates had enough cereal in their house for 2 people to have 15 servings each. Out of that same amount of cereal, how many servings each could 5 people have?

273

6. A builder reckons he can build a house in 15 weeks using 6 men. How long would it take to build the house using 9 men, if they all worked at the same rate?

7. Walking at a steady 6 km per hour I should cover a certain distance in 45 min. How long should I take to walk the same distance at a steady 5 km per hour?

8 Ohm's law gives the current flowing in a resistor to be inversely proportional to the resistance. If a current of 3 A flows in an 80 Ω resistor, find the resistance when a 5 A current is flowing.

9. The frequency of a wave is inversely proportional to its wavelength. The Radio 1 transmitter sends out waves of wavelength 275 m and frequency 1089 kHz (kilohertz). If the Radio 4 transmitter sends out waves of wavelength 1500 m, find the frequency.

Change of Units

Use the given information, as necessary, to help in the following exercises.

$$5 \text{ miles} = 8 \text{ kg}$$
$$2.54 \text{ cm} = 1 \text{ in}$$
$$1 \text{ kg} = 2.2 \text{ lb}$$
$$1 \text{ lb} = 454 \text{ g}$$
$$1 \text{ t} = 0.984 \text{ tons}$$
$$(\text{metric}) \quad (\text{imperial})$$

$$4.55 \ \ell = 1 \text{ gal}$$
$$3.79 \ \ell = 1 \text{ US gal}$$

Exercise 6

1. A car travelled at 40 miles per hour. Express the speed in kilometres per hour.

2. Change 6 kg to pounds.

3. Change 2 lb to grams.

4. (a) Change 4 in to centimetres.

(b) Change 21 in to centimetres.

(c) Convert 7.5 in to centimetres.

(d) Given that $12 \text{ in} = 1 \text{ ft}$, convert 1 ft to centimetres.

(e) (i) Convert 4 ft to centimetres.

(ii) Write 4 ft in metres (correct to three significant figures).

(f) Given that $3 \text{ ft} = 1 \text{ yd}$, convert 1 yd to metres.

5. Each side of the given square measures 1 in:

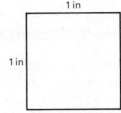

(a) What is the area of the square in square inches?

(b) How long is each side of the square in centimetres?

(c) What is the area of the square in square centimetres?

(d) How many square centimetres are there in a square inch?

6. Change 15 cm to inches, giving the answer to one decimal place.

7. Copy and complete:

$$\boxed{?} = 1 \text{ in}$$
$$1 \text{ cm} = \boxed{?} \text{ in}$$
$$1 \text{ m} = \boxed{?} \text{ in}$$
$$1 \text{ m} = \boxed{?} \text{ yd} \qquad (36 \text{ in} = 1 \text{ yd})$$
$$100 \text{ m} = \boxed{?} \text{ yd}$$

8. Convert:

(a) 3 gal to litres,

(b) 50 ℓ to gallons, giving the answer to the nearest gallon,

(c) 3 US gal to litres.

9. How many litres difference is there between 8 imperial gal and 8 US gal?

10. (a) Given that $16 \text{ oz} = 1 \text{ lb}$, how many grams are there in 1 oz?

(b) If rich gingerbread needs 5 oz of butter, how many grams of butter does it need?

(c) A chocolate log uses $1\frac{1}{2}$ oz of plain flour. How many grams is that?

11. Mrs Way has a mass of 8 st 12 lb:
  (*a*) How many pounds is that, if 14 lb = 1 st?
  (*b*) Convert her mass to kilograms.

12. (*a*) How many tons are there in 7 t?
  (*b*) How many tonnes are there in 1 ton?
  (*c*) A lorry has a mass of 30 tons. Write that mass in tonnes.

Exercise 7 Foreign Currencies

Answer the following using the given exchange rates where necessary:

1. Max changed £30 into Greek drachmas. How many should he have received?

Rates of Exchange Equivalent to £1 Sterling

Country	Currency
Belgium	61.43 francs
France	9.85 francs
W Germany	2.94 marks
Greece	215 drachmas
Switzerland	2.41 francs
USA	1.67 dollars

2. Nicola changed £45 into Swiss francs. How many should she have received?

3. (*a*) If the exchange rate was 2 US dollars to the pound, how many pence is 1 US dollar worth?
  (*b*) Using the exchange rate of 1.67 US dollars to the pound, how many pence is 1 US dollar worth?

4. Calvin paid 81.06 francs for a meal, while in France. How much was that in pounds sterling?

5. Mr Bairstow spent 42.50 marks in a shop in Germany. Using an exchange rate of 34 p to 1 mark, find the amount spent in pounds.

6. A coach driver bought some diesel in Belgium and paid 16.60 francs per litre:
  (*a*) Using an exchange rate of 1.63 p to 1 franc, find the cost, in pence, of 1 ℓ of diesel.
  (*b*) If 1 gal is the same as 4.55 ℓ, find the cost, in pounds (to the nearest penny), of 1 gal of diesel in Belgium.

7. Mrs Etchells visited Iceland and used the rule $5\,\mathrm{p} = 3\,\mathrm{kr\acute{o}nur}$ to convert between Icelandic and British currencies. Use the rule to find:

   (*a*) the amount spent in pounds if 270 krónur was spent,

   (*b*) the number of krónur obtained for £20.

8. Beth had 909 pesetas left in Spanish currency when she returned from holiday. If it was worth £4.50, what was the exchange rate in pesetas to one pound?

Exercise 8   Common Measures of Rate

1. Find the average speed:

   (*a*) 150 km in 3 h (in km/h),

   (*b*) 106 miles in 2 h (in m.p.h.),

   (*c*) 100 miles in $2\frac{1}{2}$ h (in m.p.h.),

   (*d*) 70 miles in 50 min (in m.p.h.),

   (*e*) 150 m in 6 s (in km/h).

2. A train averages 84 km per hour:

   (*a*) How far will it travel in 5 h?

   (*b*) How long will it take to travel 252 km?

   (*c*) How long will it take to travel 210 km?

3. A car took 4 h 5 min to travel 160 miles. *Estimate* the average speed of the car to the nearest 10 m.p.h.

4. The government petrol consumption figures for a certain make of car give 46.8 miles per gallon at a constant 56 m.p.h.:

   (*a*) How far should the car travel on $5\frac{1}{2}$ gal of petrol if it travels at a steady 56 m.p.h.?

   (*b*) How much petrol should the car use in travelling 280 miles at a steady 56 m.p.h.? (Give your answer correct to the nearest gallon.)

5. Marsha walked at a constant 5 km/h:

   (*a*) How far did she walk in 4 h?

   (*b*) How far did she walk in 2 h 15 min?

   (*c*) How long did it take her to walk 28.75 km?

6. A wheel turns at a rate of 12 rev/min:
   (*a*) How many revolutions does it make in 1 h?
   (*b*) How long does it take to make 3000 revolutions?

7. A car travelled 198 km in 2 h 45 min. Calculate its average speed in kilometres per hour.

8. A motorcycle completed a race in 1 h 12 min, averaging 105 m.p.h. Another motorcycle completed the same race 2 min faster. What was the average speed of this faster motorcycle?

9.

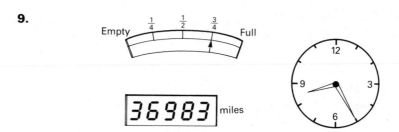

The petrol tank on my car holds 8 gal when full. It averages 46 m.p.g. The clocks above show the amount of petrol in my car, the mileage and time at the beginning of a journey. At the end of the journey the readings are as below.

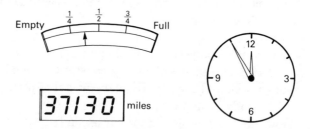

   (*a*) About how many miles could my car have travelled before running out of petrol?
   (*b*) How long did my journey take?
   (*c*) How many miles was my journey?
   (*d*) What was the average speed of my journey?
   (*e*) At the end of the journey, about how many more miles could my car travel before running out of petrol?

10. Silver has a density of 10.5 g per cubic centimetre. Calculate the mass of 8 cm^3 of silver.

11. If concrete has a density of 2080 kg per cubic metre, calculate the mass of 3.5 m^3 of concrete giving the answer in tonnes.

12. A train travelled from London to Glasgow at a constant speed. It left London Euston at 07.45 and passed through Crewe, a distance of 158.4 miles, at 09.57. The train eventually arrived at Glasgow Central at 13.20. How far is it from Crewe to Glasgow Central?

13. A bus travelled 60 miles at an average speed of 30 m.p.h., and then it travelled a further 120 miles at an average speed of 40 m.p.h.. Calculate the average speed for the whole journey.

14. A car travelled 96 km at an average speed of 48 km/h, then it travelled a further 60 km during the next hour. Calculate the average speed for the whole journey.

23 Bearings and Scale Drawings

Bearings

Exercise 1

1. The diagram shows a compass:

   (a) If you face west then turn clockwise until you face north-east, through how many degrees will you have turned?

   (b) If you face SW, then turn anticlockwise until you face north, through how many degrees will you have turned?

   (c) Which directions are at right-angles to SE?

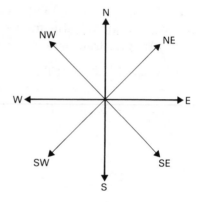

2. For each diagram, choose the answer that gives the bearing of P from O:

(a)

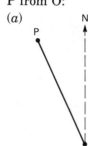

   A.   25°
   B. 155°
   C. 025°
   D. 335°

(b)

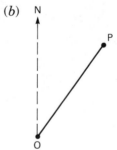

   A.   36°
   B. 036°
   C. 144°
   D. 324°

(c)

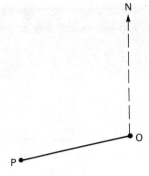

A. 258°
B. 102°
C. 78°
D. 078°

3. What is the bearing of:
   (a) Douglas from Peel?
   (b) Peel from Douglas?

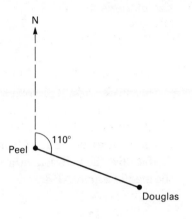

4. What is the bearing of:
   (a) Ballymagorry from
      Ballyclare?
   (b) Ballyclare from
      Ballymagorry?

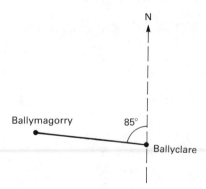

5. A ship is at a bearing of 192° from a lighthouse. What is the bearing of the lighthouse from the ship?

6. What is the bearing of north-west?

7. A ship is sailing on a bearing of 072°. Another ship is sailing in exactly the opposite direction. On what bearing is this second ship sailing?

8. A ship is sailing on a bearing of 194°. Find its new bearing if it turns 42° to port (to the left)?

Exercise 2

1. If Perth is at a bearing of 317° from Alnwick, find the size of angle θ.

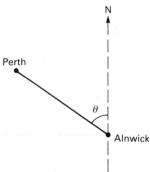

2. P is on a bearing of 123° from A and 064° from B. Calculate the size of angle APB.

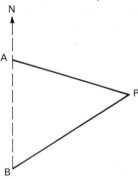

3. In the given diagram, find the bearing of:
   (a) Y from X
   (b) X from Y
   (c) Z from X
   (d) Z from Y
   (e) X from Z

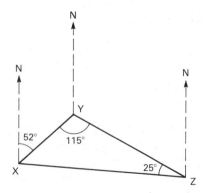

4 The diagram below shows the relative positions of Lowestoft, Luton and Stafford.

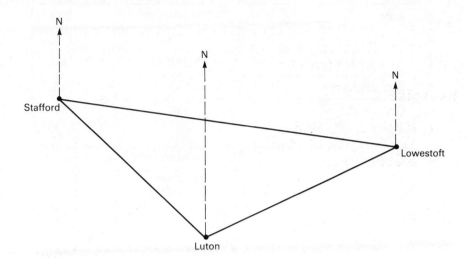

Find the bearing of:
(a) Lowestoft from Luton,
(b) Stafford from Luton,
(c) Lowestoft from Stafford,

(d) Luton from Stafford,
(e) Stafford from Lowestoft,
(f) Luton from Lowestoft.

Scale Drawings Involving Bearings

Exercise 3

Mark a point near the centre of your page and label it Bradford. Mark a North line starting at that point.

Using a scale of 1 cm to 20 km, find and label the places given in the table on the next page.

	Place	Distance from Bradford (km)	Bearing
1.	Bridlington	120	072°
2.	Bala	160	231°
3.	Workington	150	312°
4.	Newcastle-upon-Tyne	140	006°
5.	Birmingham	155	181°
6.	Grimsby	130	103°
7.	Peterborough	184	141°
8.	Carlisle	144	331°

Exercise 4 M

1. The given diagram has been drawn to a scale of 1 cm to 10 km.

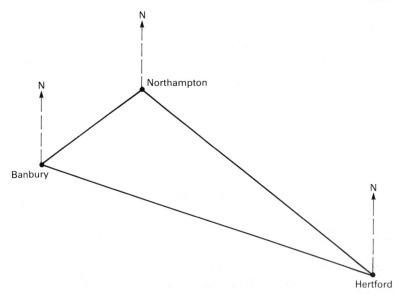

By measuring, find:
(a) the distance from Northampton to Hertford,
(b) the distance from Banbury to Hertford,
(c) the distance from Banbury to Northampton,
(d) the bearing of Northampton from Hertford,
(e) the bearing of Banbury from Hertford.

2. Presteigne is 100 km due west of Warwick.

(a) Measure the line joining Presteigne to Warwick. Hence, find and write the scale used:

   1 cm represents ? km

(b) Copy the given line and label Presteigne and Warwick. (You need to leave 4 cm space above the line and 7.5 cm space below the line. You also need 1.5 cm space east of Warwick (to the right).) Mark the North lines.

On your diagram, find and label the following places using the given information.

(c) Stafford is 90 km from Presteigne and 70 km from Warwick. (It is north of both places.) By measuring, find the bearing of Stafford from Presteigne and from Warwick.

(d) Derby is at a bearing of 055° from Presteigne and 005° from Warwick. By measuring, find the distance of Derby from Presteigne and from Warwick.

(e) Oxford is 140 km from Presteigne and at a bearing of 115°. How far is Oxford from Warwick?

(f) Salisbury is at a bearing of 184° from Warwick and is 170 km from Presteigne. How far is Salisbury from Warwick?

3. A ship sails from A to B, a distance of 40 km on a bearing of 070°. It then changes direction and sails 32 km on a bearing of 155° to C.

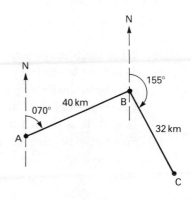

(a) Make a scale drawing using a scale of 1 cm to 5 km.
(b) (i) Join AC and measure its length to the nearest millimetre.
    (ii) How many kilometres is the straight-line distance from A to C?
(c) (i) Measure and write the size of angle BAC.
    (ii) Write the bearing of C from A.
    (iii) Write the bearing of A from C.
(d) By drawing further lines on your scale drawing, find how far C is south of B.

4. A ship sailed 160 km due south from a point J to a point K. It then changed course and sailed 120 km due east to point L. From L, it sailed 80 km on a bearing of 345° until it reached M.
(a) Make a scale drawing using a scale of 1 cm to 20 km.
(b) From your drawing find:
    (i) the straight-line distance from J to M,
    (ii) the bearing of M from J to the nearest degree,
    (iii) the distance that J is west of M,
    (iv) the distance that J is north of M.

Scale Drawings

Exercise 5

1. A model was made to the scale of 1 to 32. If the model was 8.5 cm long, what was the real length?

2. A scale drawing of a rectangular garden is shown. It is 24 m long.
    24 m
(a) What scale has it been drawn to? Write the answer in the form:
1 cm represents ⬚ ? m
(b) How wide is the actual garden?
(c) Calculate the area of the actual garden.
(d) If three-fifths of the garden is lawn, calculate the area of the lawn.

3. The house has been drawn to a scale of 1 : 200.

Scale: 1:200

For the actual house, find:
(a) the overall width of the house and garage,
(b) the dimensions of the garage door,
(c) the area of the square window,
(d) the area of the downstairs window,
(e) the area of the whole of the front of the garage.

4. The scale of a map is 1 : 200 000:
(a) Find the distance in kilometres represented by:
(i) 1 cm on the map,
(ii) 7.5 cm on the map.
(b) Find the distance in centimetres that represents a map distance of:
(i) 8 km
(ii) 3 km

5. A field is in the shape of a quadrilateral PQRS. PQ = 160 m, QR = 90 m and RS = 140 m. Angle PQR = 90° and angle QRS = 110°.
Using a scale of 1 cm to represent 20 m, make a scale drawing of the field.
(a) From your scale drawing, find the length of side PS.

287

(b) A farmer fixed a post in the field. It was positioned at the point of intersection of the perpendicular bisector of side RS and the bisector of angle RSP. Using only a pencil, ruler and pair of compasses, construct and indicate the position of the post.

(c) Find the distance of the post from corner P of the field.

(d) A second post was positioned so that it was no more than 60 m from RS, and no more than 90 m from corner P. By shading, show the region where the post may be sited.

6. On a set of plans, a 20 m long garden has been drawn to a length of 5 cm:

(a) Calculate the length, on the plan, of a road that is 92 m long.

(b) Calculate the actual length of a fence that has been drawn to be 29 cm long on the plan.

Exercise 6

1. The angle of elevation of the top of a tower, from a point on the ground 55 m from the foot of the tower, is 36°. Using a scale of 1 cm to 10 m, make a scale drawing and find the height of the tower.

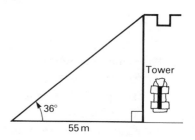

2. From the top of a multi-storey car-park, the angle of depression of a car is 25°. If the car is 150 m away from the bottom of the car-park, make a scale drawing (use a scale of 1 cm to 20 m). From the scale drawing, find the height of the multi-storey car-park.

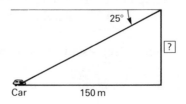

3. The angles of elevation of the top of a tree from two points, A and B, that are 40 m apart and in line with the tree are 12° and 21° respectively. Using a scale of 1 cm to 10 m, make a scale drawing. From your scale drawing, find:

(*a*) the height of the tree,

(*b*) the distance of point B from the foot of the tree.

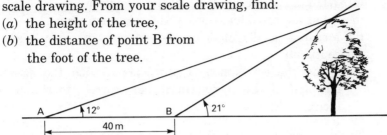

Exercise 7   Plans and Elevations

1. Three views of a television set are shown below.

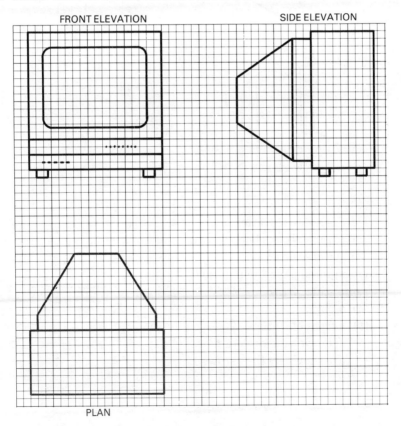

FRONT ELEVATION

SIDE ELEVATION

PLAN

Each view has been drawn using the scale 1 : 10.
(a) What is the overall height of the television?
(b) What is the width of the television?
(c) What is the overall depth of the television?
(d) What are the dimensions of the television screen?
(e) Measure a diagonal of the screen, giving its size in centimetres.
(f) Using the conversion 1 in = 2.54 cm, find the size of a diagonal of the screen in inches (correct to the nearest inch).

2. The drawing shows a coffee table. Its dimensions are given.

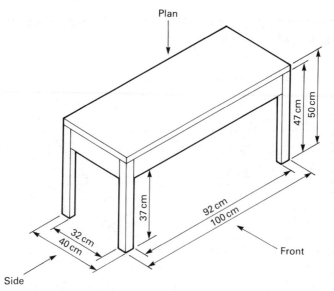

Here is a side elevation of the coffee table. It has been drawn using the scale 1 : 20.
On squared paper, using the same scale, draw:
(a) a plan,
(b) a front elevation.
  (The viewing directions are shown by the arrows.)

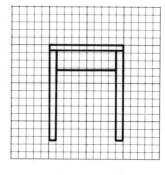

24 Graphs in Practical Situations

Exercise 1   Conversion Graphs

1. The conversion graph shows the rate of exchange from pounds
sterling to Swiss francs.

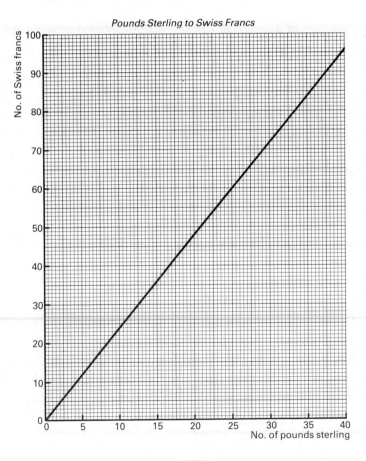

Pounds Sterling to Swiss Francs

Using the graph on the previous page, find

(a) the number of Swiss francs equivalent to:
    (i) £25   (ii) £10   (iii) £32.50

(b) the number of pounds sterling equivalent to:
    (i) 36 Swiss francs (ii) 30 Swiss francs (iii) 21 Swiss francs

2. The exchange rate of pounds sterling to US dollars was $1.60 to £1.

Draw a pair of axes using a scale of 2 cm to £5 and 1 cm to $5. The axes should show up to £50 sterling and up to $80.

Draw a conversion graph to convert pounds to dollars. Use your graph to find:

(a) the number of dollars in:
    (i) £30   (ii) £25   (iii) £45   (iv) £37.50

(b) the number of pounds in:
    (i) $64   (ii) $56   (iii) $20   (iv) $50

3. Draw a pair of axes using a scale of 1 cm to 5 m.p.g. and 4 cm to 5 km/ℓ. (Show up to 80 m.p.g. and 25 km/ℓ.)

Using the fact that 25 km/ℓ is equivalent to 71 m.p.g., draw a conversion graph.

From your graph, find:

(a) the number of km/ℓ in:
    (i) 37 m.p.g.   (ii) 54 m.p.g.   (iii) 17 m.p.g.

(b) the number of m.p.g. in:
    (i) 12 km/ℓ   (ii) 14 km/ℓ   (iii) 22 km/ℓ

Exercise 2   Drawing Graphs from Given Data **M**

1. The graph opposite shows the hire charges of a machine from Archer's.

(a) Copy the graph.

(b) Find the cost of 3 h hire of the machine.

(c) Find the cost of 1 h hire of the machine.

(d) The graph shows that there is a fixed charge followed by a certain rate per hour. How much is the fixed charge?

(e) What rate per hour is charged?

(f) For how many hours can the machine be hired for a total charge of £15?

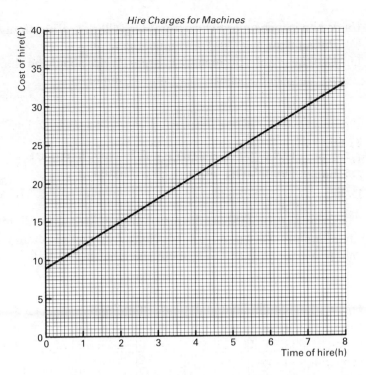

Hire Charges for Machines

2. The same sort of machine, as in question 1, can be hired from Banks Bros. The following table shows some of their hire charges.

Time (h)	2	3	5	7	8
Hire charge (£)	10	15	25	35	40

(a) On the same pair of axes as for question 1, draw a graph to show Banks Bros.' hire charges.
(b) How much do Banks Bros. charge for 7 h hire?
(c) How much do Banks Bros. charge for $2\frac{1}{2}$ h hire?
(d) For how many hours can the machine be hired from Banks Bros. for a total charge of £20?
(e) Use your graphs to find out when it is cheaper to hire from Archer's.

3. H. E. Clarke charges £30 per day, or for part of a day, for the hire of the same sort of machine:
(a) Show H. E. Clarke's charges on the same pair of axes as for questions 1 and 2.

(*b*) When is it cheaper to hire from H. E. Clarke rather than from Banks Bros.?

(*c*) Use the graphs to compare charges. Write about the charges, stating when it is cheaper to hire from each firm.

Exercise 3   Interpretation and Sketching of Graphs Representing Some Practical Situation ━━━━━━━━━━━━━━━━━━━━━━━━━━━━━ **M**

1. The following points show the mass (in grams) and the 'diameter' (in millimetres) of 1 p, 2 p, 5 p, 10 p, 20 p, 50 p and £1 coins. Which coin is which? (Match the coins to the labelled points.)

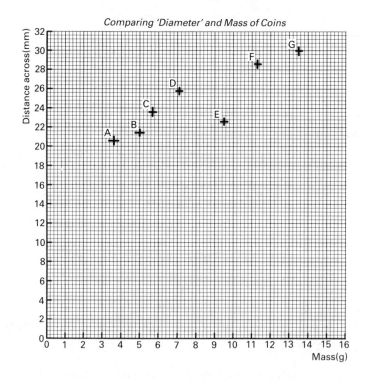

2. The following three sketch graphs describe two cars (labelled A and B on the graphs).

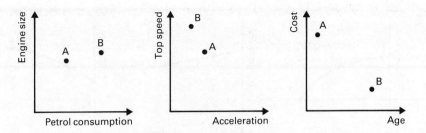

(a) For each statement, write whether it is true or false:
   (i) The car with the larger engine uses more petrol.
   (ii) The car with the higher top speed has faster acceleration.
   (iii) The cheaper car uses less petrol.
   (iv) The newer car has greater acceleration.
   (v) The car with the greater acceleration uses more petrol.
(b) Copy the following pairs of axes. On each one, mark and label points to represent cars A and B.

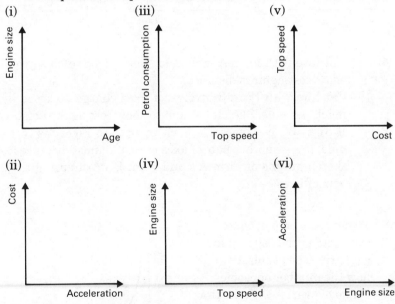

3. (a) The nurse noticed that Mrs Payne's temperature was still rising, but not as fast as before. Which of the graphs on the next page is the best representation of this statement?

   (b) Which graph would indicate that Mrs Payne's temperature was falling at a steady rate?

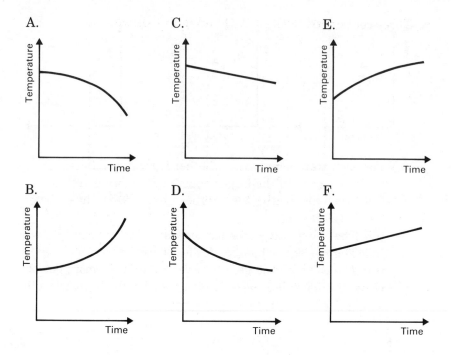

A.

C.

E.

B.

D.

F.

4. (*a*) Car hire with Firm A is so much per mile. Sketch a graph to show cost against distance.

(*b*) Car hire with Firm B involves a fixed charge, followed by so much per mile. Sketch a graph to show cost against distance.

(*c*) If Firm B's cost per mile is cheaper than Firm A's cost per mile, draw another pair of axes of cost against distance, then sketch graphs of Firm A's and Firm B's costs using the one pair of axes.

5. People were employed to collect and grade eggs at an egg farm. The graph shows how the number of people employed varies with the time taken to collect and grade all the eggs.

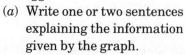
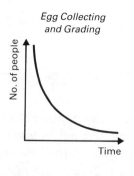

Egg Collecting and Grading

(*a*) Write one or two sentences explaining the information given by the graph.

(*b*) Why doesn't the graph meet the axes?

296

6. Three containers, labelled P, Q and R, are shown.

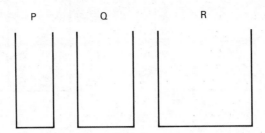

They are each filled with water at the same steady rate.

(a) Which container will be the first to be filled to the brim?

(b) The graph shows how the depth of the water in container P varies with time. Copy the graph then, using the same pair of axes, sketch graphs to show the depth of water in containers Q and R as they are steadily filled. (Label the graphs.)

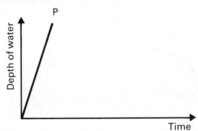

7. Two conical flasks are shown. They can each hold the same amount of water.

Both flasks are filled with water at the same steady rate.

The graphs on the next page show how the depth of water in a flask can vary with the volume of the water.

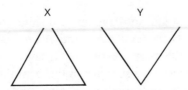

(a) Which graph is the best representation of filling flask X?

(b) Which graph is the best representation of filling flask Y?

A.

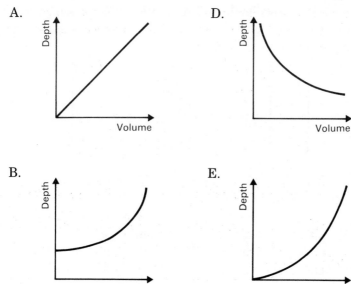

D.

B.

E.

C.

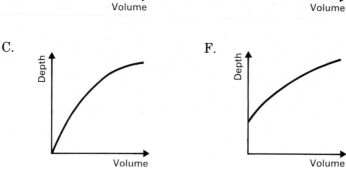

F.

8. A garage sold petrol. On a certain day, they opened at 7 a.m. and their 4-star storage tank was about one-quarter full. Sales were slow and steady until about 2.30 p.m., except for two busy periods – one between 8 a.m. and 9 a.m. and the other from 12.30 p.m. to 1.30 p.m. A tanker arrived with a delivery at 2.30 p.m. It took between 10 and 15 min to fill the storage tank. Sales then continued to be slow and steady until 4 p.m., and then increased until 6 p.m. From 6 p.m. to 7.30 p.m. the number of sales decreased, and no petrol was sold after 7.30 p.m. The garage closed at 8 p.m.

Draw a pair of axes as shown below and *sketch* a graph to show how the total amount of petrol in the storage tank may have varied throughout the day.

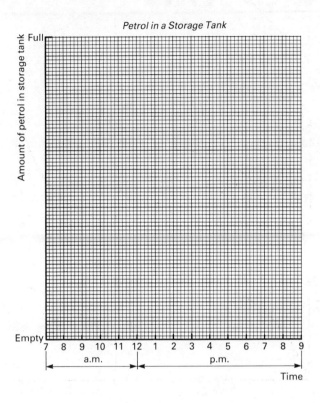

Revision Exercises XVII to XXIV

Revision Exercise XVII

1. Solve for x:

   (a) $7x = 63$ (b) $\dfrac{x}{3} = 12$ (c) $x + 18 = 26$

2. Solve for x:

   (a) $3x - 10 = 14$ (b) $4 = 2x - 9$ (c) $5 = 4x + 13$

3. Solve for x:

   (a) $12 - x = 5$ (b) $8 - x = 17$ (c) $40 - 3x = 4$

4. If $3x - 17 = 28 - 2x$, find the value of x.

5. Solve the equations:

   (a) $4(2t - 5) = 28$ (b) $25 - 2(9 - x) = 3(2x - 7)$

6. Solve the equations:

   (a) $\dfrac{n}{15} = \dfrac{1}{3}$ (b) $\dfrac{2f}{21} = \dfrac{6}{7}$ (c) $\dfrac{1}{g} = \dfrac{4}{3}$ (d) $\dfrac{12}{y} = 3$

7. If $\dfrac{3u + 5}{2} = 10$, find the value of u.

8. Solve for x:

   (a) $\dfrac{x}{4} - \dfrac{x}{6} = 1$ (b) $\dfrac{3x}{4} - \dfrac{(2x - 3)}{5} = 2$

9. Liam, Moira and Ronan were three candidates in a school election. Moira got 40 more votes than Ronan, while Liam got twice as many votes as Ronan.

   (a) If Ronan got v votes, express the number of votes each of the others got in terms of v.

   (b) If the total number who voted for the three candidates was 340, form an equation in v and solve it to find out the number of votes each candidate received.

300

10. (*a*) If $2x^2 = 98$, find possible values of x.

(*b*) If $4x^2 = 81$, find possible values of x.

11. If x is an integer, list the set of values of x where:

(*a*) $x + 5 \leqslant 7$

(*b*) $^-4 \leqslant x < 4$

12. If x is an integer, list all possible values of x where:
$$1 < 2x + 7 \leqslant 19$$

Revision Exercise XVIII

1. In the given flow chart, if n is input:

(*a*) Write an expression in n for the final answer obtained.

(*b*) If the final answer was 30, find the starting number, n.

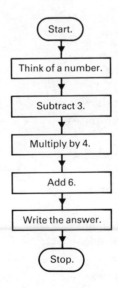

2. (*a*) Follow the instructions in the flow chart on the next page.

(*b*) What sort of numbers have you written?

(*c*) Draw a dot pattern to show the seventh number written.

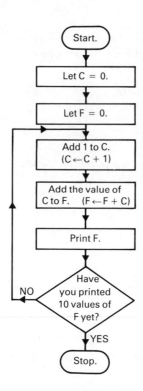

Revision Exercise XIX

1. Draw a pair of axes as shown:
   (a) What are the co-ordinates of P?
   (b) Copy the point P and plot Q(2, ⁻7) and R(3, 1). Join the points to form △PQR.
   (c) Mark and label the point M, the mid-point of side PQ.
   (d) Write the co-ordinates of M.
   (e) Join RM, then calculate its length.
   (f) Write the co-ordinates of the mid-point of PR.

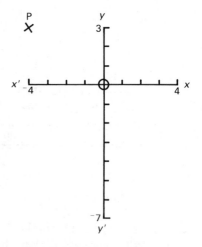

2. Draw a pair of axes where x ranges from 0 to 5 $(0 \leqslant x \leqslant 5)$ and y ranges from $^-4$ to 5 $(^-4 \leqslant y \leqslant 5)$. Use a scale of 2 cm to 1 unit on both axes.
   (a) Draw the graph of $y = 2x - 4$.
   (b) On the same pair of axes, draw the graph of $x + y = 5$.
   (c) Write the co-ordinates of the point of intersection of the two graphs.

3. A stone is thrown downwards from the top of a tower. Its velocity, v m/s, at a time, t s, is given by the formula $v = 8 + 10t$.
   (a) Copy and complete the table:

Time, t(s)	0	1	2	3	4
Velocity, v(m/s)			28		

   (b) Draw a pair of axes. Use a scale of 4 cm to 1 s on the time axis and 2 cm to 5 m/s on the velocity axis (the velocity ranges from 0 to 50 m/s).
   (c) Draw a graph of v against t, using the table to help you.

   Using your graph, find:
   (d) the velocity of the stone after $1\frac{1}{2}$ s,
   (e) the time taken for the stone to reach a velocity of 33 m/s,
   (f) the time taken (to the nearest $\frac{1}{10}$ s) for the stone to reach a velocity of 40 m/s.

4. (a) Draw a pair of axes.
       The x-values should range from $^-4$ to 4 (use a scale of 2 cm to 1 unit) while the y-values should range from 0 to 80 (use a scale of 1 cm to 5 units).
   (b) Draw the graph of $y = 5x^2$.
   (c) Using the same pair of axes, draw the graph of $y = 5x + 30$.
   (d) Write the co-ordinates of the point of intersection of the two graphs.
   (e) By drawing a tangent to the curve, estimate the gradient of the graph of $y = 5x^2$ at the point $(1, 5)$.

5. (a) Draw a pair of axes where the x-values range from $^-7$ to $^+7$ and the y-values from $^-20$ to $^+30$.

(b) Draw the graph of $y = x^2 - 20$.

(c) By drawing one straight-line graph to intersect the graph drawn in part (b), solve the equation $x^2 - 20 = 12$.

6. (a) Copy and complete the following table for the equation $y = x^2 + 4x - 6$.

	x	$^-6$	$^-5$	$^-4$	$^-3$	$^-2$	$^-1$	0	1	2	
+	x^2		25		9						+
+	$+ 4x$				$^-12$						+
+	$^-6$	$^-6$		$^-6$	$^-6$					$^-6$	+
	$y = x^2 + 4x - 6$				$^-9$						

(b) Draw a pair of axes as shown, where the x-values range from $^-6$ to 2 and the y-values range from $^-10$ to 6.

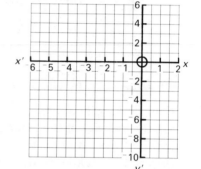

(c) Using the table to help you, draw the graph of $y = x^2 + 4x - 6$.

(d) What is the minimum point for the graph?

(e) At which points does the graph cross the x-axis? (Give the x-values to one place of decimals.)

(f) At which point does the graph cross the y-axis?

(g) Using the graph, find the value of y when $x = {^-3.4}$.

(h) Using the graph, find the values of x when $y = {^-3}$.

(i) Draw the line of symmetry of the graph of $y = x^2 + 4x - 6$.

(j) By drawing a straight line, use the graph to solve the equation $x^2 + 4x - 6 = {^-1}$.

7. (a) Copy and complete the following table for the equation $y = (x + 4)(x - 3)$.

x	$^-7$	$^-6$	$^-5$	$^-4$	$^-3$	$^-2$	$^-1$	0	1	2	3	4	5	6
$(x + 4)$														
$(x - 3)$														
$y = (x + 4)(x - 3)$														

(b) Draw a pair of axes where the x-values range from ⁻7 to 6 (use a scale of 1 cm to 1 unit) and where the y-values range from ⁻15 to 30 (use a scale of 2 cm to 5 units).

(c) Draw the graph of $y = (x + 4)(x - 3)$.

(d) Where does the graph cross the y-axis?

(e) Write the co-ordinates of the points where the graph crosses the x-axis.

(f) By drawing a straight line to cross the graph of $y = (x + 4)(x - 3)$, solve the equation $(x + 4)(x - 3) = 15$.

8. (a) For the equation $y = \frac{6}{x}$, copy and complete the following table.

x	1	2	3	4	5	6
$y = \frac{6}{x}$					1.2	

(b) Draw a pair of axes where both the x- and y-values range from 0 to 6 (use a scale of 2 cm to 1 unit).
Now draw the graph of $y = \frac{6}{x}$ for $1 \leqslant x \leqslant 6$.

(c) Using your graph, estimate a solution of the equation $\frac{6}{x} = 2.4$.

Revision Exercise XX

1. Write inequalities to show the shaded regions:

(a)

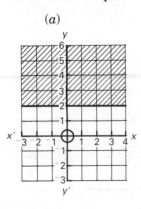

(b)

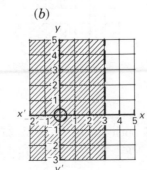

(c)

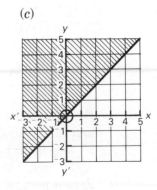

2. For each part of this question, draw a pair of axes as shown. Shade the following regions.
   (a) $y > 1$
   (b) $x \leqslant 1$
   (c) $x > {}^-3$

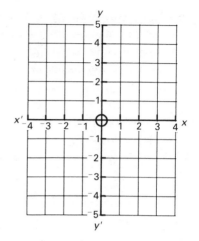

3. For each part of this question, draw a pair of axes as shown for question 2. Leave unshaded the regions described by the following inequalities.
   (a) $x \geqslant {}^-1$ (b) $y \leqslant 3$ (c) $y > x$

4. Use inequalities to describe the unshaded regions in the following diagrams:

(a)   (b)   (c)

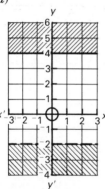 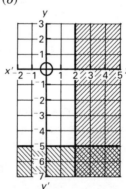 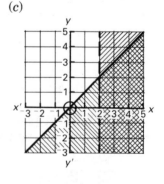

5. (a) Draw a pair of axes as for question 4(c) where the x-values and the y-values both range from ${}^-3$ to ${}^+5$. Shade the part of the diagram that is not described by the inequalities $x < 3$ and $y \geqslant 2$.
   (b) Repeat part (a) for the inequalities $y < x$ and $y \leqslant 3$.

6. The unshaded region in the diagram can be described by three inequalities. What are the three inequalities?

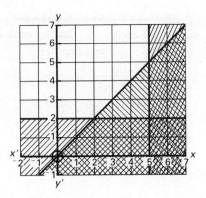

Revision Exercise XXI

1. Draw a pair of axes as shown:
($^-2 \leqslant x \leqslant 14$ and
$^-6 \leqslant y \leqslant 10$)
By drawing two graphs, solve the simultaneous equations:
$$y = x - 4$$
$$x + 2y = 13$$

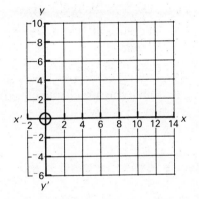

2. For the given rectangle, we can write $3x + 2y = 21$:

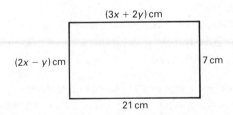

(3x + 2y) cm

(2x − y) cm

7 cm

21 cm

(*a*) Write another equation from the information given on the diagram.

(b) Draw a pair of axes as shown, then draw graphs of the two equations obtained for this problem.

(c) What is the value of x?

(d) What is the value of y?

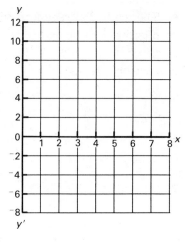

3. Solve the simultaneous equations:

(a) $2x + 5y = 22$
   $2x + 3y = 18$

(b) $5x + 2y = 14$
   $3x - 2y = 18$

4. The sum of two numbers is 10. If the second number is added to twice the first, the answer is 16.
Find both numbers.

5. Solve the simultaneous equations:

(a) $2x + y = 10$
   $8x + 3y = 36$

(b) $3x - 2y = 21$
   $4x + 3y = 11$

Revision Exercise XXII

1. A recipe for flaky pastry uses 200 g plain flour and 150 g butter:
   (a) Write, as a ratio in its simplest form, the amount of butter to the amount of flour.
   (b) How much flour is needed when 450 g of butter is used?
   (c) How much butter is needed when 1 kg of plain flour is used?
   (d) How much butter is needed when 700 g of plain flour is used?
   (e) If the flour and butter used have a total mass of 1.4 kg, how much of each was used?

2. Write the following ratios in their simplest form:
   (a) $45:27$ (b) $1\frac{1}{4}:5:10$ (c) £1.80 to £2.40

3. £3600 was shared amongst three people in the ratio $3:2:4$. Calculate the largest share.

4. If 20 kg of concentrated farm manure is diluted with 80 gal of water, how many gallons are used to dilute 15 kg of the manure?

5. In picking potatoes, 7 people filled several sacks in 45 min. Working at that same rate per person, how long would it take 9 people to fill the same number of sacks?

6. A desk is 29 in high. What is its height in centimetres if 2.54 cm = 1 in?

7. Mrs Kelsall paid 16 692 lire for a meal in Italy. If the exchange rate was 2140 lire to £1 sterling, find the cost of the meal in pounds.

8. A motorist set off on a 171 mile journey at 09.35 and arrived at his destination at 14.05. Calculate the average speed for the journey.

9. An article made of ebony (density 1.2 g/cm³) has a mass of 168 g:
 (*a*) Calculate the volume of the article.
 (*b*) If the article was made of copper (density 8.93 g/cm³), what would it weigh? (Give the answer in kilograms rounded to two decimal places.)

Revision Exercise XXIII

1. (*a*) What is the bearing of Ilfracombe from Dorchester?
 (*b*) What is the bearing of Dorchester from Ilfracombe?

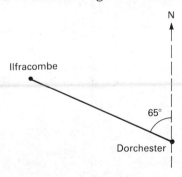

2. A ship sails north-east. At what bearing is it sailing?

3. Port G is 8 km due north of port H. A ship is at S, where the bearing of S from G is 120° and the bearing of S from H is 030°.

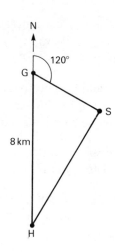

(*a*) Explain why angle GSH is a right-angle.

(*b*) Make a scale drawing. Use a scale of 1 cm to 1 km.

(*c*) By measuring, find the distance of the ship S from:

(i) G   (ii) H

4. The angle of elevation of the top of a tower from a point at one side is 35°, while the angle of elevation from a point at the other side is 25°. The distance between the two points is 125 m. Make a scale drawing. (Use a scale of 1 cm to 10 m.) Find the height of the tower.

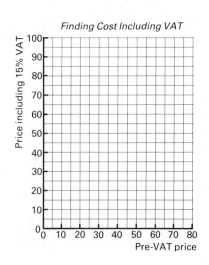

Revision Exercise XXIV

1. Draw a pair of axes as shown.

Finding Cost Including VAT

If the VAT rate is 15%, an article costing £80 before VAT is sold at £92 after VAT has been added. Using this fact, draw a conversion graph to find the VAT inclusive prices from the pre-VAT prices. Use your graph to find:

(a) the price including VAT if the pre-VAT price is:

    (i) £20   (iii) £30

    (ii) £70   (iv) £5

(b) the pre-VAT price when the VAT inclusive price is:

    (i) £69   (iii) £11.50

    (ii) £46   (iv) £57.50

2. A stone fell from the top of a skyscraper. The table shows the distance fallen (in metres) at a given time (in seconds).

Time, t (s)	0	1	2	3	$3\frac{1}{2}$	4	$4\frac{1}{2}$	5	$5\frac{1}{2}$	6
Distance, s (m)	0	5	20	45	61.25	80	101.25	125	151.25	180

(a) Draw a pair of axes as shown. Use a scale of 2 cm to 1 s and 1 cm to 10 m.

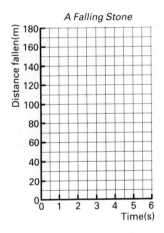

A Falling Stone

(b) Draw a graph using the given table.

(c) from your graph, find:

    (i) the distance fallen in 2.9 s,

    (ii) the time taken for the stone to fall 120 m.

3. 'The inflation rate is still falling, but by less each month.' Which of the graphs on the next page is the best representation of this statement?

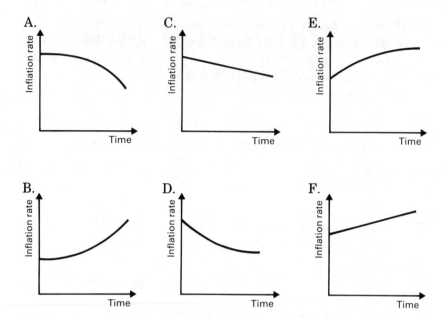

A.

Inflation rate

Time

C.

Inflation rate

Time

E.

Inflation rate

Time

B.

Inflation rate

Time

D.

Inflation rate

Time

F.

Inflation rate

Time

4. 'The inflation rate is falling by more each month.' Which of the six graphs in question 3 is the best representation of this statement?

25 Similarity and Congruency

Similarity

Exercise 1

1.

NOT TO SCALE

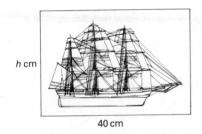

h cm

40 cm

25 cm

50 cm

Two drawings of a clipper ship are shown. One drawing is an enlargement of the other. Calculate the height, h cm, of the smaller drawing.

2. The diagrams show the Brough Superior (1924). This was the first production motor bike that was generally available and had a top speed of more than 100 m.p.h (160 km/h). The 1930 version is shown. One diagram is an enlargement of the other.
Find the missing dimension marked ⬚?⬚ on the small diagram.

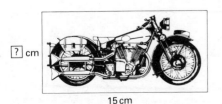

?⬚ cm

15 cm

10 cm

20 cm

3.

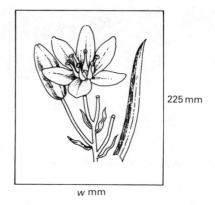

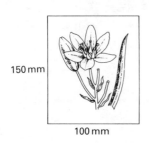

150 mm

100 mm

225 mm

w mm

Two pictures of the Star of Bethlehem are shown. (It is named after its white, star-like flowers.)

(*a*) Calculate the width, *w*, of the larger picture.

(*b*) If the flower in the larger picture is 180 mm tall, how tall is the flower in the smaller picture?

(*c*) In another enlargement of the picture, the full-sized flower is 300 mm tall.

Find the dimensions of this new enlargement.

Exercise 2

In each question, write whether or not the two triangles are similar. Give reasons for your answers.

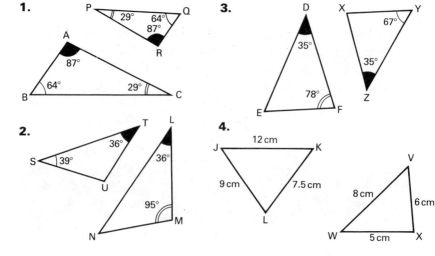

1.

2.

3.

4.

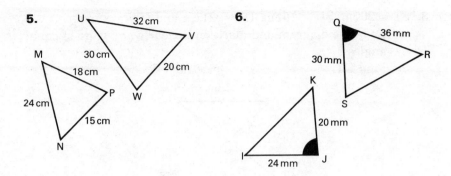

5.

6.

Exercise 3

1. AC = 15 cm, BC = 18 cm, LM = 25 cm and LN = 40 cm. Find:
  (a) AB (b) MN

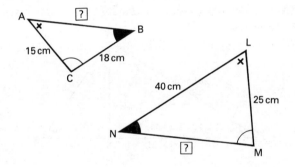

2. ID = 30 mm, DE = 24 mm and JK = 32 mm. Find:
  (a) IJ (b) DJ

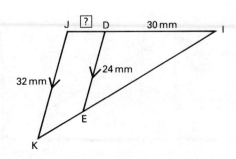

3. ST = 20 cm, SU = 16 cm, UV = 21 cm and UW = 28 cm.
  (*a*) Copy the diagram and mark on it clearly any pairs of equal angles.
  (*b*) Find UT   (*c*) Find VW

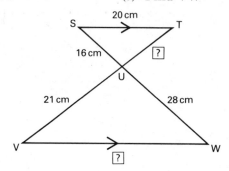

4. In the diagram, the equal angles have been marked. RS = 20 cm, RT = 15 cm and SX = 16 cm. Find:
  (*a*) RX   (*b*) XT

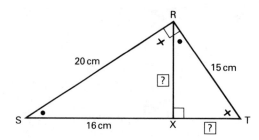

5. AB = 35 mm, AC = 40 mm, CD = 48 mm and CE = 64 mm. Find:
  (*a*) CB   (*b*) DE

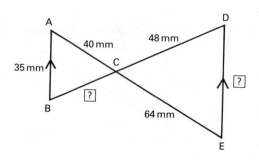

Exercise 4

A **1.** A boat is sailing across a river that is 48 m wide. Although it tries to sail straight across, the current sweeps it downstream so that the path followed is as shown. How far is the boat from the South Bank?

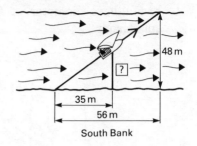

South Bank

2. An end elevation of a small, folding stool is shown. Calculate the length x cm.

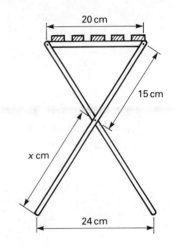

3. A church spire cast a shadow 27 m long, while a 2 m post cast a shadow 1.5 m long. How tall is the church spire?

B **1.** A table is 180 cm long, 90 cm wide and 75 cm high. A model of the table is made to fit inside a doll's house. The model is 6 cm long.
(a) How wide is the model?
(b) Calculate the height of the model.
(c) What scale has been used in making the model?

2. A rectangular lawn is 18 m long and 12 m wide:
(a) If, on a plan, the width drawn is 3 cm, how long should the length be drawn?
(b) If, on the plan, the length drawn is 12 cm, how long should the width be drawn?

3. Two similar jam jars are shown. The larger jar has a base diameter of 75 mm and a height of 120 mm. The smaller jar has a base diameter of 55 mm. Calculate the height of the smaller jar.

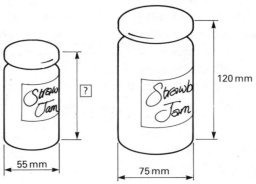

4. Two tubes of toothpaste are mathematically similar in shape. Using the dimensions given in the diagram, calculate the width of the smaller tube.

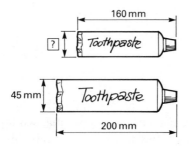

5. How far is it from Sapphire Coast to Paradise View?

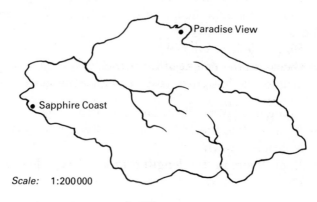

Scale: 1:200 000

> *Reminder*: Two shapes are similar if corresponding angles are equal *and* corresponding sides are in the same ratio.

Exercise 5

1. A square has sides measuring 3 cm. Each side is increased in length by 2 cm. Is the new square similar to the old?

2. A rectangle has sides measuring 5 cm by 3 cm. Each side is increased in length by 2 cm. Is the new rectangle similar to the old?

3. (*a*) Draw any square.
   (*b*) Draw another square with sides that are twice as big.
   (*c*) Are the two squares similar?

4. (*a*) Draw any rectangle.
   (*b*) Draw another rectangle with sides that are twice as big.
   (*c*) Are the two rectangles similar?

5. (*a*) Are all squares similar?
   (*b*) Are all rectangles similar?
   (*c*) Are all triangles similar?
   (*d*) Are all equilateral triangles similar?
   (*e*) Are all isosceles triangles similar?
   (*f*) Are all right-angled isosceles triangles similar?
   (*g*) Are all rhombuses similar?
   (*h*) Are all semi-circles similar?

Exercise 6   Area Ratio

A 1. (*a*) Choose any size of square, then calculate its area.
   (*b*) Double the lengths, then calculate the area of a new square having this new length of side.
   (*c*) Find the ratio:

$$\frac{\text{Area of new square}}{\text{Area of original square}}$$

giving the ratio in its simplest form.

2. Repeat question 1, choosing a different square.

Write what you notice about the answers to part (*c*).

(You may repeat question 1 as many times as you need, choosing a different starting square each time.)

B Repeat part A, using a rectangle instead of a square.

C Repeat part A, using a parallelogram instead of a square.

D 1. The lengths of the sides of two squares are 2 cm and 5 cm:

  (*a*) Calculate the areas of the squares.

  (*b*) Write down the ratio:

$$\frac{\text{Length of side of large square}}{\text{Length of side of small square}}$$

  (*c*) Write down the ratio:

$$\frac{\text{Area of large square}}{\text{Area of small square}}$$

  (*d*) Square the answer to part (*b*), then compare the answer with the answer to part (*c*). Write what you notice.

2. Repeat question 1 for squares with sides measuring 3 cm and 4 cm.

3. The lengths of the sides of two squares are 4 cm and 7 cm. Find the ratio:

$$\frac{\text{Area of the large square}}{\text{Area of the small square}}$$

giving the ratio in its simplest form.

4. (*a*) A rectangle measures 6 cm by 4 cm. Calculate its area.

  (*b*) Calculate the area of a rectangle with sides $1\frac{1}{2}$ times as long as the sides of the rectangle in part (*a*).

  (*c*) Write down the ratio:

$$\frac{\text{Length of large rectangle}}{\text{Length of small rectangle}}$$

(d) Write down the ratio:

$$\frac{\text{Breadth of large rectangle}}{\text{Breadth of small rectangle}}$$

(e) Write down the ratio:

$$\frac{\text{Area of large rectangle}}{\text{Area of small rectangle}}$$

(f) Square the answer to part (c), then compare the answer with the answer to part (e). Write what you notice.

Exercise 7   Volume Ratio

1. The lengths of the sides of two cubes are 2 cm and 4 cm:
   (a) Calculate the volumes of the cubes.
   (b) Find the ratio:

   $$\frac{\text{Length of side of large cube}}{\text{Length of side of small cube}}$$

   giving your answer in its simplest form.
   (c) Find the ratio:

   $$\frac{\text{Volume of large cube}}{\text{Volume of small cube}}$$

   giving your answer in its simplest form.

2. The lengths of the sides of two cubes are 2 cm and 3 cm. Find the ratio:

   $$\frac{\text{Volume of small cube}}{\text{Volume of large cube}}$$

3. The lengths of the sides of two cubes are 3 cm and 10 cm. Find the ratio:

   $$\frac{\text{Volume of large cube}}{\text{Volume of small cube}}$$

4. (a) Find the volume of a cuboid measuring 5 cm by 3 cm by 2 cm.
   (b) Find the volume of a similar cuboid to the one in part (a) but with all the dimensions doubled.
   (c) Find the ratio:

   $$\frac{\text{Volume of larger cuboid}}{\text{Volume of smaller cuboid}}$$

Congruency

Exercise 8

For each question, write whether or not the given pair of triangles is congruent:

1.

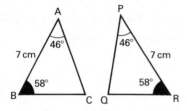

5.

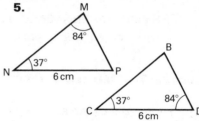

2.

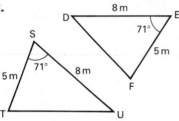

6.

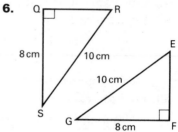

3.

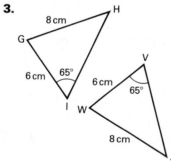

7.

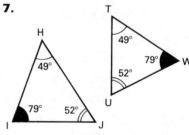

4.

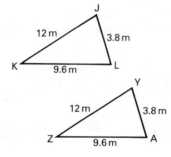

8.

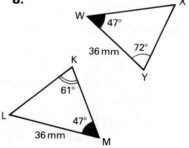

Exercise 9

A For each question, which two of the triangles are congruent?

1.

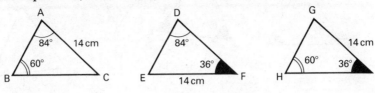

2.

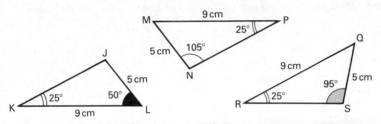

3.

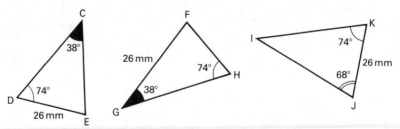

4.

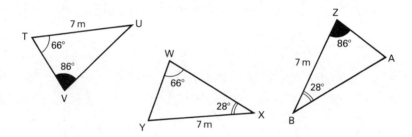

5.

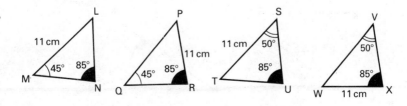

6.

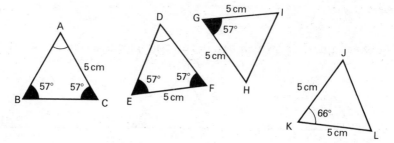

B For each question, name two pairs of congruent triangles:

1.

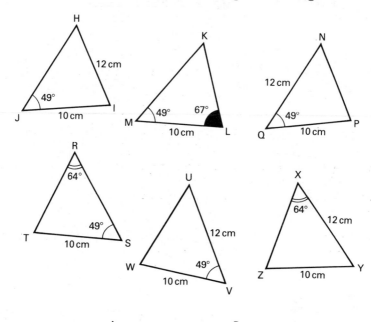

2.

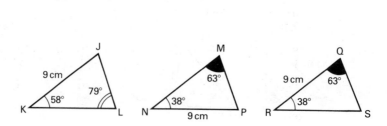

26 Pythagoras

The Theorem of Pythagoras in an Arabic mathematical manuscript from the 14th century. A part is shown in the following diagram.

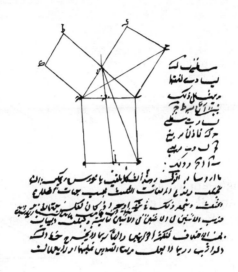

Exercise 1

1. △ABC is right-angled at B.
    AB = 7.2 m and BC = 5.4 m.
    Find:

    (a) the area of the square on side AB,

    (b) the area of the square on side BC,

    (c) the area of the square on side AC,

    (d) the length of side AC.

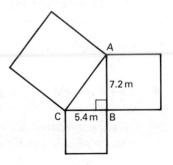

2. △LMN is right-angled at M.
LM = 9.6 cm and LN = 12 cm.
Find:
(a) the area of the square on side LN,
(b) the area of the square on side LM,
(c) the area of the square on side MN,
(d) the length of side MN.

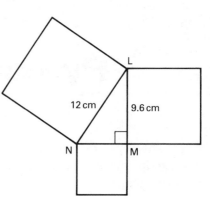

3. △DEF is right-angled at E.
DE = 7 cm and EF = 5 cm.
Find the length of DF correct to two significant figures.

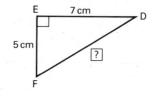

4. △STU is right-angled at T.
ST = 3 cm and SU = 10 cm.
Find the length of TU correct to one decimal place.

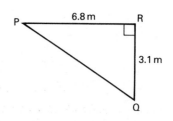

5. △PQR is right-angled at R.
PR = 6.8 m and RQ = 3.1 m.
Find the length of PQ correct to one decimal place.

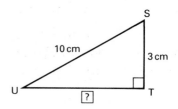

6. △XYZ is right-angled at Y.
XZ = 15 cm and XY = 8.6 cm.
Find the length of YZ correct to three significant figures.

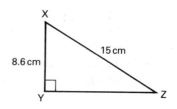

Exercise 2

1. Calculate the length of the bar supporting the inn sign. Use the measurements in the diagram and give the answer correct to the nearest centimetre.

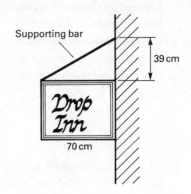

Supporting bar

39 cm

Drop Inn

70 cm

2. A farmer wanted to fence the triangular piece of land shown.
   Calculate the total length of fencing needed, giving your answer to the nearest metre.

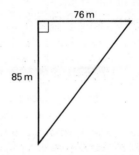

76 m

85 m

3. The height of a loft is 1.8 m. It is 7 m wide. Calculate the length of the sloping roof.

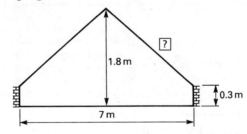

?

1.8 m

0.3 m

7 m

4. Calculate the perimeter and the area of each field:

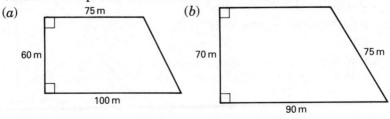

(a)

75 m

60 m

100 m

(b)

70 m

75 m

90 m

5. A shop blind is 4 m long. Using the distances given in the diagram, calculate:
   (a) the width of the blind,
   (b) the area of canvas used in making the blind.

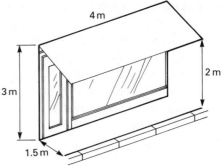

6. The diagram shows a tiled porch roof. Using the lengths given in the diagram, calculate the value of x.

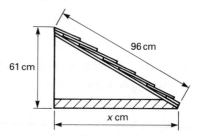

7. A 4.8 m ladder is placed against a garage as shown. Using the dimensions given, calculate the amount by which the top part of the ladder is above the top edge of the wall of the garage.

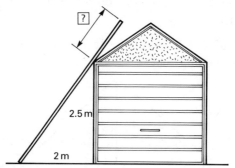

8. A ship sailed 46 km due east, followed by a journey of 58 km due north. How far would the ship have sailed if it had sailed a direct route?

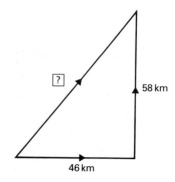

9. A clothes prop is 3 m long. If the bottom of the prop is placed on level ground, 1.9 m from a point directly under the washing line, how far is the washing line above the ground at the position where the clothes prop meets it?

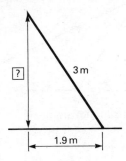

10. A 14 ft ladder is placed against the wall of a house. The foot of the ladder is on level ground and is 4 ft from the wall. A house window in that wall is just above the ladder, and is 15 ft from the ground. How far is the ladder below the window?

(*a*) Give the answer in feet correct to two decimal places.

(*b*) Give the answer in feet and inches correct to the nearest inch. (12 in = 1 ft.)

Exercise 3

Calculate the length marked with a question mark. Explain the method used.

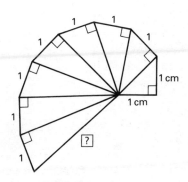

329

Exercise 4

A **1.** Draw any obtuse-angled triangle.

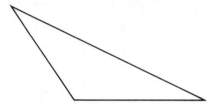

    2. Measure all three sides.

    3. Square the long side.

    4. Square the two short sides, then add the two answers.

    5. Compare the square of the long side (the answer to question 3) with the sum of the squares of the other two sides (the answer to question 4).
Write what you notice.

    6. Repeat questions 1 to 5 as many times as you need, using a different obtuse-angled triangle each time, until you notice a special property in question 5.

B Repeat part A using acute-angled triangles.

C In each question, three sides of a triangle are given.
Write whether the triangle is right-angled, acute-angled or obtuse-angled.

    1. 15 cm, 39 cm, 36 cm

    2. 8 m, 9 m, 13 m

    3. 15 m, 12 m, 9 m

    4. 18 m, 7 m, 16 m

    5. 6 cm, 10 cm, 9 cm

    6. 3 cm, 4 cm, 5 cm

Exercise 5

1. Consider a triangle with sides twice as long as those of the given triangle.

   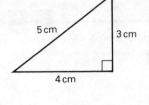

   (a) Square all three sides of the new triangle.

   (b) Add the two smaller squares.

   (c) Write what you notice.

2. Consider a triangle with sides three times as long as the 3, 4, 5 triangle.

   Repeat question 1 for this new triangle.

3. Multiply all three sides of the 3, 4, 5 triangle by any number you wish, then repeat question 1 for a triangle having sides with these calculated sizes.

27 Trigonometry

Exercise 1

A Find, to three decimal places:

1. $\tan 38°$

2. $\sin 61°$

3. $\cos 12°$

4. $\tan 27.9°$

5. $\sin 75.2°$

6. $\cos 34.5°$

7. $\sin 4.6°$

8. $\cos 63.1°$

B Find to three decimal places:

1. (a) $\sin 24°$ (b) $\cos 66°$

2. (a) $\sin 75°$ (b) $\cos 15°$

3. (a) $\sin 33°$ (b) $\cos 57°$

4. (a) $\sin 17°$ (b) $\cos 73°$

5. (a) $\sin 36.5°$ (b) $\cos 53.5°$

6. (a) $\sin 82.4°$ (b) $\cos 7.6°$

7. (a) $\sin 42.1°$ (b) $\cos 47.9°$

8. (a) $\sin 54.9°$ (b) $\cos 35.1°$

C Find angle θ to one decimal place:

1. $\sin \theta = 0.833$ **4.** $\cos \theta = 0.993$ **7.** $\tan \theta = 3.006$

2. $\tan \theta = 2.675$ **5.** $\cos \theta = 0.89$ **8.** $\cos \theta = 0.073$

3. $\tan \theta = 0.642$ **6.** $\sin \theta = 0.314$ **9.** $\sin \theta = 0.693$

Exercise 2

A Write which trig. ratio (sin, cos or tan) should be used in each of the following right-angled triangles in order to find the required side or angle:

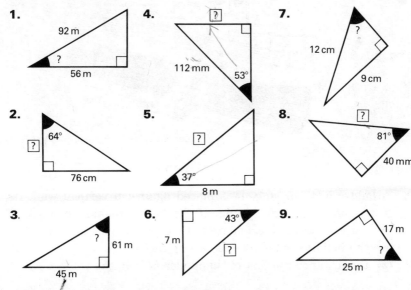

1.
92 m
?
56 m

4.
?
112 mm
53°

7.
?
12 cm
9 cm

2.
64°
?
76 cm

5.
?
37°
8 m

8.
?
81°
40 mm

3.
?
61 m
45 m

6.
43°
7 m
?

9.
17 m
?
25 m

B Calculate the required side or angle in each triangle in part A.

Exercise 3

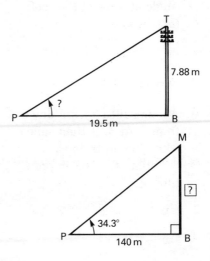

1. A telegraph pole is 7.88 m tall. Find the angle of elevation of the top of the pole from a point on level ground, which is 19.5 m from the bottom of the pole.

T
7.88 m
?
P
19.5 m
B

2. Point P lies on level ground and is 140 m from the bottom of a mast. The angle of elevation of the top of the mast from P, is 34.3°. Calculate the height of the mast.

M
?
34.3°
P
140 m
B

333

3. A ship's gangplank is 5.6 m long. When it reaches from the ship's deck to the dock it makes an angle of 25.4° with the dock. How high is the ship's deck above the dock?

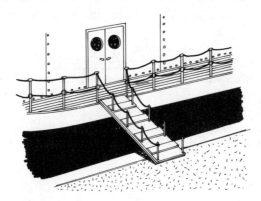

4. A ladder is 4.5 m long. It is placed against a vertical wall. Its foot is on horizontal ground. If the ladder makes an angle of 69° with the ground, calculate to three significant figures:
(a) the height the ladder reaches up the wall,
(b) the distance the foot of the ladder is from the wall.

5. The diagram shows a dormer window. Using the given dimensions, calculate the angle of slope of the roof.

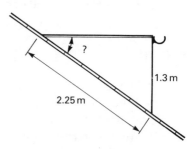

?

1.3 m

2.25 m

6. A ship sailed 7.2 km due east from A to B. It then sailed 8 km due north to C. Calculate the bearing of C from A.

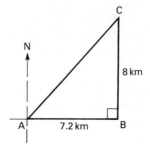

C

N

8 km

A   7.2 km   B

7. Two places, labelled P and Q in the diagram, are 11 km apart. P is due west of Q. A ship S is at a bearing of 063° from P and 333° from Q.

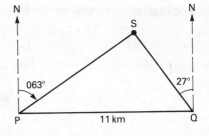

(a) Calculate the angles of triangle PSQ.

(b) Calculate, to the nearest tenth of a kilometre, the distance of the ship S from P.

(c) Calculate, to the nearest tenth of a kilometre, the distance of the ship S from Q.

8. The angle of depression of a buoy from the top of a lighthouse is 7.4°. If the buoy is 400 m from the base of the lighthouse, calculate the height of the lighthouse to the nearest metre.

9. The diagram shows an end elevation of a folding table. Its tubular steel legs are 107.5 cm long, and make an angle of 43.5° with the table top. Ignoring the thickness of the legs and of the top, calculate:

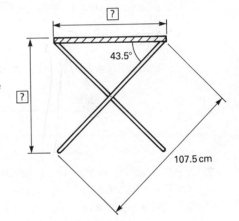

(a) the width of the table top,

(b) the height of the table.

10. From a point that is 157 m from the foot of a tower, the angles of elevation of the top and bottom of a flagpole are 29° and 27° respectively. Calculate the length of the flagpole.

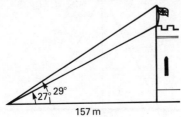

Exercise 4

1. Using the information given in the diagram, calculate:
   (a) the size of angle ABP,   (b) the length of PC.

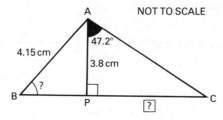

2. ABCD is a parallelogram. AB = 9 cm, AD = 6 cm and angle D = 76°. AE is perpendicular to DC.
   Calculate, giving your answers correct to two significant figures:
   (a) the length of AE,
   (b) the area of parallelogram ABCD.

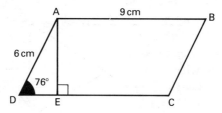

3. XYZ is an isosceles triangle in which YX = YZ = 77 mm and ∠XYZ = 38°. Calculate, correct to two significant figures:
   (a) the length of YP,
   (b) the length of XP,
   (c) the area of the isosceles triangle XYZ.

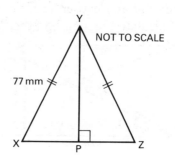

4. ABCD is a field. BD = 130 m, ∠ADB = 24° and ∠CBD = 58°.
Calculate, correct to two significant figures:

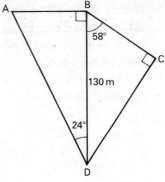

(*a*) the length of AB,
(*b*) the length of BC,
(*c*) the length of CD,
(*d*) the area of triangle ABD,
(*e*) the area of triangle BCD,
(*f*) the total area of field ABCD.

5. In rectangle ABCD, AB = 10 cm and BC = 7 cm. Calculate:
(*a*) angle BAC,
(*b*) the acute angle between the diagonals of the rectangle.

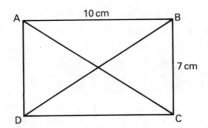

6. TA and TB are tangents to a circle centre O. The tangents are
20 cm in length and the circle has a radius of 7 cm.

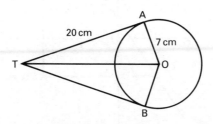

Calculate the angle between the tangents (∠ATB in the
diagram), giving your answer correct to one place of decimals.

7. AB is a diameter of circle, centre O. AP and AQ are chords of the circle and AP = AQ = 7 cm. PQ is perpendicular to AB and crosses AB at X, ∠PAB = 37°.

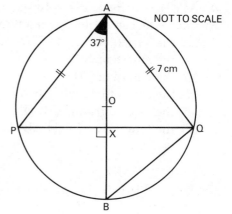

NOT TO SCALE

(a) Find the size of:
- (i)   ∠AQB
- (ii) ∠AQP
- (iii) ∠BQX
- (iv) ∠QBX

(b) If AQ = 7 cm, calculate, correct to two significant figures, the length of:

(i) QX   (ii) AX   (iii) BX   (iv) diameter AB

8. A is the point (⁻2, ⁻2) and B the point (4, 7):
- (a) Write the co-ordinates of C.
- (b) BC is 9 units long. How long is AC?
- (c) Find the value of tan BÂC.

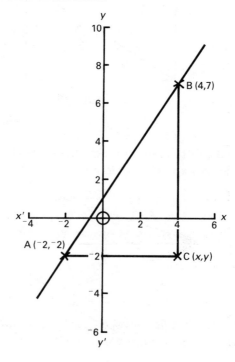

Exercise 5

A For each question, find the value of x:

1. $4 = \dfrac{8}{x}$ **3.** $5 = \dfrac{20}{x}$ **5.** $6 = \dfrac{18}{x}$ **7.** $8 = \dfrac{32}{x}$

2. $3 = \dfrac{12}{x}$ **4.** $2 = \dfrac{10}{x}$ **6.** $2 = \dfrac{18}{x}$ **8.** $3 = \dfrac{30}{x}$

B For each question, find the value of y giving the answer correct to two significant figures:

1. $y = \dfrac{2}{\tan 51°}$ **4.** $y = \dfrac{7}{\cos 21°}$ **7.** $y = \dfrac{1.2}{\cos 58.3°}$

2. $y = \dfrac{3}{\tan 76.5°}$ **5.** $y = \dfrac{4}{\cos 81.2°}$ **8.** $y = \dfrac{6.9}{\sin 30.7°}$

3. $y = \dfrac{4}{\sin 48°}$ **6.** $y = \dfrac{8}{\tan 16°}$ **9.** $y = \dfrac{7.8}{\sin 57.4°}$

Exercise 6

For each question, calculate the value of x giving your answers correct to two significant figures:

1.
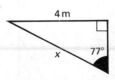

4.
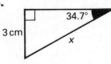

7.
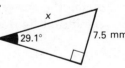

2.
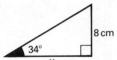

5.
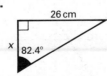

8.
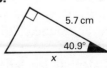

3.
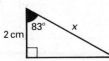

6.
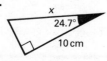

9.
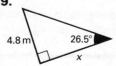

1. Triangle BAC is right-angled
   at A. AP is perpendicular to BC.
   AB = 8 cm and AP = 4 cmd.
   (*a*) Calculate angle ABP.
   (*b*) Calculate BC, giving the
   length correct to three
   significant figures.
   (*c*) Calculate the area of △BAC, giving the answer correct to
   three significant figures.

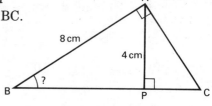

2. A rectanglar field is 100 m
   long. The angle between a
   long side and a diagonal
   is 34°.
   Calculate, to the nearest
   metre, the length of the
   diagonals.

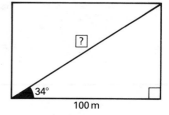

3. A ship sailed on a bearing of
   063° until it reached a point
   B, that was 8 km east of the
   starting point A. Calculate
   the distance travelled AB,
   giving the answer to three
   significant figures.

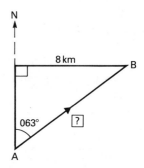

4. A ladder is placed against a
   vertical wall with its foot on
   level ground, 1.25 m from the
   wall.
   Calculate the length of the
   ladder if it makes an angle
   of 71.3° with the ground. Give
   your answer in metres,
   correct to one decimal place.

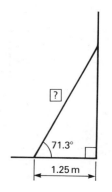

5. A ship sailed due west from P. It then turned and sailed 20 km due south until it reached Q, which was at a bearing of 240° from P. Calculate:

(a) the distance sailed due west,

(b) the total distance sailed.

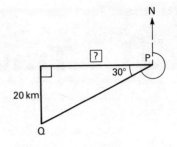

28 Travel Graphs

Exercise 1

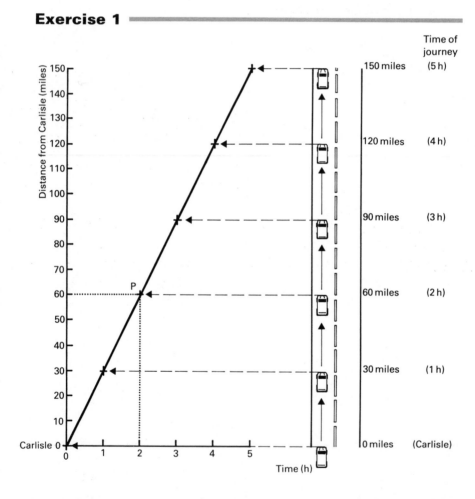

On the right of the diagram above, a car is travelling at a steady 30 m.p.h. The distance/time graph shown on the left illustrates the journey. The point labelled P shows that the car is 60 miles from its starting place (Carlisle), after 2 h.

342

Using the graph, find:

1. the distance the car is from Carlisle after:
    (*a*) 4 h   (*b*) 5 h   (*c*) $1\frac{1}{2}$ h

2. the time taken for the car to travel:
    (*a*) 90 miles   (*b*) 75 miles   (*c*) 135 miles

Exercise 2

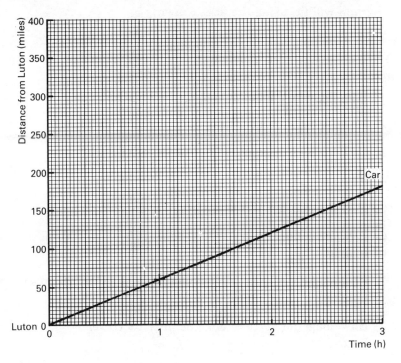

A **1.** Copy the pair of axes shown.

    2. A car set off from Luton and travelled at a steady 60 m.p.h. This is shown on the graph above (60 miles after 1 h, 120 miles after 2 h, 180 miles after 3 h). Copy the graph and label it as shown.

B Each of the following left Luton at the same time as the car in part A and followed the same route. Draw a graph for each journey using the same pair of axes as for part A. Label each graph.

1. a bus travelling at a steady 30 m.p.h.,

2. a cyclist travelling at a steady 10 m.p.h.,

3. a pedestrian walking at a steady 4 m.p.h.,

4. a motorcyclist travelling at a steady 70 m.p.h.,

5. a helicopter flying at a steady 100 m.p.h.,

6. an aeroplane flying at a steady 400 m.p.h. (only part of this graph will fit, using the axes drawn).

C Answer the following questions using the graphs drawn in parts A and B:

1. How far was the bus from Luton after 2 h?

2. How far was the helicopter from Luton after 30 min?

3. How far was the cyclist from Luton after $2\frac{1}{2}$ h?

4. How far was the car from Luton after 1 h 40 min?

5. How far was the aeroplane from Luton after 45 min?

6. How long did it take for the helicopter to be 150 miles from Luton?

7. How long did it take for the motorcyclist to be 175 miles from Luton?

8. How long did it take for the bus to travel 40 miles from Luton?

9. How long did it take for the pedestrian to walk 11 miles from Luton?

10. Explain how to recognise, from a distance/time graph, which of the journeys shown is the fastest.

11. How far was the motorcyclist ahead of the car after 2 h?

12. How far was the motorcyclist ahead of the bus after $1\frac{1}{2}$ h?

13. How far behind the car was the bus after:
    (a) $2\frac{1}{2}$ h?   (b) 1 h 50 min?

344

14. How far was the aeroplane ahead of the helicopter after 24 min?

15. (*a*) How far behind the cyclist was the pedestrian after $2\frac{1}{4}$ h?
(*b*) How many minutes after the cyclist did the pedestrian reach a point that was 5 miles from Luton?

16. After how long was the bus ahead of the cyclist by:
(*a*) 30 miles?   (*b*) 18 miles?

Exercise 3   Finding the Speed

A For each journey shown, find the speed in the units stated:

1.

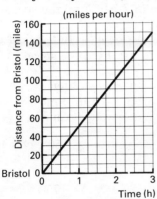

2.

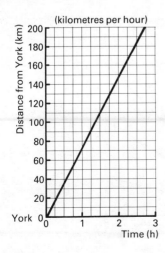

3.

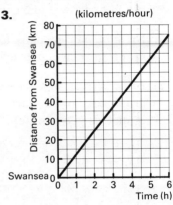

4.

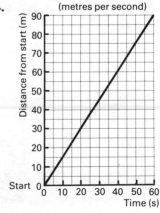

5.

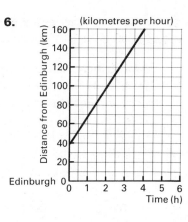

6.

B **1.** Draw a pair of axes as for question 2 of section A. Draw a graph to show a journey of $175\,km$ in $2\frac{1}{2}\,h$. Find the speed.

2. Draw a pair of axes as for question 3 of section A. Draw a graph to show a journey of $75\,km$ in $5\,h$. Find the speed.

3. Draw a pair of axes as for question 5 of section A. Draw a graph to show a journey of $1275\,m$ in $8\frac{1}{2}\,min$. Find the speed in metres per minute.

Exercise 4

1.

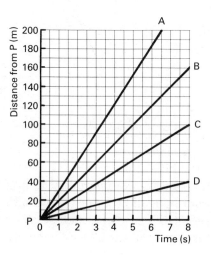

The bottom graph on the previous page shows four different journeys starting at P at the same time:

(a) Which journey is the fastest?
(b) Which is the third fastest journey?
(c) On which journey is 100 m travelled in 5 s?
(d) After 6 s, how many more metres have been travelled on journey C than on D?
(e) Write the speeds of all four journeys in metres per second.
(f) Write the speeds of all four journeys in kilometres per hour.
(g) How many times faster is B than D?
(h) Write the ratio of the speeds of A to C in its simplest form.

2. A cyclist left Ingle at 3 o'clock to cycle to Moreton. Later, a car driver left Ingle for Wakeham.

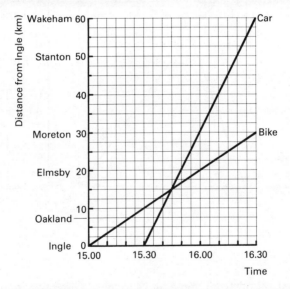

(a) At what time did the car leave Ingle?
(b) What was the car's speed?
(c) What was the bike's speed?
(d) At what time did the car overtake the bike?
(e) How far from Ingle did the car overtake the bike?
(f) Who arrived at Elmsby first, the car driver or the cyclist?
(g) At what time was the car 20 km ahead of the bike?

347

3. The graph and diagram show the journeys of a car C and a bus B. The diagram shows the road positions every 15 min (the times are given next to each vehicle).

(a) Write the distances of the car from Ingle at:
  (i) 10.15   (ii) 10.30   (iii) 10.45

(b) Write the distances of the bus from Ingle at:
  (i) 10.00   (iii) 10.30   (v) 11.00
  (ii) 10.15   (iv) 10.45   (vi) 11.15

(c) Write what you notice about the directions travelled by the car and the bus.

(d) (i) At what time are the car and bus at the same place?
    (ii) How far from Ingle are the car and bus when they are at the same place?

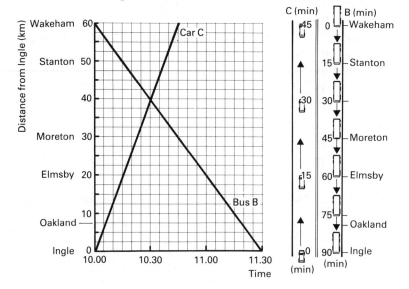

Exercise 5

1. A cyclist set off from home at 12 o'clock. The following graph and diagram show the journey.

(a) How far was the cyclist from home after:
  (i) 15 min?   (iii) 45 min?   (v) 1 h 15 min?
  (ii) 30 min?   (iv) 1 h?   (vi) 1 h 30 min?

(b) Opposite Dorton, what does the horizontal line mean on the graph?

(c) How far is Dorton from the cyclist's home?

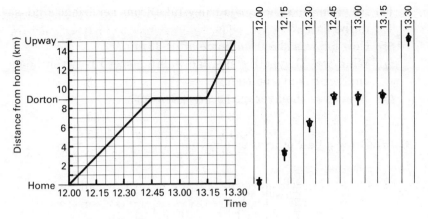

(d) How far is Upway from the cyclist's home?

(e) For how long did the cyclist stop?

(f) What was the cyclist's average speed:
   (i) from home to Dorton?
   (ii) from Dorton to Upway?
   (iii) for the whole journey?

2. Gwyneth walked from home to her friend's house, where she waited for her friend to get ready. They then set off by car to the swimming baths. The graph below shows the journey.

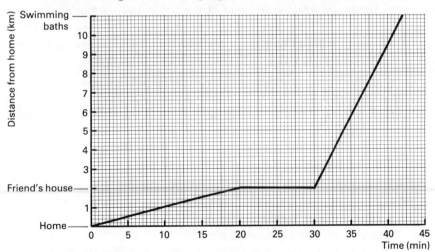

(a) How long did it take her to walk to her friend's house?

(b) How long did she wait at her friend's house?

(c) How far is her friend's house from the swimming baths?

349

(d) How long did the car journey take from her friend's house to the baths?

(e) How far was she from home after 38 min?

(f) What was Gwyneth's average walking speed between home and her friend's house?

(g) What was the average speed of the car?

3. (a) Draw a pair of axes as shown.

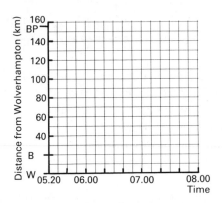

(b) Draw a travel graph from the given information:
A train left Wolverhampton at 05.20 and arrived in Birmingham, a journey of 20 km, after half an hour.
After a stop in Birmingham, the train set off again at 06.25 and continued to Bristol Parkway to arrive there at 07.55 (Bristol Parkway is 155 km from Wolverhampton).

(c) At what time did the train arrive in Birmingham?

(d) How long did the train stop in Birmingham?

(e) How long did the journey take from Birmingham to Bristol Parkway?

(f) How long did it take to travel from Wolverhampton to Bristol Parkway?

(g) How far was the train from Wolverhampton at 07.05?

(h) How far was the train from Wolverhampton one hour after leaving Birmingham?

(i) Calculate the average speed for:
   (i) the journey from Wolverhampton to Birmingham,
   (ii) the journey from Birmingham to Bristol Parkway,
   (iii) the whole journey from Wolverhampton to Bristol Parkway.

1. The graph shows a flight made by an aeroplane:

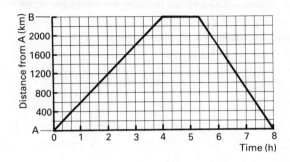

(a) What was the aeroplane's average speed on the outward flight (Airport A to B)?

(b) How long was spent at airport B?

(c) How long was the return flight?

(d) What was the average speed of the return flight?

2. Mrs McKay set off from Glasgow at 10 o'clock to go to Perth. She stopped for petrol on the way. After visiting her friend in Perth, she returned home to Glasgow.

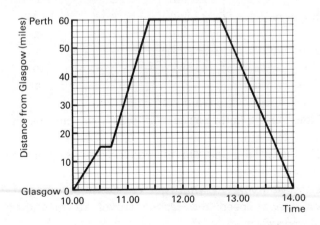

(a) (i) At what time did Mrs McKay stop for petrol?

  (ii) What was Mrs McKay's average speed from home to the service station?

(b) How long did Mrs McKay stop at the service station for petrol?

(c) (i) After leaving the service station, how long did it take Mrs McKay to get to Perth?
  (ii) How far was the service station from Perth?
  (iii) What was Mrs McKay's average speed from the service station to Perth?
(d) How long did Mrs McKay spend in Perth?
(e) (i) How long did her journey home take?
  (ii) What was Mrs McKay's average speed for her journey home?

3. David cycled from his home in Morcott to visit his uncle in Somerby, a distance of 20 km. He left home at 1 o'clock and made one short stop on the way.
The graph shows the journey to his uncle's house.

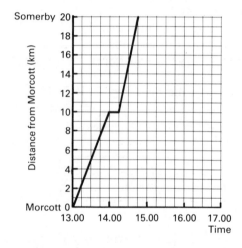

(a) Copy the graph but use a scale of 1 cm to 15 min and 1 cm to 1 km.
(b) For how long did David stop on the way to his uncle's house?
(c) After stopping, at what time did David set off again?
(d) At what speed did David travel to his uncle's after stopping?
(e) David stayed at his uncle's for 45 min before setting off for home:
  (i) At what time did he leave Somerby?
  (ii) Draw a line on your graph to represent David's stay at his uncle's.

(*f*) David set off from Somerby at a steady 16 km per hour, but after quarter of an hour he had a puncture which took 21 min to repair. He then cycled home at 20 km per hour.

   (i) Complete the travel graph to show the rest of David's journey.

   (ii) At what time did David arrive back in Morcott?

4. Kevin cycled to Gloria's house, left his bike there and walked with Gloria to a disco. After leaving the disco, they slowly walked back to Gloria's house then, after saying goodnight, Kevin cycled home. The following graph shows Kevin's journey.

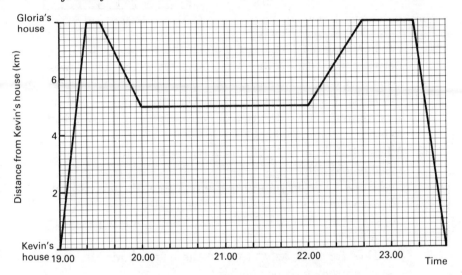

(*a*) (i) How long did it take Kevin to cycle to Gloria's house?

    (ii) What was his average speed in cycling to Gloria's?

(*b*) How long did he wait at Gloria's?

(*c*) (i) How far did they walk to the disco?

    (ii) How long did it take them to walk to the disco?

(*d*) For how long were they at the disco?

(*e*) (i) How long did it take to walk from the disco to Gloria's house?

    (ii) At what time did they arrive at Gloria's house?

(*f*) (i) How long did Kevin stay at Gloria's house before setting off for home?

    (ii) At what time did Kevin set off for home?

(*g*) How long did it take Kevin to cycle home?

1. (*a*) Copy the graph which shows Mrs Baird's journey by car between Ashton and Belton.

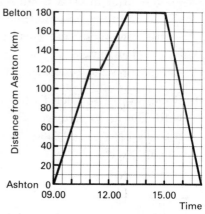

(*b*) For how long did Mrs Baird stop on the way to Belton?

(*c*) Between what times was Mrs Baird travelling her slowest average speed?

(*d*) If Mrs Baird's car averaged 14 km per litre of petrol, find the least number of whole litres of petrol needed to travel from Ashton to Belton and back again.

(*e*) A bus left Ashton at 12.30 and travelled to Belton at a steady speed of 45 km/h:

   (i) Draw a line on your graph to represent the bus journey.

   (ii) At what time did the bus arrive in Belton?

   (iii) At what time would Mrs Baird and the bus pass each other?

   (iv) How far from Ashton would the bus and Mrs Baird be when they pass each other?

2.

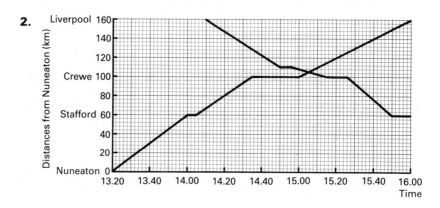

The previous graph shows the journeys of two trains:
(a) One train leaves Nuneaton:
    (i) Where does the other train leave?
    (ii) What is the destination of the train in part (i)?
(b) Describe the journeys of both trains, mentioning times, distances and average speeds.
(c) (i) At what time do the two trains pass each other?
    (ii) How far are the trains from Nuneaton when they pass each other?
(d) Find the average speed of the journey from:
    (i)   Nuneaton to Crewe,
    (ii) Nuneaton to Liverpool,
    (iii) Liverpool to Stafford.

Exercise 8 Acceleration and Deceleration

A For each graph shown, write whether it shows an acceleration, a deceleration or neither:

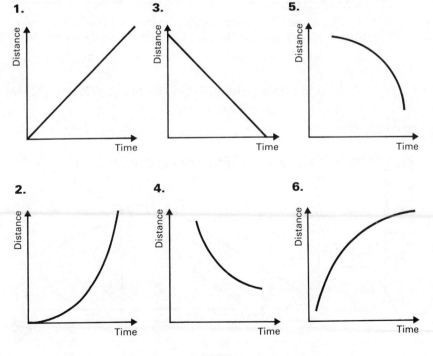

1.

3.

5.

2.

4.

6.

B Each graph below shows a car journey in which the car stops. For each graph, write whether it shows the car stopping 'immediately', 'quickly' or 'gently'.

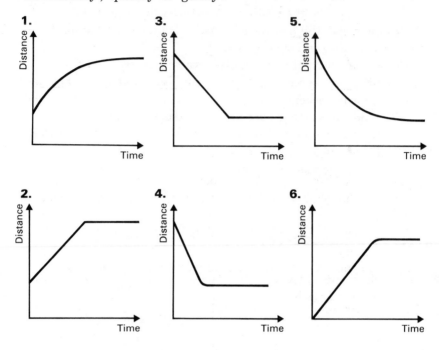

Exercise 9

Explain what is wrong about the following graphs:

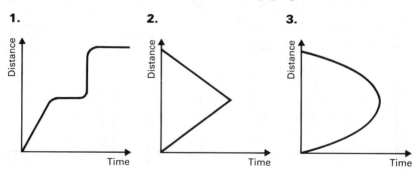

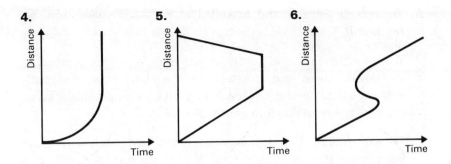

Exercise 10

Here are some travel graphs numbered 1 to 12.

Following the graphs are 7 stories of journeys. These are labelled A to G.

For each graph, find the story that matches it. If there is no suitable story for any particular graph, then write one of your own. (You can be more imaginative with your stories.)

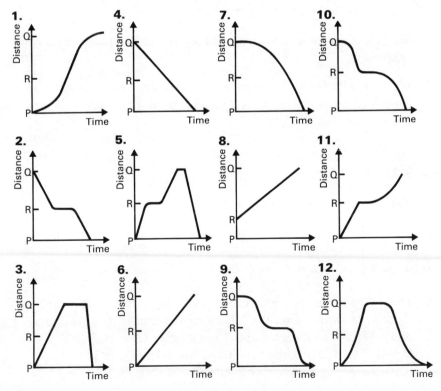

A. We set off from Q and travelled at a steady speed until we reached P.

B. We set off from P and gently accelerated. When we reached Q, we slowed down and stopped. After a short stay, we gently accelerated as we headed back to P. As we approached P, we gradually slowed down to gently stop at P.

C. We set off from P at a steady speed until we reached Q where we quickly stopped. After a short stay, we returned to P at a steady speed but faster than before.

D. We set off from Q and gradually increased our speed. At R, we slowed down to a halt. After a while, we set off again, gently accelerating away from R on our journey to P. At P, we gradually slowed down then stopped.

E. We set off from Q and gradually increased our speed. At R, we slowed down to a halt. After a while, we set off again, gently accelerating away from R on our journey to P. We did not slow down when we reached P.

F. We set off from P and travelled at a steady speed until we reached Q.

G. We set off from P, gradually increasing our speed. We continued on our journey at a steady speed, then gently slowed down to stop at Q.

Exercise 11   M

1. The following map and graph illustrate a car journey from Preston to Swindon on the M6 motorway and on the A417 and A419. Write about each stage of the journey (A to B, B to C, C to D and D to E) using the graph and the map to help you.
   (Give distances, times, speeds and reasons where possible.)

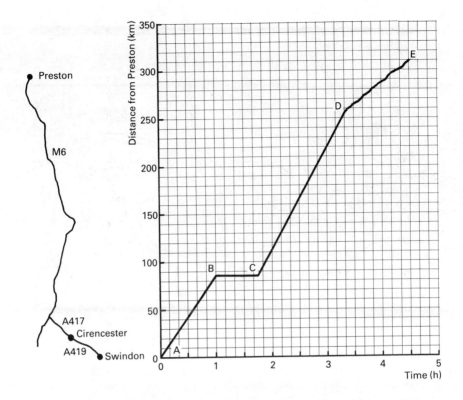

2. Mr and Mrs Rambler walked from Barmoor Castle to Etal along the B6353. The graph shows their journey.

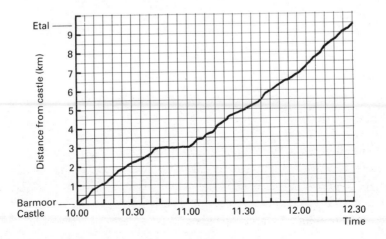

359

(*a*) On a copy of the map, mark a point X where they stopped for a rest.

(*b*) Mark a point Y to show where they were at 12.05.

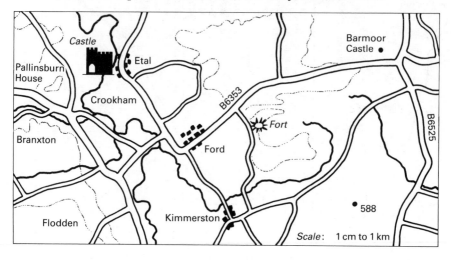

29 Probability

Single Events

Exercise 1

1. (a) Faye spins the spinner.
   What is the probability of
   her getting:
   - (i) a 1?   (iii) a 4?
   - (ii) a 2?   (iv) a 6?

   (b) Reg spins the 5-sided
   spinner.
   What is the probability of
   his getting:
   - (i) a 1?   (iii) a 4?
   - (ii) a 2?   (iv) a 5?

   (c) Who has the greater chance of getting:
   - (i) a 1?   (iii) a 3?
   - (ii) a 2?   (iv) a 4?

2. (a) In throwing an ordinary, unbiased die, what is the
   probability of obtaining a 5?

   (b) In throwing an ordinary, unbiased die 540 times, how many
   times would you expect to get a 5?

3. In throwing an ordinary, unbiased die, what is the probability
   of obtaining a number greater than 4?

4. (a) 100 tickets were sold in a raffle. If Mr Eaton bought 5
   tickets, what is the probability that he wins the only prize?

   (b) Isabel bought 4 raffle tickets, while Rose bought 6 raffle
   tickets. If 120 tickets were sold together, what is the
   probability that one of them wins the only prize?

5. In the game shown, the pointer is spun and comes to rest pointing at a number. What is the probability of the pointer pointing to:

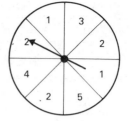

(a) a 1?
(b) a 5?
(c) a 2?
(d) an odd number?
(e) a prime number?
(f) a number less than 4?

6. 18 boys' and 12 girls' names are put in a hat. If one name is drawn at random, find the probability that the first name drawn out of the hat is a girl's name.

7. A letter is chosen at random from the word MATHEMATICS. What is the probability that it is:
(a) an M?
(b) a vowel?
(c) not a T?

8. Three boys take it in turns to toss a coin. What is the probability that the third boy will toss a head?

9. There were some glasses of fruit juice on a table. Half of the glasses contained orange juice, 8 contained pineapple juice, 6 contained apple juice, while the other 4 contained tomato juice. If Mrs Ives picked up one of the glasses without looking, what is the probability that:
(a) the glass contained apple juice?
(b) the glass contained tomato juice?
(c) the glass did not contain pineapple juice?

10. Throughout a month, several reasons were given for lateness. The following table gives the reason and the percentage of pupils who gave that reason.

Reason	Percentage
'I missed the bus.'	40%
'I overslept.'	25%
'The car broke down.'	5%
'My bike had a puncture.'	10%
'I forgot my bag and went home for it.'	20%

What is the probability that the reason given was:

(a) 'I overslept.'?

(b) 'I missed the bus.'?

(c) 'The car broke down.'?

(d) *Not* 'My bike had a puncture.'?

11. If the probability of a bus being late was $\frac{3}{5}$ and the probability of it being early was $\frac{1}{10}$, what is the probability that it arrived on time?

12. There are 10 black, 8 white and 6 red balls in a bag:

(a) What is the probability of taking a white ball out of the bag?

(b) How many black balls would you expect to take out of the bag out of 180 turns, if the ball taken out of the bag is replaced each time?

13. The table gives the ages of pupils in a school.

Age next birthday	12	13	14	15	16	17
Number of boys	50	85	80	76	84	60
Number of girls	90	72	83	81	64	75

If one of the pupils had their photograph printed in their local paper then:

(a) What is the probability that it was a girl who would be 17 years old on her next birthday?

(b) What is the probability that it was someone under 14 years of age?

(c) What is the probability that it was a boy?

Simple Combined Probabilities ━━━━━━━━

Exercise 2   Use of Venn Diagrams ━━━━━━━━

Answer the following questions using the given Venn diagrams which show the numbers in each set:

1. $\mathscr{E}$ = the set of people in a
  room who drink tea or
  coffee or both.
  T = the set of people who
  drink tea.
  C = the set of people who
  drink coffee.

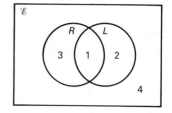

If someone in the room spills a drink, what is the probability that the person drinks:

(a) coffee?   (b) only tea?   (c) tea and coffee?

2. $\mathscr{E}$ = {cars parked on a road}
  R = {red cars}
  L = {2-litre cars}
  If one car is driven off, what is
  the probability that it is:
  (a) a red car?
  (b) a 2-litre red car?
  (c) a 2-litre car that is not red?
  (d) not a red car?
  (e) not a 2-litre car?

3. $\mathscr{E}$ = a set of 5th-year pupils.
  F = the set of 5th-year pupils who take French.
  H = the set of 5th-year pupils who take history.
  If one of the set wrote a brilliant essay, what is the probability that the person takes:
  (a) only history?
  (b) only French?
  (c) both history and French?
  (d) either history or French?

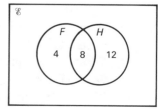

4.

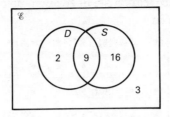

$\mathscr{E} = \{\text{pupils}\}$
$D = \{\text{those in drama group}\}$
$S = \{\text{those in swimming group}\}$
If one of the group can play the guitar, what is the probability that the person is:

(a) in the swimming group?
(b) in the swimming group and the drama group?
(c) in either the swimming group or the drama group?
(d) neither in the swimming group nor the drama group?

Possibility Spaces

A spinner has the numbers 1, 2, 3, 3, 4, 5, 5, 6 on it, while another has the numbers 2, 2, 3, 4, 4, 4, on it. If the spinners are spun and their totals noted, one way of recording the results is to use a *possibility space* (sometimes called a *sample space* or an *outcome space*, or a *probability space*).

A possibility space showing the totals for the two spinners is given.
It has 48 points.

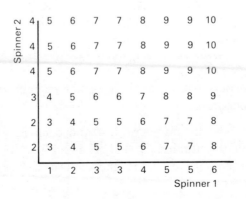

The possibility space can also be drawn using dots. (The totals need not be written in.)

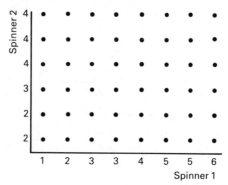

The possibility space can be used to find probabilities.

e.g. Using the two spinners mentioned above, find the probability of obtaining a total of 7.

The probability of a total of 7 = $\dfrac{11}{48}$

(The diagram shows that 11 of the 48 possible outcomes have a total of 7.)

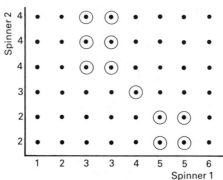

Exercise 3

For each question, use a possibility space to help you to find the required probabilities:

1. A spinner has the numbers 3, 4 and 5 on it, while a second spinner has the numbers 3, 3, 3, 4, 5 and 5 on it.
   If the two spinners are spun, find the probability of obtaining a total of 8.

2. A coin was tossed and an ordinary die was thrown:

   (a) Copy and complete the diagram.

	1	2	3	4	5	6
H				H4		
T						

   (b) Find the probability of getting:

      (i)   a head *and* a 2,

      (ii)   a tail *and* a number bigger than 4,

      (iii)   a head *and* a prime number,

      (iv)   a head *and* a factor of 12,

      (v)   either a tail *or* a 5 *or* both,

      (vi)   either a tail *or* a 5 but not both.

3. There were two bags of marbles. The first bag contained 2 red, 3 blue and 1 green while the second bag contained 1 red, 2 blue and 1 green. A marble was removed from each bag.

   (a) Copy and complete the diagram.

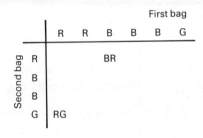

   (b) Find the probability of:

      (i)   2 red,

      (ii)   2 blue,

      (iii)   a red and a blue,

      (iv)   a red followed by a blue,

      (v)   a blue followed by a red.

4. A coin was tossed and a spinner containing the numbers 0, 1, 3, 4 and 8 was spun:

   (a) Draw a possibility space diagram.

   (b) Find the probability of getting:

      (i)   a tail and a 4,

      (ii)   a tail and an odd number,

      (iii)   a head and a number less than 4,

      (iv)   either a head *or* a 3 or both.

Use of the Multiplication Law for Independent Events

A spinner has the numbers 1, 2, 3 and 4 on it, while a second spinner has the letters P, Q and R on it.

		First spinner			
		1	2	3	4
Second spinner	P	1P	2P	3P	4P
	Q	1Q	2Q	3Q	4Q
	R	1R	2R	3R	4R

The possible outcomes are shown in the possibility space.

For the first spinner, $p(3) = \frac{1}{4}$.

[*Note* $p(3)$ means 'the probability of getting a 3'.]

For the second spinner, $p(R) = \frac{1}{3}$.

From the diagram:

$$p(3 \; and \; R) = \frac{1}{12} = \frac{1}{4} \times \frac{1}{3} = p(3) \times p(R)$$

[*Note* $p(3 \; and \; R)$ means 'the probability of getting a 3 *and* an R.' $p(3 \; and \; R)$ can also be written as $p(3 \cap R)$.]

In general, if A and B are two independent events (that is, the outcome of one does not affect the outcome of the other):

$$p(A \; and \; B) = p(A) \times p(B)$$

which can be written as

$$p(A \cap B) = p(A) \times p(B)$$

Also, for more than two *independent* events:

if p_1, p_2, p_3, ... are the separate probabilities, then the probability that *all* the events will occur $= p_1 \times p_2 \times p_3 \times \ldots$

e.g. 1   A coin and an ordinary die are tossed, find the probability of:

(*a*) a head and a 3,

(*b*) a tail and an even number.

(*a*) $p(H) = \frac{1}{2}$, $p(3) = \frac{1}{6}$

$p(H \; and \; 3) = p(H) \times p(3) = \frac{1}{2} \times \frac{1}{6} = \underline{\underline{\frac{1}{12}}}$

(b) $p(\text{T}) = \frac{1}{2}$, $p(\text{even number}) = \frac{1}{2}$

$p(\text{T and even number}) = p(\text{T}) \times p(\text{even number})$

$$= \frac{1}{2} \times \frac{1}{2}$$

$$= \underline{\underline{\frac{1}{4}}}$$

e.g. 2   A coin is tossed 3 times, find the probability of getting 3 tails.

$p(\text{T}) = \frac{1}{2}$

Since the tosses of 3 coins are independent events:

$p(3 \text{ tails}) = p(\text{T}) \times p(\text{T}) \times p(\text{T}) = \frac{1}{2} \times \frac{1}{2} \times \frac{1}{2} = \underline{\underline{\frac{1}{8}}}$

Exercise 4

1. (a) A card is drawn from a pack of 52 cards. What is the probability that it is a heart?
   (b) A coin is tossed. What is the probability of a head?
   (c) A card is drawn from a pack of 52 cards at the same time as a coin is tossed. What is the probability that the card is a heart and the coin shows a head?

2. If there is an equal chance of a mother giving birth to a boy or a girl, what is the probability of:
   (a) a boy being born?
   (b) two children being born who are both girls?

3. On any given day, the probabilities that Eric and Peter will be wearing brown trousers are 0.4 and 0.7 respectively. What is the probability that both will be wearing brown trousers tomorrow?

4. At a certain station, the probability of a particular train arriving late is $\frac{1}{2}$, while the probability of it arriving exactly on time is $\frac{1}{3}$. Find the probability:
   (a) that the train arrives early,
   (b) that the train does not arrive late,
   (c) that the train arrives late on two successive days,
   (d) that the train is late on one day and then early on the next.

5. A coin is tossed 4 times. What is the probability of 4 heads?

6. One bag contains 2 red and 3 blue marbles, while a second bag contains 4 red and 2 blue marbles. If one marble is taken from each bag, find the probability:
(a) that the marble taken from the first bag is red,
(b) that the marble taken from the second bag is red,
(c) that both marbles are red,
(d) that the first marble is blue and the second red,
(e) that the first marble is red and the second blue.

7. The probability that Keith wins the 100 m is $\frac{1}{4}$, and the probability that Julia wins the high jump is $\frac{2}{5}$. What is the probability that:
(a) both of them win their events?
(b) neither of them win their events?

Dependent and Independent Events

A bag contains 3 black and 2 red balls.

If one ball is taken out of the bag, the probability that the ball taken out will be black $= \frac{3}{5}$.

If the ball that was taken out is replaced in the bag, then, if a ball is again taken out of the bag, the probability of a black ball this time is again $\frac{3}{5}$. This result does not depend on the previous outcome. The removals of the balls are two separate and *independent* events.

Consider again a bag containing 3 black and 2 red balls. If a ball is taken out but *not replaced* then 4 balls remain in the bag and two different situations arise:

Either   2 black and 2 red remain
            (if the removed ball was black)
or   3 black and 1 red remain
            (if the removed ball was red)

If a second ball is now removed from the bag, then there are two possible answers for the probability of drawing out a black ball.

In the first case (with 2 black and 2 red balls in the bag), the probability of drawing out a black ball $= \frac{2}{4} = \frac{1}{2}$.

In the second case (with 3 black and 1 red ball in the bag), the probability of drawing out a black ball $= \frac{3}{4}$.

Note that the outcome of the second event is totally *dependent* on the outcome of the first event.

The events are therefore called *dependent events*.

Note that the multiplication law also applies to dependent events.

e.g. What is the probability of drawing out 2 black balls from a bag containing 3 black and 2 red balls if:
(a) the first ball is replaced?
(b) the first ball is not replaced?

(a) The probability that the first ball is black $= \frac{3}{5}$

The probability that the second ball is black $= \frac{3}{5}$

The probability of drawing out 2 black balls $= \frac{3}{5} \times \frac{3}{5} = \underline{\underline{\frac{9}{25}}}$

(b) The probability of the first ball being black $= \frac{3}{5}$
The probability of the second ball being black $= \frac{2}{4} = \frac{1}{2}$

(*Note* Since we require the probability of getting 2 black balls, we only consider the outcomes where black balls are removed.)

The probability of drawing out 2 black balls $= \frac{3}{5} \times \frac{1}{2} = \underline{\underline{\frac{3}{10}}}$

Note also that drawing out 2 balls at the same time gives the same probability as drawing out 2 balls separately without replacing them.

Exercise 5

1. There are 3 red and 5 blue counters in a box. A counter is taken at random from the box and not replaced. A second counter is then drawn. Find the probability that:
(a) both counters will be blue,
(b) both counters will be red,
(c) the first counter will be red and the second counter blue.

2. 5 red, 3 white and 2 blue balls are placed in a bag. A ball is taken at random from the bag.

(a) What is the probability that the chosen ball is blue?

(b) If the first ball chosen is red and is not replaced, what is the probability that the second ball chosen is also red?

(c) What is the probability of the first ball being white and the second ball red, if:

(i) the first ball is replaced?

(ii) the first ball is not replaced?

(d) If the first three balls drawn are red then white then red, and are not replaced, what is the probability of the next ball being red?

(e) If the first nine balls drawn are, in order, red, blue, red, white, white, red, red, white, blue, and are not replaced, what is the probability that the next ball will be red?

3. There are 9 girls' and 3 boys' names in a hat. Two names are drawn out at random and are not replaced.

(a) Find the probability that the first name drawn will be a boy's name.

(b) Find the probability that both names drawn will be boys' names.

4. Two cards are selected at random from an ordinary pack of 52 playing cards and are not replaced. Find the probability that the selected cards are:

(a) both black,

(b) red followed by black,

(c) both spades,

(d) both picture cards.

5. Two people are chosen from a group containing 10 men and 8 women. Find the probability that they are:

(a) both men,

(b) both women.

Use of the Addition Law for Mutually Exclusive Events

If two events can not happen at the same time they are said to be *mutually exclusive*.

For example, if an ordinary die is thrown once, it is impossible to get a 5 *and* a 6 at the same time. So the events of throwing a 5 and a 6, if a die is thrown once, are mutually exclusive.

If a bag contains red beads and blue beads only, it is impossible to take out one bead and for that bead to be red *and* blue (the beads are either red or blue). These events are mutually exclusive.

If two events are mutually exclusive, the probability of *one* of the events occurring is the *sum* of the separate probabilities.
If A and B are two mutually exclusive events:

$$p(A \ or \ B) = p(A) + p(B)$$

which is the same as:

$$p(A \cup B) = p(A) + p(B)$$

For more than two mutually exclusive events, if $p_1, p_2, p_3, \ldots$ are the separate probabilities, then, the probability that *one* of the events will occur $= p_1 + p_2 + p_3 + \ldots$

e.g. An ordinary die is thrown once. What is the probability of scoring either a 5 or a 6?

Probability of scoring a $5 = \frac{1}{6}$
Probability of scoring a $6 = \frac{1}{6}$
Probability of scoring a $5 \ or \ a \ 6 = \frac{1}{6} + \frac{1}{6} = \underline{\underline{\frac{1}{3}}}$

(Sometimes the addition law is called the OR law, while the multiplication law is called the AND law.)

Exercise 6

1. There are 15 British and 5 foreign stamps in a packet. One is taken out at random. What is the probability that it is:
   (a) British?
   (b) foreign?
   (c) either British or foreign? Explain your answer.

2. 3 green, 6 red and 9 blue balls are in a box. One ball is taken out of the box at random. What is the probability that it is:
(*a*) a red ball?   (*b*) either a green or a blue ball?

3. The probability that Len will win the 400 m is $\frac{1}{4}$ while the probability that Glyn will win is $\frac{1}{3}$:
(*a*) Who is most likely to win?
(*b*) If the race did not end in a dead heat, what is the probability that either Glyn or Len won?

4. A spinner has the numbers 2, 3, 5, 6 and 8 on it. If it is spun, what is the probability of getting:
(*a*) a number bigger than 5?
(*b*) either a 3 or a 5?

5. A card is dealt from an ordinary pack of 52 playing cards. What is the probability the card is:
(*a*) either a heart or a club?
(*b*) either a king or a queen?

Use of Tree Diagrams

A train leaving Birmingham, New Street never leaves early. The probability it leaves on time is $\frac{4}{5}$, so the probability it leaves late is $\frac{1}{5}$.

Different examining groups may set out their tree diagrams in slightly different ways. For the train and the given probabilities, three versions of a tree diagram are shown (figs. 1–3).

Fig. 1   Fig. 2

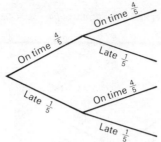

Fig. 3   First day   Second day

Note also that the outcomes and the probabilities of the combined events may be given at the end branches:

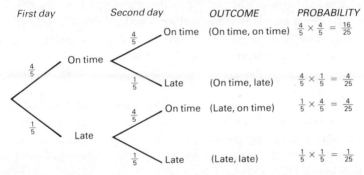

First day	Second day	OUTCOME	PROBABILITY
	On time	(On time, on time)	$\frac{4}{5} \times \frac{4}{5} = \frac{16}{25}$
	Late	(On time, late)	$\frac{4}{5} \times \frac{1}{5} = \frac{4}{25}$
	On time	(Late, on time)	$\frac{1}{5} \times \frac{4}{5} = \frac{4}{25}$
	Late	(Late, late)	$\frac{1}{5} \times \frac{1}{5} = \frac{1}{25}$

Using the tree diagram:

e.g. 1   The probability of the train being late on both days is $\frac{1}{5} \times \frac{1}{5} = \underline{\frac{1}{25}}$.

e.g. 2   The probability of the train being on time on the first day *AND* late on the second day $= \frac{4}{5} \times \frac{1}{5} = \underline{\frac{4}{25}}$.

e.g. 3   The probability of the train being on time on both days *OR* late on both days $= \frac{16}{25} + \frac{1}{25} = \underline{\frac{17}{25}}$.

Exercise 7   M

1. At a particular school, the probability that a pupil lives less than 3 miles from the school is $\frac{1}{3}$, that is, $p(L) = \frac{1}{3}$. No one lives exactly 3 miles from the school, so the probability that a pupil lives more than 3 miles from the school is $\frac{2}{3}$, that is, $p(M) = \frac{2}{3}$.

(a) Copy and complete the tree diagram for two pupils.

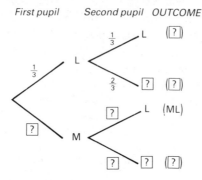

First pupil   Second pupil   OUTCOME

(b) Find the probability of the following events:
   (i) Both pupils live more than 3 miles from the school.
   (ii) The first pupil lives more than 3 miles and the second pupil less than 3 miles from the school.

2. A card was drawn from an ordinary pack of 52 playing cards. It was noted whether or not a heart was obtained. The card was *returned* to the pack. A card was once again drawn, and again it was noted whether or not it was a heart before it was returned to the pack.
   (a) Copy and complete the tree diagram to show all the outcomes and probabilities.
   (b) Find the probability of each of the following events:
      (i) two hearts,   (ii) no hearts.

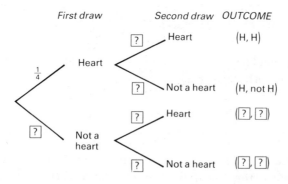

First draw   Second draw   OUTCOME

3. Repeat question 2, but this time after the first card is removed from the pack, it is *not replaced* before a second card is drawn.

4. There are two teams, A and B. A has 4 women and 7 men in it, while B has 3 women and 6 men. One person is picked at random from team A and put into team B. One person from team B is then picked at random to start the game.

   (*a*) Copy the tree diagram, then write the probabilities on its branches and fill in the outcomes.

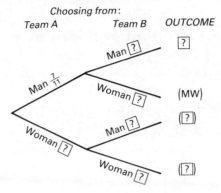

Choosing from:

Team A   Team B   OUTCOME

Man $\frac{7}{11}$

Man [?] → [?]

Woman [?] → (MW)

([?])

Woman [?]

Man [?] → ([?])

Woman [?] → ([?])

   (*b*) What is the probability that a woman is picked to start the game?

5. A bag contained fruit sweets. There were 10 red, 3 green and 2 yellow. $\frac{2}{5}$ of them were hard, while $\frac{3}{5}$ were soft.

   (*a*) Copy the tree diagram, and complete your copy to show all the outcomes and probabilities for a sweet being taken from the bag at random.

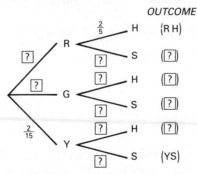

OUTCOME

[?] — R — $\frac{2}{5}$ H (RH)

[?] — S ([?])

[?] — G — [?] H ([?])

[?] — S ([?])

$\frac{2}{15}$ — Y — [?] H ([?])

[?] — S (YS)

   (*b*) Find the probability that the selected sweet is:
   (i)   a soft, red sweet,
   (ii) either a hard, green sweet *or* a soft, yellow sweet,
   (iii) either a soft sweet *or* a red sweet *or* a soft, red sweet.

30 Statistics

Averages: Mean, Median and Mode

Exercise 1

1. Lesley got the following marks in her examinations:

   57, 76, 45, 54, 51, 67, 42

   Calculate her mean mark.

2. Jeff's times in running 400 m were:

   82 s, 80 s, 74 s, 76 s, 71 s, 73 s, 78 s, 74 s

   Calculate the mean value of these times.

3. The number of children in 15 families were:

   2, 1, 3, 2, 5, 1, 3, 4, 2, 2, 3, 2, 4, 3, 5

   Find: (a) the mode,
   (b) the median.

4. Here are the collar sizes of 7 men (in inches):

   15, 16, $15\frac{1}{2}$, 15, $15\frac{1}{2}$, $16\frac{1}{2}$, 15

   Find: (a) the mode,
   (b) the median,
   (c) the mean.

5. Attendance at a concert on 4 nights was 276, 321, 285 and 302. Calculate the average nightly attendance.

6. In a certain household, 9 kg of coffee was used in one year. How many grams is this on average per week? (Give the answer correct to the nearest gram.)

7. The actual number of tissues in each of ten boxes was:

$$198, 203, 197, 201, 199, 204, 198, 199, 198, 203$$

Find:

(*a*) the mode,

(*b*) the median,

(*c*) the mean number of tissues per box.

8. In a diving competition, the scores awarded by 7 judges were:

$$7.5, 7.4, 7.6, 8.2, 8.5, 7.9, 7.8$$

Delete the highest and lowest score, then calculate the mean of the remaining 5 scores.

Exercise 2

1. If the average of 4 numbers is 9, what must the 4 numbers total?

2. The average price of 6 ballpoint pens was 47 p.
What was the total cost of the pens?

3. In 7 examinations, Graham's average mark was 56%:

(*a*) What was Graham's total for the 7 exams?

(*b*) If in an eighth exam, Graham got 64%, find:

(i) the new total mark,   (ii) the new average mark.

4. Ingrid's average mark in seven exams was 63%:

(*a*) Find her total mark.

(*b*) Find her chemistry mark if her other results were:
maths 68%, physics 73%, biology 70%,
French 67%, English language 52%, English literature 62%

5. (*a*) If Janet averaged 48% in six exams, what was her total mark?

(*b*) What mark must Janet get in a seventh exam to increase her average to 49%?

6. For the last 3 h, Mr Kirby had averaged 39 m.p.h. What speed must he average during the next hour for his average to become 42 m.p.h.?

Exercise 3

1. 20 people were asked how much they paid to see a play at a theatre:

    2 paid £10 each
    4 paid £8 each
    10 paid £6 each
    4 paid £5 each

    (a) Calculate the total amount paid by the 20 people.
    (b) Calculate the mean amount paid by the 20 people.
    (c) Which amount is the mode?
    (d) Find the median amount paid.

2. The table shows the number of ink cartridges used in a month by 25 people:

Number of cartridges	6	8	10	12	15	20
Number of people	3	4	9	5	3	1

    Find: (a) the mode,
           (b) the median,
           (c) the mean,
           (d) the range.

3. The table shows the number of hours worked on a Saturday in a factory:

Number of hours	0	1	2	3	4	5	6	7	8	9	10
Number of people	10	0	0	5	2	14	9	4	5	0	1

    Find: (a) the mode,
           (b) the median,
           (c) the mean.

4. The following numbers of goals were scored throughout a season by a local football team:

    2 1 3 0 1 2 4 3 0 2 2 0 3 1 2
    1 4 1 1 1 2 3 0 4 2 6 1 0 2 3

380

(a) Copy and complete the tally chart.
(b) Find:
  (i) the mode,
  (ii) the median,
  (iii) the mean.
(c) What is the range?

Number of goals	Tally	Frequency
0		
1		
2		
3		
4		
5		
6		

Exercise 4

For each question, find:
(a) the modal class,   (b) the class containing the median.

1.

Time taken to travel to school (min)	0–4	5–9	10–14	15–19	20–24	25–29
Number of people	2	10	18	7	6	2

2.

Mass (kg)	0–9	10–19	20–29	30–39	40–49	50–59	60–69
Frequency	3	12	4	9	6	11	15

3.

Age (years)	Frequency
2–5	3
6–9	35
10–13	9
14–17	12
18–19	27
20–25	33

4.

Cost (£s)	Frequency
10–18	6
19–27	8
28–36	20
37–45	9
46–54	15
55–63	17

1. In a survey on teenagers, the statements shown were made to 80 people.
   It was noted whether or not they agreed.
   The bar chart illustrates the results.

   'Teenagers These Days!'

   A   'They don't want to work.'
   B   'They watch too much television.'
   C   'They are bad-mannered.'
   D   'They help with washing-up.'
   E   'They don't like to get up in the morning.'
   F   'They spend too much money.'
   G   'They help other people.'
   H   'They stay out too late.'
   I   'They have plenty of self-confidence.'

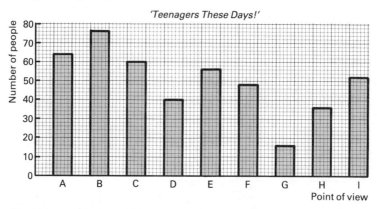

   (a) How many people thought that teenagers watched too much television?

   (b) How many thought that teenagers did not like to get up in the morning?

   (c) What percentage thought that teenagers were bad-mannered?

   (d) What percentage thought that teenagers spent too much money?

   (e) How many thought that teenagers did not stay out too late?

2. The number of examination entries in several subjects are given. Some are given in the table and some in the bar chart.

Subject	Maths	Phys.	Chem.	Biol.	Hist.	Geog.
Number of entries	120		36			75

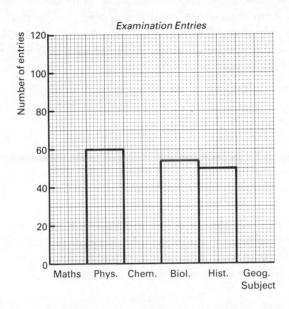

(a) Copy and complete the table and the bar chart.

(b) How many physics entries were there?

(c) How many more candidates were entered for geography than for chemistry?

(d) Which of the subjects had the second smallest number of entries?

(e) If there were 150 examination candidates altogether:
    (i)   What fraction of them were entered for physics?
    (ii) What fraction of them were entered for biology?
    (iii) What fraction of them were entered for history?
    (iv) What percentage were entered for geography?
    (v) What percentage were entered for maths?
    (vi) What percentage were entered for chemistry?

(f) (i)   What was the total number of entries for the three sciences?

(ii) What was the total number of entries for all six subjects?

(iii) What was the probability that a particular candidate was entered for history?

(iv) What was the probability that a particular candidate was entered for one of the three sciences?

(g) If the given entry is typical of the entries for a whole county with 25 000 candidates, how many of the candidates throughout the county would be entered for maths?

(h) (i) If in the following year the number of chemistry candidates increased by 25%, calculate the new number of chemistry candidates.

(ii) If in the following year the number of geography candidates was 20% less, calculate the new number of geography candidates.

(iii) Calculate the total number of entries for the given six subjects for the following year, if the number of entries in maths, physics, biology and history remained unchanged.

3. A deputy head decided to draw a graph to show the examination entries given in question 2. To save time, he drew lines instead of blocks.

Copy and complete the line graph.

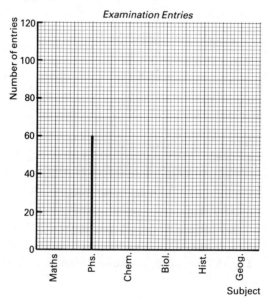

4. The daily travel costs of 40 people are given below (they have been rounded to the nearest 10 p):

70 p	90 p	60 p	90 p	80 p	£1	£1.30	90 p
60 p	80 p	£1	£1.20	70 p	90 p	£1	£1.10
£1.20	80 p	60 p	80 p	90 p	£1	£1.20	80 p
£1	90 p	70 p	90 p	£1.10	80 p	£1.10	£1.20
80 p	60 p	£1.20	£1.30	90 p	£1.10	90 p	£1

(*a*) Copy and complete the tally chart:

Amount	Tally	Frequency
60 p		
70 p		
80 p		
90 p		
£1		
£1.10		
£1.20		
£1.30		

(*b*) Draw a bar chart for the distribution.
(*c*) Write the mode of the distribution.
(*d*) Find the probability that someone chosen at random from the 40 people pays:
    (i) £1.20 per day,   (ii) between 75 p and 95 p daily.
(*e*) Calculate the mean daily travel costs of the 40 people.

5. Fifty people leaving a station's platform were asked how long they had waited to catch their train. The times, to the nearest minute, were:

3	6	21	12	14	7	9	26	15	16
8	10	16	4	2	22	11	8	13	19
5	1	13	6	8	19	5	12	28	7
23	9	18	10	20	6	3	11	12	5
3	14	2	17	27	13	9	8	18	24

(a) Copy and complete the tally chart:

Time (min)	Tally	Frequency
0–		
5–		
10–		
15–		
20–		
25–		

(b) Draw a histogram for the distribution:

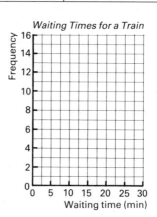

Waiting Times for a Train

6. The graph shows the daily crisp sales at a school:

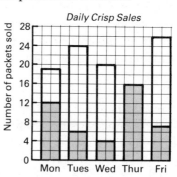

Key:
☐ Salt and Vinegar
▨ Cheese and Onion

Daily Crisp Sales

(a) Calculate the average daily sales for each type of crisp.
(b) If the total sales for the given week were 20% of the total monthly sales, find the total monthly sales.

Exercise 6

1. The table gives the daily TV repairs carried out by a firm:

Day	Mon	Tue	Wed	Thur	Fri
Number of repairs	12	14	11	18	13

Using 🖵 to represent two TV sets, draw a pictogram to represent the information.

2. The pie chart illustrates the annual running costs of Mrs Ellison's car:

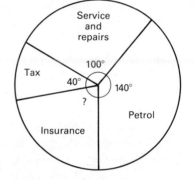

  (a) Calculate the missing angle.
  (b) If car tax was £100, calculate:
    (i)   service and repair costs,
    (ii) petrol costs,
    (iii) the total running costs.
  (c) What fraction of the total running costs was the cost of service and repairs?
  (d) If next year, *all* the costs were increased by 5%, what angle should petrol be on a pie chart?

3. The number of votes obtained by three candidates in an election were as follows:

  N. Archer   15 000
  A. Bowman   9 000
  J. Arrowsmith   6 000

Show these results on a pie chart.

4. The graph shows the number of units of electricity used throughout a year:

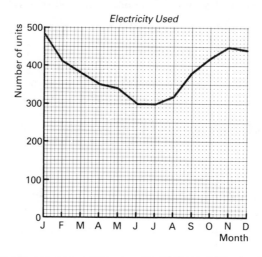

Electricity Used

(*a*) During which months was the least number of units used?

(*b*) What was the least number of units used?

(*c*) How many units were used in the quarter involving the months of February, March and April?

(*d*) Calculate the total cost of electricity for February, March and April, if each unit used cost 5.7 p and there was a standing charge of £6.60.

5. Explain why the diagram shown is misleading:

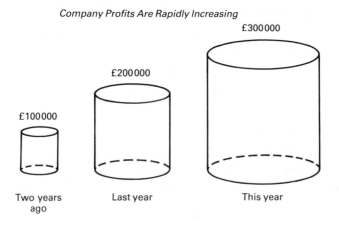

Company Profits Are Rapidly Increasing

£300 000

£200 000

£100 000

Two years ago

Last year

This year

Exercise 7   Scatter Diagrams

The table compares the number of years teachers have taught with the number of grey hairs they have:

Number of years taught	20	4	17	23	37	11	31	38	7	20	34	13	24	30	28
Number of grey hairs	62	16	50	80	128	30	108	140	12	78	130	46	94	110	90

1. Draw a pair of axes as shown and construct a scatter diagram.

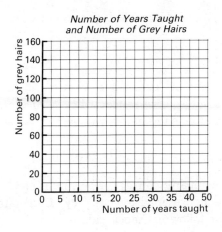

Number of Years Taught
and Number of Grey Hairs

2. Draw a line of best fit.

3. Use your line to estimate the number of grey hairs for a teacher who has taught for:
(*a*) 15 years,   (*b*) 33 years.

4. If a teacher has 62 grey hairs, estimate the number of years he has taught.

31 Insurance and Taxation

Property Insurance

Exercise 1

A Building Insurance

1. An insurance company charges a premium of £2.10 per £1000 insured on its house insurance policy. Calculate the annual premium on the following house values.
   - (a) £30 000
   - (b) £40 000
   - (c) £52 000
   - (d) £108 000

2. An insurance company charges a premium of £1.80 per £1000 insured on its house insurance policy. Calculate the annual premium on the following house values.
   - (a) £20 000
   - (b) £35 000
   - (c) £29 000
   - (d) £72 000

3. A householder insured his house for £32 000:
   - (a) Calculate the annual premium paid if an insurance company charged £1.80 per £1000 insured.
   - (b) If the premium was increased to £1.90 per £1000 insured, how much extra did the householder have to pay?

B Contents Insurance

1. If the annual premium for insuring the contents of a house is £3 per £1000 insured, calculate the annual premium payable on contents valued at:
   - (a) £12 000
   - (b) £14 500
   - (c) £16 200
   - (d) £9800

2. If the contents insurance annual premium is £7.20 per £1000 insured, calculate the annual premium payable on contents valued at:

(a) £9000

(c) £21 300

(b) £13 600

(d) £15 900

3. Mrs Ogden insured the contents of her home for £15 500 and paid an annual premium of £5.60 per £1000 insured. She also paid an annual premium of £5 for her freezer insurance and £8 to insure her bicycle. Calculate the total annual premium paid.

4. Mr Waddington insured the contents of his home for £14 000 and paid an annual premium of £44.80. Calculate the rate of his premium in pounds per £1000 insured.

C Personal Possessions Insurance

1. If the cost of insuring personal possessions is £1.50 per £100 insured, find the annual premium on articles valued at:

(a) £1000

(c) £420

(b) £1200

(d) £260

2. If the cost of insuring personal possessions is £1.25 per £100 of cover, find the annual premium on articles valued at:

(a) £280

(c) £2400

(b) £860

(d) £1360

3. Mrs Pickles insured a ring for £340 at an annual premium of £1.75 per £100 insured. Calculate the total premium paid.

Exercise 2

An insurance company issued the following information:

Section A — Buildings

Premium per £1000 insured   £2.10

Minimum annual premium   £46.20

Section B—Contents

Standard cover Premium per £1000 insured
(minimum annual premium in brackets)

Area A	£2.40 (£16.80)	Area D	£3.60 (£25.20)	Area K	£7.20 (£50.40)
Area B	£2.80 (£19.60)	Area F	£4.40 (£30.80)	Area L	£8.00 (£56.00)
Area C	£3.20 (£22.40)	Area I	£6.00 (£42.00)	Area N	£9.00 (£63.00)

Standard plus cover Premium per £1000 insured
(minimum annual premium in brackets)

Area A	£3.00 (£42.00)	Area D	£4.60 (£64.40)	Area K	£10.00 (£140.00)
Area B	£3.50 (£49.00)	Area F	£5.80 (£81.20)	Area L	£12.00 (£168.00)
Area C	£4.00 (£56.00)	Area I	£8.00 (£112.00)	Area N	£14.00 (£196.00)

Section C—Personal possessions ('All-risks')

	Rating area				
	A (£)	B (£)	C (£)	D (£)	E (£)
Premium for the minimum sum insured of £1000	22.50	25.00	27.50	30.00	37.50
For each £100 insured in excess of £1000 *add*	1.25	1.50	1.75	2.25	3.25

Using the information given:

1. Calculate the insurance premium paid on a house valued at £21 000.

2. Calculate the insurance premium paid on contents valued at £16 500 in area D, if the standard plus policy was taken out.

3. Mrs Mason's jewellery was insured for £2600. What premium did she pay if she lived in rating area D?

4. Calculate the total insurance premium on a house valued at £42 000 and contents insured for £12 000 (area K, standard cover policy).

5. Calculate the total insurance premium on:
A house valued at £26 000,
contents insured for £10 000 (area D, standard plus cover),
personal possessions insured for £1300 (area C for 'all-risks' is the same area as area D for contents).

Motor Insurance

Exercise 3

A 1. A motorist's car insurance totalled £380. However, he was allowed a no-claims discount* of 65%.
  (*a*) Calculate the discount.
  (*b*) Calculate the premium payable.

2. Mr Ford's car insurance was £510. If he was given a no-claims discount of 40%, calculate Mr Ford's premium payable.

3. The insurance on Mrs Morris's car totalled £320. Her no-claims discount was 60%. Calculate the premium payable.

4. The insurance on Conor's motorbike was £166 and he was given 30% discount. Calculate the premium payable.

5. Mrs Fairhurst insured her car for £426.80 less 45% no-claims discount. Calculate her insurance premium for the year.

B 1. Mr Gibbs travelled 10 000 miles last year in his car:
  (*a*) If his car averaged 40 m.p.g.:
    (i) How much petrol did he use?
    (ii) How much did the petrol cost for one year at £1.80 per gallon?
  (*b*) Mr Gibbs's car insurance was £452.40 less 60% no-claims discount. Calculate the premium payable.
  (*c*) (i) Copy and complete:

Tax	= £100
Insurance	= ⍰ [from part (*b*)]
Servicing and repairs	= £320
Petrol costs	= ⍰ [from part (*a*)]
Depreciation	= £1200
Total cost for the year	= ⍰

    (ii) Work out the cost per mile of running the car.

*See the glossary, p. 469.

2. Repeat question 1 using the following information:
The car travelled 13 300 km during the year.
It averaged 14 km to the litre.
Petrol costs were 39.4 p per litre.
Insurance costs were £224.80 less 30% no-claims discount.
Other costs were the same as in question 1.
(Note that throughout the question you need to use litres instead of gallons, kilometres instead of miles and kilometres per litre instead of miles per gallon.)

Life Assurance

Exercise 4

The following tables give the monthly premiums for a life assurance policy that matures after 20 years:

Age next birthday		Monthly premium rate per £1000	Age next birthday		Monthly premium rate per £1000
Male	Female		Male	Female	
up to 30	up to 34	£4.46	43	47	£4.64
31	35	£4.47	44	48	£4.67
32	36	£4.47	45	49	£4.70
33	37	£4.48	46	50	£4.73
34	38	£4.49	47	51	£4.77
35	39	£4.50	48	52	£4.81
36	40	£4.51	49	53	£4.86
37	41	£4.52	50	54	£4.91
38	42	£4.54	51	55	£4.96
39	43	£4.55	52	56	£5.02
40	44	£4.57	53	57	£5.09
41	45	£4.59	54	58	£5.16
42	46	£4.61	55	59	£5.24

A Use the given tables to help with the following:

1. Mr Gornall will be 37 years old on his next birthday:
   (a) If he takes out a life assurance policy for £10 000, find:
      (i) the monthly premium,   (ii) the annual premium.
   (b) His wife, aged 37 years, take out a policy for £9000, find:
      (i) her monthly premium,   (ii) her annual premium.

2. Mrs Stalker is now 48 years old. If she takes out a life assurance policy for £2000, find:
   (a) her monthly premium,   (b) her annual premium.

3. Mr Thornley is 23 years old. If he takes out a life assurance policy for £7500, find:
   (a) his monthly premium,   (b) his annual premium.

4. Mr Gamble's life assurance policy is for £15 000. If he will be 32 years old next year, find:
   (a) his monthly premium,   (b) his annual premium.

B 1. Mrs Bligh's life assurance premium worked out to be £4.47 per £1000 each month. Her policy was for £18 000. Calculate:
   (a) her annual premium,   (b) her monthly premium.

2. Mr Ashcroft paid a monthly premium of £31.74 for life assurance. If his insurance company's premium worked out to be £5.29 per £1000 per month, find:
   (a) how much he was assured for,
   (b) his annual premium.

3. Mrs Metcalfe paid a monthly premium of £36.32 on a life assurance policy that had a guaranteed maturity value of £8000 after 10 years:
   (a) Find the total amount paid in the 10 years.
   (b) If Mrs Metcalfe's policy was a 'with profits' policy, and with the profits the maturity value turned out to be £20 947, find:
      (i) the profits when compared with the guaranteed maturity value,
      (ii) the profits when compared with the total amount paid.

Taxation

Exercise 5

1. For each taxable income and rate of tax given, calculate the income tax due:
   (a) taxable income £2000;   rate of tax 30%,
   (b) taxable income £9000;   rate of tax 29%,
   (c) taxable income £7500;   rate of tax 27%,
   (d) taxable income £12 960;   rate of tax 32%,
   (e) taxable income £8465;   rate of tax 28%.

2. A man earned £4370 in a year and his total tax allowances were £2750:
   (a) Calculate the man's taxable income.
   (b) Calculate the amount of income tax paid during the year if the rate of tax was:
      (i) 30% of the taxable income,
      (ii) 27% of the taxable income.

3. Miss Kerfoot earned £9480 per year. Her total tax allowances came to £2640.
   (a) Calculate her average gross monthly salary.
   (b) Calculate her taxable income.
   (c) Calculate the total amount of tax paid during the year if the tax rate was 30%.
   (d) Calculate the average amount of tax paid each month.
   (e) Calculate Miss Kerfoot's average monthly earnings after tax.

4. Mr Locke earned £15 000 p.a. His total tax allowances were £4250.
   (a) Calculate Mr Locke's taxable income.
   (b) Calculate the amount of tax paid by Mr Locke during the year if the tax rate was 29%.
   (c) Calculate how much Mr Locke would have saved in tax if the rate had only been 27%.

5. Mrs Hurley earned £6350 p.a. Her total tax allowances were £3890. Calculate the income tax due for the year if the tax rate was 27%.

6. A man's taxable income came to £20 000. If £2100 of this was taxed at 40% and if the remaining amount was taxed at 27%:
   (a) Find the amount of tax due at the higher rate of 40%.
   (b) Find the amount of tax due at the lower rate of 27%.
   (c) Find the total amount of tax due.

7. Mrs Malik's taxable income came to £18 750. Using the given table, calculate the amount of tax due.

   Income Tax Rates

Taxable income (£)	Rate (%)
1–17 900	27
17 901–20 400	40
20 401–25 400	45
25 401–33 300	50
33 301–41 200	55
Over 41 200	60

8. Mr Frost earned £28 320 during the year. His tax allowances were £4640.
   (a) Calculate his taxable income.
   (b) Using the table of income tax rates, calculate the total amount of tax due.

32 Vectors

Exercise 1

1.

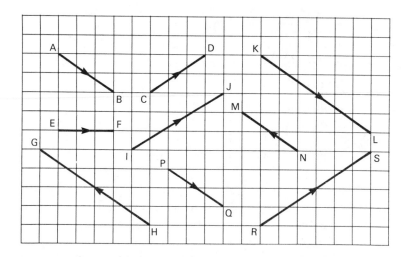

The diagram above shows nine vectors:

(*a*) Write down two equal vectors.

(*b*) Write down two vectors that are equal in magnitude but opposite in direction.

(*c*) Which vector is equal to $2\overrightarrow{CD}$?

(*d*) Which vector is equal to $2\overrightarrow{AB}$?

(*e*) Write $\overrightarrow{PQ}$ as a column vector.

(*f*) Write $\overrightarrow{IJ}$ as a column vector.

(*g*) Write $\overrightarrow{HG}$ as a column vector.

(*h*) Which vector is equal to $\frac{1}{2}\overrightarrow{RS}$?

(*i*) Write $\overrightarrow{EF}$ as a column vector.

2. (a) Write the co-ordinates of A, B, C and D.

(b) Write vector $\overrightarrow{CD}$ as a column vector.

(c) Write vector $\overrightarrow{DC}$ as a column vector.

(d) Write vector $\overrightarrow{AB}$ as a column vector.

(e) Write vector $\overrightarrow{BA}$ as a column vector.

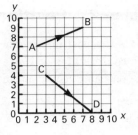

3. A translation moves P(3, 5) to Q(5, 1):

(a) Write the column vector for this translation.

(b) Give the co-ordinates of the point (2, 7) under the same translation.

(c) Give the co-ordinates of the point (4, 2) under the same translation.

(d) Write $\overrightarrow{QP}$ as a column vector.

4. The vector $\begin{pmatrix} ^{-}1 \\ -3 \end{pmatrix}$ maps the point L(4, 5) to the point M.

What are the co-ordinates of M?

5. Write each of the following as a column vector:

(a) the vector $\overrightarrow{AB}$,

(b) the vector $\overrightarrow{CD}$,

(c) a vector that is perpendicular to vector $\overrightarrow{AB}$ *and* has the same magnitude,

(d) a vector that is perpendicular to vector $\overrightarrow{CD}$ *and* has the same magnitude.

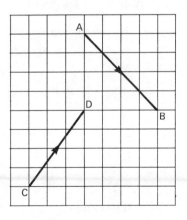

6. Write a vector that is perpendicular to the vector:

(a) $\begin{pmatrix} 3 \\ 3 \end{pmatrix}$ (b) $\begin{pmatrix} 2 \\ 3 \end{pmatrix}$ (c) $\begin{pmatrix} 1 \\ -2 \end{pmatrix}$

Exercise 2   Position Vectors

$\overrightarrow{OP}$ is the position vector of point P.
The co-ordinates of P are (3, 5).
The position vector of point P, when written as a column vector,

is $\begin{pmatrix} 3 \\ 5 \end{pmatrix}$.

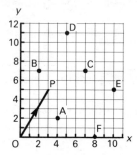

Write the position vectors of the following points as column vectors:

1. A   **3.** C   **5.** E
2. B   **4.** D   **6.** F

Magnitude of a Vector

The *magnitude* of a vector is its size (that is, its length).

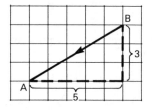

e.g. 1   In the diagram, the vector $\overrightarrow{BA}$ is shown, where

$\overrightarrow{BA} = \begin{pmatrix} ^-5 \\ ^-3 \end{pmatrix}$.

The length of $\overrightarrow{BA}$ can be found using Pythagoras:

$BA^2 = 5^2 + 3^2$

$BA^2 = 25 + 9$

$BA^2 = 34$

$BA = \sqrt{34}$

$BA = 5.83$ units (to 3 s.f.)

so the magnitude of $\overrightarrow{BA} = \underline{\underline{5.83 \text{ units}}}$ (to 3 s.f.)

400

e.g. 2   Consider the vector $\overrightarrow{MN} = \begin{pmatrix} 4 \\ -2 \end{pmatrix}$

$$\begin{aligned} \text{The magnitude of } \overrightarrow{MN} &= \sqrt{(4^2 + {}^-2^2)} \\ &= \sqrt{(16 + 4)} \\ &= \sqrt{20} \\ &= \underline{4.47 \text{ units}} \text{ (to 2 d.p.)} \end{aligned}$$

Exercise 3

Find the magnitude of each of the given vectors. (Give each answer correct to two decimal places.)

1. (*a*) $\overrightarrow{AB}$
   (*b*) $\overrightarrow{DC}$
   (*c*) $\overrightarrow{EF}$
   (*d*) $\overrightarrow{HG}$
   (*e*) $\overrightarrow{IJ}$

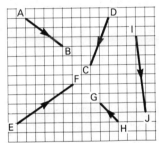

2. $\overrightarrow{KL} = \begin{pmatrix} 2 \\ 7 \end{pmatrix}$ **5.** $\overrightarrow{QR} = \begin{pmatrix} 8 \\ -6 \end{pmatrix}$ **8.** $\overrightarrow{WX} = \begin{pmatrix} 10 \\ -7 \end{pmatrix}$

3. $\overrightarrow{MN} = \begin{pmatrix} -5 \\ 12 \end{pmatrix}$ **6.** $\overrightarrow{ST} = \begin{pmatrix} 4 \\ 5 \end{pmatrix}$ **9.** $\overrightarrow{YZ} = \begin{pmatrix} 0 \\ 7 \end{pmatrix}$

4. $\overrightarrow{OP} = \begin{pmatrix} 6 \\ -8 \end{pmatrix}$ **7.** $\overrightarrow{UV} = \begin{pmatrix} -4 \\ -5 \end{pmatrix}$ **10.** $\overrightarrow{RM} = \begin{pmatrix} -9 \\ 9 \end{pmatrix}$

Exercise 4   Addition of Vectors

1. The diagram shows that:

$$\overrightarrow{AB} + \overrightarrow{BC} = \begin{pmatrix} 5 \\ 2 \end{pmatrix} + \begin{pmatrix} -3 \\ 3 \end{pmatrix} = \begin{pmatrix} 2 \\ 5 \end{pmatrix} = \overrightarrow{AC}$$

For each of the diagrams, write a vector sum similar to the one on the previous page:

(a)   (b)   (c)

2. Draw a diagram to show each sum:

(a) $\overrightarrow{PQ} + \overrightarrow{QR}$ where $\overrightarrow{PQ} = \begin{pmatrix} 1 \\ 3 \end{pmatrix}$ and $\overrightarrow{QR} = \begin{pmatrix} 2 \\ -2 \end{pmatrix}$,

(b) $\overrightarrow{YZ} + \overrightarrow{ZX}$ where $\overrightarrow{YZ} = \begin{pmatrix} -5 \\ 3 \end{pmatrix}$ and $\overrightarrow{ZX} = \begin{pmatrix} 4 \\ 2 \end{pmatrix}$.

3. Draw a diagram to show each sum:

(a) $\begin{pmatrix} 2 \\ -2 \end{pmatrix} + \begin{pmatrix} 4 \\ 4 \end{pmatrix}$ (b) $\begin{pmatrix} 3 \\ -5 \end{pmatrix} + \begin{pmatrix} -3 \\ 5 \end{pmatrix}$ (c) $\begin{pmatrix} -6 \\ 4 \end{pmatrix} + \begin{pmatrix} 2 \\ -1 \end{pmatrix}$

4. Add the following vectors giving each sum as a column vector:

(a) Find $\overrightarrow{PQ} + \overrightarrow{RS}$.

(d) Find $\overrightarrow{EF} + \overrightarrow{EG}$.

(b) Find $\overrightarrow{AB} + \overrightarrow{CD}$.

(e) Find $\overrightarrow{OT} + \overrightarrow{OU}$.

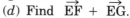

(c) Find $\overrightarrow{PQ} + \overrightarrow{PR}$.

(f) Find $\overrightarrow{VW} + \overrightarrow{VX}$.

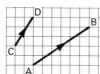

(g) Find $\overrightarrow{XZ} + \overrightarrow{XY}$.

(h) Find $\overrightarrow{ML} + \overrightarrow{JK}$.

5. In the given vector sums, find the missing components:

(a) $\begin{pmatrix} 6 \\ 2 \end{pmatrix} + \begin{pmatrix} \boxed{?} \\ \boxed{?} \end{pmatrix} = \begin{pmatrix} 7 \\ 4 \end{pmatrix}$

(d) $\begin{pmatrix} -2 \\ 8 \end{pmatrix} + \begin{pmatrix} \boxed{?} \\ \boxed{?} \end{pmatrix} = \begin{pmatrix} 4 \\ 3 \end{pmatrix}$

(b) $\begin{pmatrix} -5 \\ -1 \end{pmatrix} + \begin{pmatrix} \boxed{?} \\ \boxed{?} \end{pmatrix} = \begin{pmatrix} -2 \\ 0 \end{pmatrix}$

(e) $\begin{pmatrix} 5 \\ -3 \end{pmatrix} + \begin{pmatrix} \boxed{?} \\ \boxed{?} \end{pmatrix} = \begin{pmatrix} 7 \\ 7 \end{pmatrix}$

(c) $\begin{pmatrix} 9 \\ -6 \end{pmatrix} + \begin{pmatrix} \boxed{?} \\ \boxed{?} \end{pmatrix} = \begin{pmatrix} 7 \\ -2 \end{pmatrix}$

(f) $\begin{pmatrix} -8 \\ 2 \end{pmatrix} + \begin{pmatrix} \boxed{?} \\ \boxed{?} \end{pmatrix} = \begin{pmatrix} -7 \\ 0 \end{pmatrix}$

Multiplication of a Vector by a Scalar

Exercise 5

1. Find:

(a) $3\begin{pmatrix} 1 \\ 3 \end{pmatrix}$

(b) $6\begin{pmatrix} 2 \\ 4 \end{pmatrix}$

(c) $5\begin{pmatrix} 4 \\ 2 \end{pmatrix}$

(d) $2\begin{pmatrix} 7 \\ 3 \end{pmatrix}$

2. Find:

(a) $4\begin{pmatrix} 3 \\ -2 \end{pmatrix}$

(b) $2\begin{pmatrix} 6 \\ -5 \end{pmatrix}$

(c) $8\begin{pmatrix} -2 \\ 1 \end{pmatrix}$

(d) $3\begin{pmatrix} -7 \\ -3 \end{pmatrix}$

3. Find:

(a) $-2\begin{pmatrix} 6 \\ 4 \end{pmatrix}$

(b) $-3\begin{pmatrix} 8 \\ -3 \end{pmatrix}$

(c) $-5\begin{pmatrix} 0 \\ 3 \end{pmatrix}$

(d) $-1\begin{pmatrix} -5 \\ -1 \end{pmatrix}$

4. If $\vec{AB} = \begin{pmatrix} 6 \\ 2 \end{pmatrix}$, find:

(a) $2\vec{AB}$ (b) $4\vec{AB}$ (c) $^-\vec{AB}$ (d) $^-3\vec{AB}$

5. If $\vec{MT} = \begin{pmatrix} ^-4 \\ 5 \end{pmatrix}$ find:

(a) $2\vec{MT}$ (b) $6\vec{MT}$ (c) $^-2\vec{MT}$ (d) $^-5\vec{MT}$

6. The vector $\vec{LJ}$ is shown:
(a) Write $\vec{LJ}$ as a column vector.
(b) Find:
  (i) $2\vec{LJ}$ (ii) $6\vec{LJ}$ (iii) $^-2\vec{LJ}$

7. The vector $\vec{MP}$ is given:
(a) Write $\vec{MP}$ as a column vector.
(b) Find:
  (i) $2\vec{MP}$ (ii) $6\vec{MP}$ (iii) $^-\vec{MP}$

8. The vector $\vec{XY}$ is given:
(a) Write $\vec{XY}$ as a column vector.
(b) Find:
  (i) $2\vec{XY}$ (ii) $^-3\vec{XY}$ (iii) $^-\vec{XY}$

Exercise 6

1. The vector $\vec{AB} = \begin{pmatrix} 5 \\ ^-3 \end{pmatrix}$ is shown:

(a) Find $^-\vec{AB}$.
(b) Write vector $\vec{BA}$ as a column vector.
(c) Write what you notice about the answers to parts (a) and (b).

2. The vector $\overrightarrow{NP}$ is shown:

    (a) Write $\overrightarrow{NP}$ as a column vector.

    (b) Find $^-\overrightarrow{NP}$.

    (c) Write vector $\overrightarrow{PN}$ as a column vector.

3. (a) Write vector $\overrightarrow{WV}$ as a column vector.

    (b) Find $^-\overrightarrow{WV}$.

    (c) Write $\overrightarrow{VW}$ as a column vector.

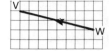

4. (a) Write $\overrightarrow{DB}$ as a column vector.

    (b) Find $^-\overrightarrow{DB}$.

    (c) Write $\overrightarrow{BD}$ as a column vector.

Graphical Representation of Subtraction of Vectors

$\overrightarrow{AB} - \overrightarrow{CD}$ may be rewritten as $\overrightarrow{AB} + \overrightarrow{DC}$
(since $^-\overrightarrow{CD} = {}^+\overrightarrow{DC}$) or as $\overrightarrow{DC} + \overrightarrow{AB}$.

The following diagrams illustrate the above subtraction.

To find $\overrightarrow{AB} - \overrightarrow{CD}$ we need to find $\overrightarrow{AB} + \overrightarrow{DC}$:

$\left[\text{i.e. } \begin{pmatrix} 5 \\ 3 \end{pmatrix} - \begin{pmatrix} 3 \\ -2 \end{pmatrix}\right]$ $\left[\text{i.e. } \begin{pmatrix} 5 \\ 3 \end{pmatrix} + \begin{pmatrix} -3 \\ 2 \end{pmatrix}\right]$

 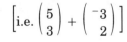

The broken line shows the addition $\overrightarrow{AB} + \overrightarrow{DC}$ which is the same as $\overrightarrow{AB} - \overrightarrow{CD}$.

405

To find $\vec{OP} - \vec{OQ}$ we can find $\vec{OP} + \vec{QO}$ instead.
This is the same as $\vec{QO} + \vec{OP}$, so the broken line shows the subtraction $\vec{OP} - \vec{OQ}$.

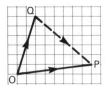

To find $\vec{OQ} - \vec{OP}$ we can find $\vec{OQ} + \vec{PO}$ instead.
This is the same as $\vec{PO} + \vec{OQ}$, so the broken line shows the subtraction.

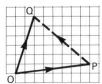

Exercise 7

Draw graphs, as above, to show the given subtractions.
Write each answer as a column vector.

1. (a) $\vec{OA} - \vec{OB}$
   (b) $\vec{OB} - \vec{OA}$

4. (a) $\vec{DE} - \vec{DF}$
   (b) $\vec{DF} - \vec{DE}$

2. (a) $\vec{OP} - \vec{OQ}$
   (b) $\vec{OQ} - \vec{OP}$

5. $\vec{MJ} - \vec{MR}$.

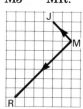

3. (a) $\vec{OX} - \vec{OY}$
   (b) $\vec{OY} - \vec{OX}$

6. $\vec{TK} - \vec{TP}$.

7. $\overrightarrow{OV} - \overrightarrow{OL}$.

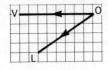

9. $\overrightarrow{HZ} - \overrightarrow{WN}$.

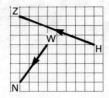

8. $\overrightarrow{GU} - \overrightarrow{GS}$.

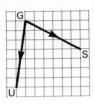

10. $\overrightarrow{CD} - \overrightarrow{DE}$.

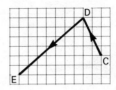

Revision Exercises
XXV to XXXII

Revision Exercise XXV

1.

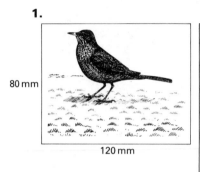

80 mm

120 mm

$b = \boxed{?}$ mm

$l = \boxed{?}$ mm

The drawing and enlargement above show a blackbird. The male blackbird has a glossy black plumage, orange-yellow bill and yellow eye-ring. The female is dark brown with a whitish throat.

Assume the small drawing measures 120 mm by 80 mm, the bird in the small drawing measures 100 mm and the bird in the enlargement shown measures 140 mm.

(*a*) Find both dimensions of the enlargement given.

(*b*) If the small drawing was enlarged still further until the blackbird was drawn at full size, the shorter sides of the drawing would measure 200 mm. Find:

    (i)   the length of the longer sides of the full-size drawing,

    (ii) the length of the full-size bird.

2. Are triangles ABC and PQR similar? Give a reason for your answer.

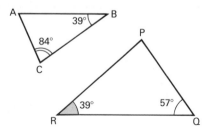

3. QS = 16 cm, SP = 12 cm,
ST = 9 cm and PT = 15 cm.
Find:
(a) QR   (b) TR

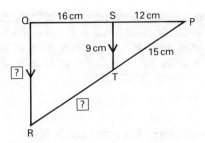

4. The diagram shows a telegraph pole and a 2 m post. The post is 9 m from the pole. Using the information given in the diagram, find the height of the telegraph pole.

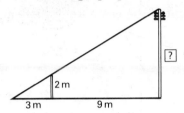

5. The lengths of the sides of two squares are 5 cm and 8 cm. Find the ratio:

$$\frac{\text{Area of small square}}{\text{Area of large square}}$$

6. The lengths of the sides of two cubes are 3 cm and 5 cm. Find the ratio:

$$\frac{\text{Volume of large cube}}{\text{Volume of small cube}}$$

7. Which two of the three triangles are congruent?

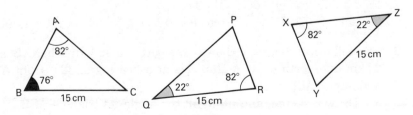

Revision Exercise XXVI

1. A rope is to be fixed to a vertical pole at a point that is 6 m above the ground. The other end of the rope is to be at horizontal ground level and 6.3 m from the pole. What length of rope is needed?

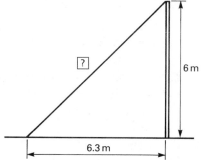

6 m

?

6.3 m

2. Calculate the height of the entrance of the tent shown.

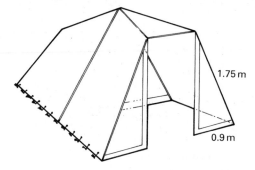

1.75 m

0.9 m

3. The three sides of a triangle measure 6 cm, 9 cm and 11 cm. Is the triangle right-angled, acute-angled or obtuse-angled?

Revision Exercise XXVII

1. Find, to three decimal places:
   (a) sin 76.2°   (b) cos 18°   (c) tan 63.5°

2. Find angle θ to one decimal place:
   (a) sin θ = 0.397   (b) cos θ = 0.134   (c) tan θ = 1.366

3. The following diagram shows two ports A and B, where B is 23 km due north of A. A ship S is at a bearing of 324° from A, and angle ASB = 90°.
   (a) Draw a sketch, and fill in all the angles of triangle ASB.

(b) What is the bearing of the ship from B?

(c) Calculate the distance of the ship from A (to the nearest tenth of a kilometre).

(d) Calculate the distance of the ship from B (to the nearest tenth of a kilometre).

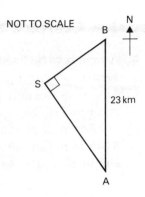

NOT TO SCALE

4. WXYZ is a rectangle and P is a point on WX. ZY = 50 cm and ZW = 20 cm. Angle WZP = 64°.

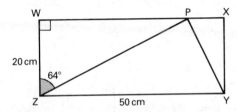

(a) Calculate the area of rectangle WXYZ.

(b) Calculate the area of triangle PYZ.

(c) Calculate the length of WP.

(d) Calculate the area of triangle PWZ.

(e) Calculate the length of PX.

(f) Calculate angle PYX to the nearest tenth of a degree.

5. What length of support is needed to fix to a shelf at a point that is 250 mm from the wall, if the support makes an angle of 44.1° with the wall? (Give your answer correct to the nearest millimetre.)

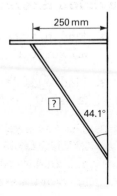

411

Revision Exercise XXVIII

1. For each journey shown, find the speed in kilometres per hour:

(a)

(b)

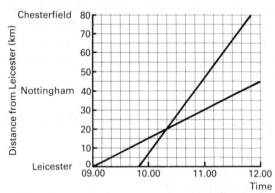

2. A cyclist set off from Leicester at 9 o'clock in the morning. A coach set off later and followed the same route.

(a) At what time did the coach leave Leicester?

(b) At what time did the coach arrive in Chesterfield?

(c) What was the average speed of the coach?

(d) (i) At what time did the coach pass the cyclist?

(ii) How far were they from Leicester when the coach passed the cyclist?

(e) How far had the cyclist travelled in 1 h 40 min?

(f) What was the cyclist's average speed?

(g) At what time were the coach and the cyclist 25 km apart?

3.

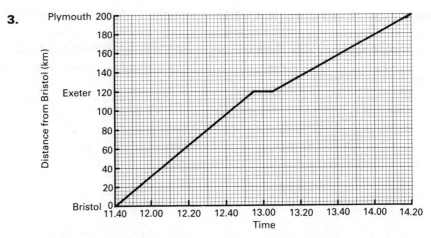

A train left Bristol at 11.40 for Plymouth, a distance of about 200 km. The graph above shows the journey.

(a) (i)   Where did the train stop?
   (ii) At what time did it stop?
   (iii) For how long did it stop?

(b) How far was the train from Bristol at:
   (i) 12.30?   (ii) 12.20?   (iii) 13.30?

(c) At what time was the train 48 km from Bristol?

(d) What was the train's average speed from Bristol to Exeter?

(e) At what times was the train 32 km from Exeter?

(f) Calculate the train's average speed for the whole journey from Bristol to Plymouth.

4. Mr Airey travelled by car from Carlisle to Berwick-upon-Tweed. The graph shows his journey.

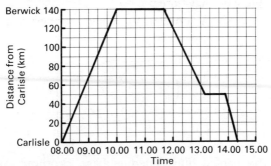

(a) How long did he stop in Berwick?

(b) How long was Mr Airey's stop on the return journey?

413

(c) Describe Mr Airey's journey. Mention distances, times and average speeds.

(d) Convert the distance between Carlisle and Berwick into miles. Use the relationship 8 km = 5 miles to help you.

5. Write a story for both of the travel graphs below:

(a)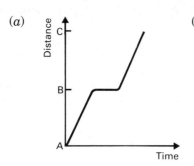

(b)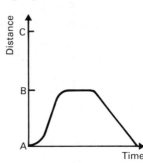

Revision Exercise XXIX

1. A coach firm had 12 red and 8 green coaches. A driver took out one of the coaches at random. What is the probability that it was:

(a) a red coach?   (b) a blue coach?

2. The probability that a certain type of seed will germinate is $\frac{1}{4}$. If 36 seeds are sown, how many are likely to germinate?

3. $\mathscr{E}$ = {people questioned in a survey}
A = {people under 21 years of age}
D = {people who drive a car}
The values in the Venn diagram show numbers of people.

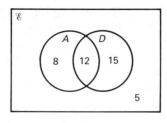

One of the people questioned is from Scotland. What is the probability that the person:

(a) is under 21?   (b) can drive a car?

414

(c) is under 21 and can drive a car?

(d) is under 21 or can drive a car or is under 21 and can drive a car?

(e) is over 21 and can drive a car?

(f) is over 21 but cannot drive a car?

4. One letter is chosen from {M, A, T, H, S} and one letter is chosen from {G, R, E, A, T}:

(a) Copy and complete the diagram.

(b) What is the probability of getting:

    (i) an A and a T?

    (ii) an A followed by a T?

    (iii) two letters that are the same?

    (iv) a consonant followed by a vowel?

	M	A	T	H	S
G				HG	
R		AR			
E					
A					
T					

5. There are 9 red and 6 green sweets in a bag. Tekla followed by Niko each took one at random. Find the probability that:

(a) Tekla took a green sweet,

(b) Niko took a green sweet given that Tekla took a red sweet,

(c) both took a red sweet,

(d) both took a green sweet.

6. There were 60 cars in a car park: 30 were red, 8 were green, 10 were blue and 12 were brown. One of the cars was driven away. What is the probability that it was:

(a) a red car?　　　　　(c) either a red or a brown car?

(b) a brown car?　　　　(d) either a blue or a green car?

7. The probability of Heather passing her maths exam was 0.8, while the probability of her passing history was 0.6:

(a) Copy and complete the tree diagram.

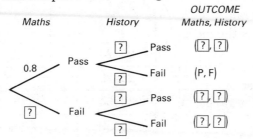

415

(b) Which of the two exams is Heather most likely to pass?

(c) Find the probabilities of the following events:

    (i) Heather passes both exams.

    (ii) Heather passes in exactly one of the two subjects.

    (iii) Heather does not fail both exams.

Revision Exercise XXX

1. The number of litres of water in 9 different containers was:

    8, 11, 7, 6, 8, 18, 7, 9, 7

Find:

(a) the median,   (b) the mode,   (c) the mean.

2. Ten people estimated, to the nearest metre, a certain distance. Their estimates were:

    24 m, 20 m, 25 m, 15 m, 23 m

    20 m, 23 m, 27 m, 20 m, 22 m

Find:

(a) the median,   (b) the mode,   (c) the mean.

3. Here are the test marks of 50 pupils:

16	25	3	8	24	19	5	32	25	15
20	11	13	37	26	4	21	22	13	29
30	23	21	10	14	23	23	12	14	6
6	12	16	23	19	7	15	20	18	21
18	18	20	20	24	14	32	22	16	19

(a) Copy and complete the tally chart.

(b) Draw a pair of axes as shown opposite, then draw a histogram.

(c) What is the modal class?

(d) Which class contains the median?

(e) Find the range.

Marks	Tally	Frequency
0–4		
5–9		
10–14		
15–19		
20–24		
25–29		
30–34		
35–39		

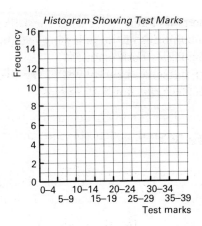

Histogram Showing Test Marks

(*f*) If one of the 50 pupils was selected at random:
  (i) What is the probability that the pupil obtained a mark between 20 and 24 inclusive?
  (ii) What is the probability that the pupil scored more than 14 marks?

4. Draw a pictogram to show the distribution in question 3.

5. Last year the sales of a particular firm totalled £240 000. The partly completed table and pie chart show some of the costs involved.

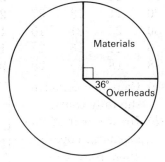

Item	Percentage of total sales
Labour	35%
Materials	25%
Overheads	
Profit	

(*a*) Copy both the table and pie chart given above.
(*b*) Calculate the angle representing labour and complete the pie chart.
(*c*) The angle for overheads is 36°. What percentage of the sales are the overheads?
(*d*) Complete the table.
(*e*) How much was spent on labour?
(*f*) How much profit was made?

417

Revision Exercise XXXI

1. An insurance company charges a premium of £1.95 per £1000 insured on its house insurance policy. Calculate the annual premium on a house valued at £24 000.

2. If the annual premium for insuring the contents of a house is £4.60 per £1000 insured, calculate the annual premium on contents valued at £13 500.

3. Mrs Coates insured her jewellery for £1420 and paid a premium of £2.25 per £100 insured. Calculate the total premium paid.

4. A motorcyclist insured his motor bike for a premium of £209.50, but received a discount of 20%.
   Calculate the premium payable.

5. Mr O'Callaghan paid a monthly premium of £4.81 per £1000 assured for life assurance. His policy was for £17 000. Calculate Mr O'Callaghan's:
   (a) monthly premium,   (b) annual premium.

6. A house has a rateable value of £215. If the rate was 170 p in the pound, work out how much the householder pays in rates.

7. Mr Illingworth earned £10 200 per year. His total tax allowances came to £3940. Calculate:
   (a) his taxable income,
   (b) the amount of tax paid if the tax rate was 27%.

Revision Exercise XXXII

1. For the following vectors:
   (a) Write down two equal vectors.
   (b) Which vector is equal to $2\overrightarrow{PQ}$?
   (c) Which vector is equal to $\frac{1}{2}\overrightarrow{LM}$?
   (d) Write down two vectors that are equal in magnitude only. (There is more than one possible answer.)
   (e) Express $\overrightarrow{RN}$ as a column vector.

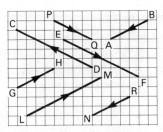

(f) Express $\overrightarrow{NR}$ as a column vector.

(g) Calculate, correct to one decimal place, the magnitude of:

    (i) $\overrightarrow{GH}$ (ii) $\overrightarrow{EF}$

2. (a) Write the position vectors of the points:

    (i) P   (iii) R

    (ii) Q   (iv) S

(b) Find the magnitude of each vector:

    (i) $\overrightarrow{OP}$ (iii) $\overrightarrow{OR}$

    (ii) $\overrightarrow{OQ}$ (iv) $\overrightarrow{OS}$

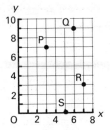

3. (a) Write the column vector for $\overrightarrow{MP}$.

(b) Find:

    (i) $2\overrightarrow{MP}$ (iii) $-\overrightarrow{MP}$

    (ii) $3\overrightarrow{MP}$ (iv) $-4\overrightarrow{MP}$

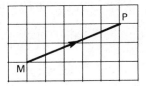

4. Make two copies of the diagram:

(a) On the first copy, show $\overrightarrow{AB} + \overrightarrow{AC}$.

(b) On the second copy, show $\overrightarrow{AB} - \overrightarrow{AC}$.

Miscellaneous Revision Papers 1–12

1. Out of a group of people, everyone had either a pen or a pencil or both. 13 had a pen, 7 did not have a pen while 8 people had both a pen and a pencil.
   (a) How many people had a pen but no pencil?
   (b) How many people had either a pen or a pencil or both?

2. 47 000 people correct to the nearest 1000, attended the pop concert. Write down the lowest and highest possible attendances.

3. Consider the numbers:
        1, 3, 7, 15, 31
   (a) Which of the numbers are prime?
   (b) Which of the numbers are triangular numbers?
   (c) Which four numbers add up to a multiple of 5?
   (d) If $a + b + 10 = c + d$, find which four of the above numbers can replace a, b, c and d to make the statement correct.
   (e) If $e + f + 20 = g + h$, find the values of e, f, g and h from the above list of five numbers.
   (f) The five numbers, written in order of size as given, form a sequence. Work out the next two numbers in the sequence.

4. (a) Write all the factors of 72. Underline those that are prime numbers.
   (b) Now write 72 as a product of prime factors.

5. Find the number of degrees difference between the readings on the following thermometers.

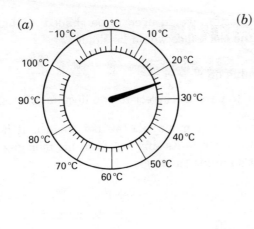

(a)

(b)

6. Total the supermarket till receipt shown:

$$
\begin{array}{r}
0.74 \\
1.29 \\
0.37 \\
0.37 \\
0.60 \\
2.06 \\
\underline{0.92} \\
\end{array}
$$

Total   £???

7. 350 people out of 500 bought a newspaper. What percentage was that?

8. Some interest rates were:

$$8.63\%, \quad 8\tfrac{3}{4}\%, \quad 8.72\%, \quad 8\tfrac{1}{2}\%, \quad 8.51\%$$

Write these interest rates in order of size giving the smallest first.

9. (a) What fraction of the clock-face has been shaded?

(b) How many more sectors would need to be shaded so that altogether $\frac{3}{4}$ of the clock-face would be shaded?

10. (a) Find the exact value of $\dfrac{18.5 + 7.3}{9.6}$.
    (b) Write the answer to part (a) correct to two decimal places.

11. Mr Howard's mortgage repayment is £140 per month. If he earns £840 per month, write in its simplest form his mortgage repayment as a fraction of his earnings.

12. The sketch is of a door canopy. If the support makes an angle of 38° with the canopy, what angle is it to the vertical?

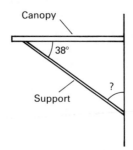

13. Calculate the labelled angles in the given parallelogram.

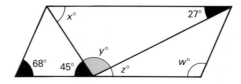

14. In the diagram, O is the centre of the circle and PT and PU are tangents. Angle TVU = 61°.
    (a) What sort of quadrilateral is PTOU?
    (b) Calculate all the angles of quadrilateral PTOU.

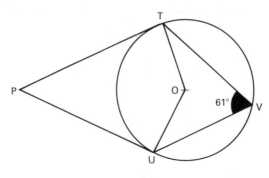

15. Copy and complete:

(a) $8.91 \text{ km} = \boxed{?} \text{ m}$

(b) $7.5 \ell \quad = \boxed{?} \text{ c}\ell$

(c) $6.4 \text{ t} \quad = \boxed{?} \text{ kg}$

16. A piece of wood measuring $28\frac{3}{4}$ in in length is cut in half. How long is each piece?

17. The ingredients for a sponge cake with low fat content are:

85 g	flour
115 g	castor sugar
30 g	melted butter
3	eggs
1	tablespoonful of hot water

Find the total mass of the ingredients. (Ignore the hot water and assume each egg has a mass of 55 g.)

18. A TV film started at 21.35 and finished at 23.41. How long was the film?

19. (a) Through how many degrees does the minute hand of a clock turn in 10 min?

(b) How many hours does it take the hour hand of a clock to rotate through 120°?

20. Idris was born on 12 May 1942. How old was he on 25 January 1971?

21. (a) Write the reading shown on the following meter (ignore the $\frac{1}{10}$ kW h dial):

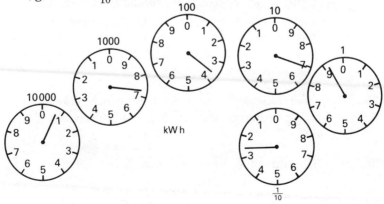

(b) If the previous reading was 06585, find the number of units used in the quarter.

(c) Calculate the cost of electricity for the quarter at a charge of 5.7 p per unit plus a quarterly charge of £6.60.

22. The table gives a guide to exposure when photographing awkward shots:

Subject	50/64 ASA	100/125 ASA	400 ASA
Full moon (NB use telephoto lens)	1/15 s f/5.6	1/15 s f/8	1/125 s f/16
Moonlit landscape	24 min f/2.8	12 min f/2.8	3 min f/2.8
TV screen (shutter speed must be 1/30th s)	1/30 s f/2	1/30 s f/2.8	1/30 s f/5.6
Fireworks—leave shutter open	10–20 s f/5.6	10–20 s f/8	10–20 s f/16
Brightly lit street scenes	1/4 s f/2.8	1/8 s f/2.8	1/8 s f/5.6
Neon signs	1/30 s f/2.8	1/30 s f/4	1/30 s f/8
Well-lit shop windows	1/15s f/2.8	1/30 s f/2.8	1/30 s f/5.6
Floodlit buildings	1 s f/2.8	1/2 s f/2.8	1/8 s f/2.8
Circus ring	1/30 s f/2.8	1/60 s f/2.8	1/250 s f/2.8
One candle as light source	1/2–1 s f/2	1/4 s f/2	1/15 s f/2
Inside tube train	1/4 s f/2	1/8 s f/2	1/30 s f/2
Star traces around Pole Star	All night f/2	All night f/2.8	All night f/5.6
Black cat in coal cellar	Pack up and go home!		

e.g. 1/30 s f/8 means a speed of 1/30 s and an aperture of f/8.

(a) If you are using 400 ASA film and are shooting a brightly-lit street scene, what speed and what aperture should you use?

(b) If you are using 100 ASA film and are photographing fireworks, what aperture should you use and for how many seconds should the shutter remain open?

(c) What speed of film should you use (that is, what ASA rating) to photograph a floodlit building allowing $\frac{1}{8}$ s at an aperture of f/2.8?

23. Using the timetable on p. 82, find which train you should catch at St Leonards Warrior Square to arrive in Eastbourne before 07.45?

24. Find the value of: (a) 6^2 (b) 3^4 (c) 2^8

25. Find the value of: (a) 2^{-5} (b) 10^{-3}

26. The Sahara has an area of $1\,554\,000\,\mathrm{km}^2$. Write this number in standard form.

27. The mass of 1 atom of hydrogen is about $1.66 \times 10^{-24}\,\mathrm{g}$.
The mass of 1 atom of oxygen is about $2.66 \times 10^{-23}\,\mathrm{g}$.
(*a*) Find the mass of 2 atoms of hydrogen (in standard form).
(*b*) Find the mass of a molecule of water which consists of 2 atoms of hydrogen and 1 atom of oxygen (in standard form).

Paper 2 (Ch. 9 to 16)

1. Mrs Lundy bought the following:

1 beauty bag	£4.25
1 box of dusting powder	£5.95
1 tin of talc	£1.65

(*a*) Work out the total cost.
(*b*) If she was given 10 p discount for each £1 spent, how much did she have to pay?

2. A compact disc player costs £200 plus VAT at 15%:
(*a*) Find the total price including VAT.
(*b*) Which is the bigger discount, 20% of the total price or £20 off the total price. (Give reasons for your answer.)

3. Draw a sketch of a cone.

4. Sketch the net of a cone without a base.

5. Which quadrilaterals have diagonals that bisect each other?

6. (*a*) Draw a triangle that has exactly one axis of symmetry.
(*b*) What sort of triangle should you have drawn in part (*a*)?

7. The diagram on the next page shows part of the pattern on a wall tile:
(*a*) Copy it.
(*b*) Complete your copy so that the pattern is symmetrical about the broken lines.

425

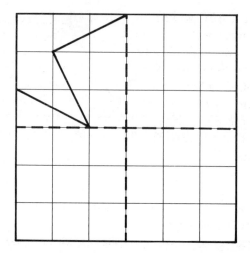

8. A gas bill totalled £C. It was made up of a standing charge of £S plus £t per therm for the n therms used. Write a formula giving C in terms of S, t and n.

9. If n is a positive whole number, what is special about the number 5n + 1? (Check the units digits.)

10. If $A = \dfrac{S}{n}$, express:

(a) S in terms of A and n,
(b) n in terms of A and S.

11. A sheet of A4 paper measures 29.7 cm by 21 cm. Calculate its area.

12. The sector shown can be cut out to make a conical hat. Calculate its area. (Use $\pi = \frac{22}{7}$.)

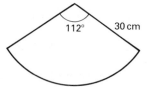

13. A hot water tank is in the shape of a cylinder of height 90 cm and of base radius 24 cm. Calculate:

(a) the volume of the tank,
(b) the number of litres of water in the tank if it is full,
(c) the total surface area of the tank (take π to be 3.14).

14. Construct △ABC where BC = 93 mm, AB = 53 mm and AC = 80 mm. Using a pair of compasses, bisect angle ABC. Using a set square, draw AD parallel to BC, where D lies on the bisector of angle ABC. How long is AD?

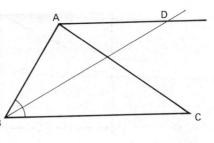

15. The diagram below shows a coastline and a ship at S. The ship is 4 miles from the coast.
  (a) A fishing boat is within 3 miles of the coast. Draw a diagram to scale, and shade it to show the possible positions of the fishing boat.
  (b) If the fishing boat is exactly 2 miles from the ship at S, indicate on your drawing the set of possible positions of the boat.
  (c) If the fishing boat had not been exactly 2 miles from the ship at S, but instead was given as being within 2 miles of S, explain how this change in the information would affect the answer.

S •

16. Copy and complete:

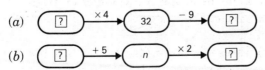

17. The function f is defined by:

Find: (a) $f(7.93)$ (b) $f(4)$ (c) $f(2.43)$

18. If $y = x^2 - 2x + 10$, find the value of y when:
(a) $x = 8$ (b) $x = 5$ (c) $x = 2$ (d) $x = {}^-5$

19. If $y = (x - 4)(x + 2)$, find the value of y when:
(a) $x = 6$ (b) $x = 4$ (c) $x = 0$ (d) $x = {}^-2$

20. If $f(x) = -\dfrac{6}{x}$, find:
(a) $f(3)$ (b) $f({}^-2)$ (c) $f({}^-6)$ (d) $f(\tfrac{1}{2})$

21. Find the simple interest on £4280 for 6 years at $4\tfrac{1}{2}\%$ p.a.

22. £750 is invested for 2 years at 8% p.a. compound interest. Find the total interest earned.

23. Mrs Spencer obtained a personal loan of £2500 repayable by equal monthly instalments over 5 years. She was charged a flat rate of 9.95% p.a.
(a) What was the interest for 1 year?
(b) What was the interest for 5 years?
(c) Calculate each monthly repayment giving the answer to the nearest penny.

24. Copy the diagram showing an object and its image and mark the centre of rotation. Label the centre using the letter C.

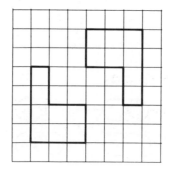

25. The given diagram is made up of congruent right-angled triangles.

Equal lengths are marked.

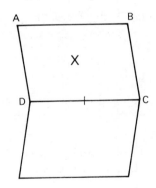

(a) Describe fully a single transformation that will map:
  (i) △BDC onto △AFB,
  (ii) △FEB onto △FAB,
  (iii) △FEB onto △DBE,
  (iv) △DBE onto △DBC.

(b) Name two isosceles triangles in the diagram.

(c) If ∠DBE = 65°, which other angles equal 65°?

26. Each diagram shows a parallelogram with its image under a transformation:

(a) Which of the diagrams, X or Y, shows a half-turn rotation about the mid-point of side CD?

(b) Describe any other transformations shown in the diagrams.

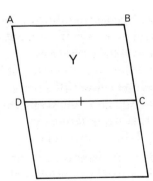

Paper 3   (Ch. 17 to 24)

1. Solve the equations:
  (a) $2x + 7 = 16$ (b) $6x - 5 = 19$ (c) $7 - 3x = 22$

2. Solve for x: $3(4x - 7) = 15$

3. Alyn is 5 years older than Nia, and Berwyn is twice as old as Alyn:

(*a*) If Nia is x years old, write expressions for the ages of Alyn and Berwyn.

(*b*) If the sum of their ages is 63 years, write an equation in x, solve it, then write the ages of all three people.

4. Using the given flow chart, find the answers obtained from the following input:

(*a*) 1   (*c*) 0

(*b*) 8   (*d*) ⁻2

(*e*) If t is input, find an expression in t for the final answer.

(*f*) If the final answer is 11, find the value of t that was input.

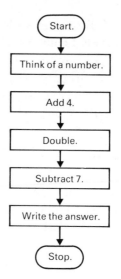

Start.

Think of a number.

Add 4.

Double.

Subtract 7.

Write the answer.

Stop.

5. (*a*) Draw a pair of axes as shown.

(*b*) Plot the points P(5, 8) and Q(2, 2). Join them with a straight line.

(*c*) Find the gradient of the line segment PQ.

(*d*) What are the co-ordinates of the mid-point of PQ?

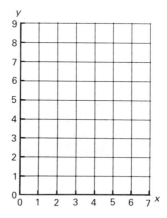

6. The formula $v = \dfrac{16}{t}$ gives the average speed, v km/h, needed to travel 16 km in a time, t h:

(*a*) Copy and complete the following table for $v = \dfrac{16}{t}$ (where necessary, give values to one decimal place).

t (h)	1	2	3	4	5	6	8	10	12	14	16
$v = \dfrac{16}{t}$			5.3							1.1	

(b) Draw a pair of axes as shown, then draw the graph of $v = \dfrac{16}{t}$ for values of t from 1 to 16 h.

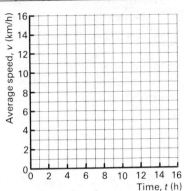

From your graph, find:
(c) the average speed for a time of 7 h,
(d) the average speed for a time of $2\frac{1}{2}$ h,
(e) the time when the average speed is 5 km/h,
(f) the time when the average speed is 3 km/h.

7. Which inequality describes the shaded region shown in the diagram?

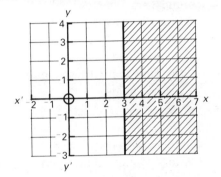

8. Draw a pair of axes as shown. Shade the part of the diagram that is *not* described by the inequalities $x \geqslant 2$ and $y > {}^-3$.

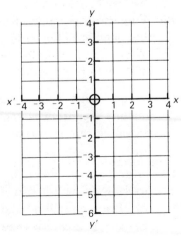

9. (a) Draw a pair of axes as shown $(0 \leqslant x \leqslant 16$ and $0 \leqslant y \leqslant 25)$.
  (b) By drawing two straight lines, solve simultaneously the equations:

$$2x + 5y = 30$$
$$4x + y = 24$$

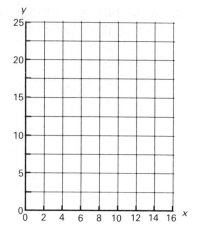

10. A firm makes two sizes of boxes. 3 large and 4 small boxes hold 108 tins. 5 large and 3 small boxes hold 136 tins. By drawing graphs, find:
  (a) How many tins a large box holds.
  (b) How many tins a small box holds.

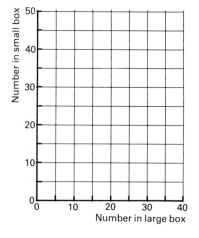

11. A recipe uses 225 g of tomatoes and 175 g of long-grain rice. How much rice should be used when 450 g of tomatoes are used?

12. Daniel spent 1456 escudos in a shop in Portugal. If the amount spent was equivalent to £6.50, what was the exchange rate in escudos to the pound?

13. A car averages 64 km/h:
  (a) How far will it travel in 7 h?
  (b) How long will it take to travel 320 km?
  (c) How long will it take to travel 208 km?

14. In the diagram, ∠RPQ = 73° and ∠QRP = 61°.
What is the bearing of:
  (a) Q from R?
  (b) Q from P?
  (c) R from Q?
  (d) P from Q?

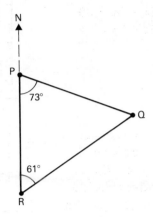

15. Using the given map, find the straight-line distance from:
  (a) Luton to Ipswich,
  (b) Lincoln to Colchester.

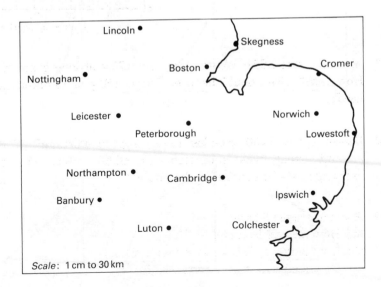

433

16. A test was marked out of 80.

Draw a pair of axes as shown, then draw a graph to convert the test marks into percentages.

(*Note* 80 marks = 100%.)

Use your graph to change the following marks into percentages:

(*a*) 60
(*b*) 24
(*c*) 32
(*d*) 56
(*e*) 72
(*f*) 64

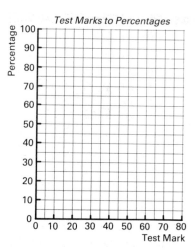

Test Marks to Percentages

17. A builder arranged to pay a team of bricklayers a fixed sum of money for a specified job. Which of the following graphs best shows the amount of money received by each person in the team, if the total sum is shared equally amongst them?

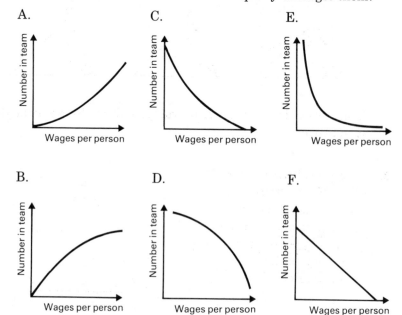

1.

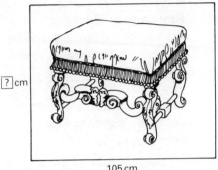

20cm

30 cm

?cm

105 cm

A picture of a William and Mary stool (*c.* 1690) together with an enlargement are shown above. Using the information given, calculate the missing dimension on the enlargement.

2.

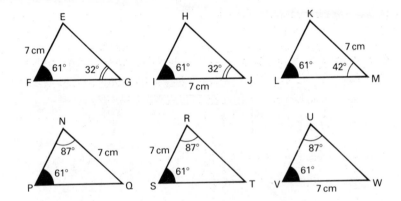

Name two pairs of congruent triangles from the six triangles given above.

3. In isosceles triangle ABC,
AB = AC = 6.8 cm and
BC = 5.6 cm. Calculate:
(*a*) the perpendicular height,
PA, of the triangle (to one decimal place),
(*b*) the area of △ABC.

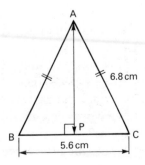

435

4. The cross-section of a full swimming pool is shown.
The pool is 20 m long. It is 1 m deep at the shallow end and 1.84 m deep at the other end.

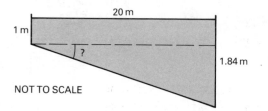

20 m

1 m

?

1.84 m

NOT TO SCALE

(a) Calculate the angle of slope of the bottom of the pool.
(b) Calculate the area of the cross-section of the pool.
(c) If the pool is 10 m wide, calculate the volume of the water in the pool.
(d) Given that 1 m³ holds 1000 ℓ, how many litres of water are in the pool when it is full?

5. Finbar cycled to see his friend. The graph shows his journey.

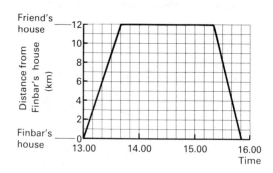

(a) At what time did he set off from home?
(b) At what time did he arrive at his friend's house?
(c) How long did he stay at his friend's house?
(d) At what time did he get back home?
(e) How long did the journey home take?
(f) At what times was he 6 km from his home?
(g) How far did he travel altogether between 13.00 and 16.00?
(h) What was his average speed for the journey to his friend's house?
(i) What was his average speed on the return journey home?

6. In a bag of mixed nuts there were 150 peanuts, 12 walnuts, 80 cashews, 20 almonds, 28 hazel-nuts and 10 brazil nuts. If one nut is taken out of the bag, what is the probability that it is:

(a) an almond? (d) a brazil nut?

(b) a cashew? (e) a hazel-nut?

(c) a walnut? (f) not a hazel-nut?

7. A pack of sweets contains 6 cherry-flavoured and 4 blackcurrant-flavoured sweets packed in a random order. Angela took the first sweet and ate it, while David took the second sweet and ate it.

(a) Copy and complete the tree diagram.

(b) Find the probability of the following events:

    (i)   Both took cherry-flavoured sweets.

    (ii) Angela took a blackcurrant-flavoured sweet *and* David took a cherry-flavoured sweet.

    (iii) One of them took a blackcurrant-flavoured sweet and the other took a cherry-flavoured sweet.

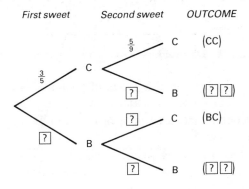

8. 60 people attended keep-fit classes. Their ages were:

Under 20 years	7 people	30–40 years	10 people
20–25 years	? people	over 40 years	5 people
25–30 years	20 people		

(a) How many people between the ages of 20 and 25 years attended?

(b) Draw a pie chart to show the information.

437

9. Mrs Underhill earned £6875 in a year. Her tax allowances were £3795. Calculate:
   (a) her taxable income,
   (b) the amount of tax paid if the tax rate was 30%.

10. (a) Copy the diagram.

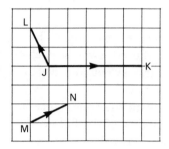

   (b) (i)   Draw the vector $\overrightarrow{JK} + \overrightarrow{JL}$.
       (ii) Express $\overrightarrow{JK} + \overrightarrow{JL}$ as a column vector.
       (iii) Express $\overrightarrow{MN}$ as a column vector.
       (iv) If $\overrightarrow{JK} + \overrightarrow{JL} = k.\ \overrightarrow{MN}$, what is the value of k ?

Paper 5   (Ch. 1 to 32)

1. It was noticed that out of a group of people 21 wore a necklace, 12 wore both a necklace and a bracelet, while 24 wore either a necklace or a bracelet or both. 17 people did not wear a bracelet.
   (a) How many did not wear a necklace?
   (b) How many wore neither a necklace nor a bracelet?
   (c) How many people were there in the group?

2. Angus had collected 80 key-rings correct to the nearest ten. Write down the lowest and highest possible number of key-rings.

3. Write down the next two numbers in the sequence:

   3, 5, 9, 17, 33, ? , ?

4. If the temperature shown on the following thermometer was increased by 12 °C, what would the new temperature be?

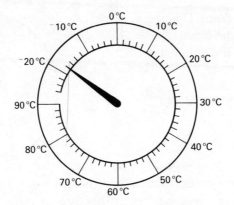

5. Mr Ingle bought a set of drill bits. The sizes ranged from $\frac{1}{16}$ in to $\frac{1}{2}$ in. If the sizes increased in intervals of one-sixteenth of an inch:

   (a) List the sizes in order from smallest to largest.
   (b) How many drill bits must there be in the set?
   (c) What size would the third smallest bit be?

6. What is the remainder when 950 is divided by 65?

7. After using $\frac{2}{3}$ of her eggs, Mrs Irvine had 8 left. How many did she have to begin with?

8. A manufacturer considered the design of a recliner chair as shown. The back would swing from a lower position making an angle of 15° with the horizontal, to an upper position making an angle of 75° with the horizontal.
   They worked out that for a three-position back, the angle made with the horizontal for the three positions would be 15°, 45° and 75° (assuming an equal amount of rotation between positions). If there is an equal amount of rotation between positions and the back swings from 15° to 75°, calculate the angles the back makes with the horizontal for:

   (a) a four-position back,
   (b) a five-position back,
   (c) a six-position back,
   (d) a seven-position back.

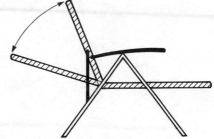

9. In the diagram, O is the centre of the circle. Calculate the value of x and y.

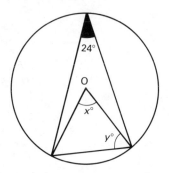

10. (*a*) To raise money for charity, people were asked to put 2 p pieces in one long line with adjacent coins touching. The coins stretched just over 1 km when the last coin was put in position. If 2 p coins have a diameter of 25.91 mm, how much was collected?

(*b*) If 10 p coins were collected instead of 2 p coins, as in part (*a*), how much would have been collected? (The diameter of a 10 p coin is 28.5 mm.)

11. Beef can be roasted for 56 min per kilogram plus 25 min. If a 1.5 kg piece of brisket is to be roasted:

(*a*) How long will it take to cook?

(*b*) What is the latest time the beef should be put in the oven to be ready for 17.30?

12. Isaac went on holiday on 2 August and returned on 14 August. For how many nights was he away?

13. Show on a digital meter (as shown on the following page) the reading given on the dials:

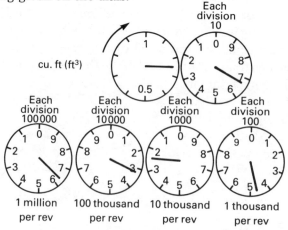

440

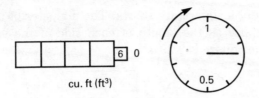

cu. ft (ft³)

14. Express $\dfrac{3^4 \times 3^7}{3^{13}}$ as a single power of 3, then find its value.

15. In the year 2000 the population of the UK will be about 62.8 million. Write this number in standard form.

16. A set of pans costs £34 plus VAT at 15%:
   (a) Calculate the cost of the set of pans.
   (b) If the pans are now sold at a discount of 12%, find the selling price of the pans.

17. (a) Draw a rectangle of length 5 cm and breadth 3 cm. On it, draw its lines of symmetry.
   (b) How many lines of symmetry has it?
   (c) It has rotational symmetry. What is its order of rotational symmetry?

18. In the diagram, is the shaded part a plane of symmetry?

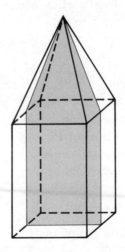

19. Factorise $12x + 8y$.

20. If $A = Ph$, express P in terms of A and h. Calculate P when $h = 8$ and $A = 28$.

441

21. A circle and a square are shown. The diameter of the circle is the same size as the length of each side of the square. The area of the square is $7.29\,\mathrm{m^2}$.

(a) Calculate the length of each side of the square.
(b) Find the perimeter of the square.
(c) Find the circumference of the circle using $\pi = 3.14$.
(d) Calculate the area of the circle using $\pi = 3.14$. Write the answer to two decimal places.

22. A cylindrical oil drum has a diameter of $30\,\mathrm{cm}$:
(a) It is filled to a depth of $140\,\mathrm{cm}$. How many litres of oil are there in the drum?

If the drum has a height of $150\,\mathrm{cm}$, calculate:
(b) its total capacity in litres,
(c) its total surface area.
   (Take π to be 3.14.)

23. Construct $\triangle\mathrm{XYZ}$ such that $\mathrm{YZ} = 95\,\mathrm{mm}$, $\angle\,\mathrm{XYZ} = 68°$ and $\mathrm{XY} = 57\,\mathrm{mm}$. Using a pencil, ruler and pair of compasses only, bisect side YZ and angle XZY and let the two bisectors meet at a point P.
(a) Measure XZ.
(b) Measure PZ.

24. Copy and complete:
(a)

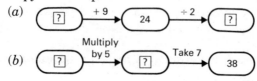

(b)

(c)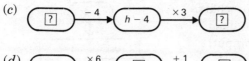

(d)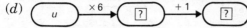

25. Mr Urmston obtained a personal loan of £1280 and repaid it by equal monthly instalments over 3 years. The interest charge was a flat rate of 10.25% p.a.
    (a) What was the interest for 1 year?
    (b) What was the interest for the 3 years?
    (c) Calculate each monthly repayment giving your answer correct to the nearest penny.

26. Describe fully two transformations that map the upper H onto the lower H.

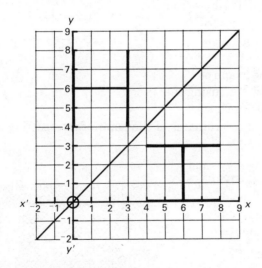

27. A motorist averaged x m.p.h. for 3 h, then averaged $(x + 10)$ m.p.h. for 2 h:
    (a) How far did the motorist travel at x m.p.h.?
    (b) How far did the motorist travel at $(x + 10)$ m.p.h.?
    (c) Write an expression in x for the total distance travelled during the 5 h.
    (d) If the total distance travelled in the 5 h was 195 miles, write an equation in x and solve it.

28. Using the given flow chart, find the answer obtained from the following input:

(a) 6   (c) 3   (e) 1
(b) 12   (d) 4.5   (f) ⁻4

(g) If x is input, find an expression in x for the final answer.

(h) If the final answer is 8, find the numerical value of x that was input.

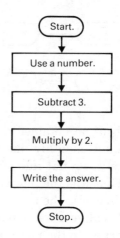

29. Draw a pair of axes as shown. x-values should range from ⁻4 to 6 ($^-4 \leqslant x \leqslant 6$). y-values should range from ⁻4 to 8 ($^-4 \leqslant y \leqslant 8$).

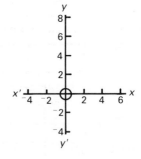

(a) Plot the graph of $y = x + 2$.

(b) Plot the graph of $y = 3x - 2$, using the same pair of axes.

(c) Find the co-ordinates of the point of intersection of the two graphs.

30. Write two inequalities that describe the unshaded region in the given diagram:

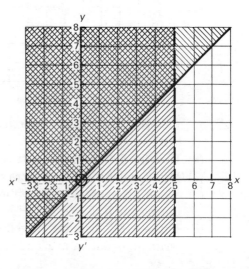

444

31. 3 rubbers and 1 ruler cost 90 p. 1 rubber and 2 rulers cost 80 p.

(a) Draw a pair of axes as shown.

(b) Using the given information, write two equations.
(Let each rubber cost b p and each ruler cost l p.)

(c) By drawing two straight lines, find the cost of a rubber.

(d) What does one ruler cost?

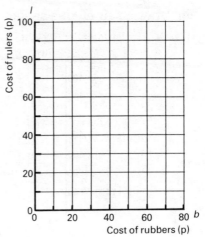

32. Oona spent 175.10 schillings in an Austrian shop. If the exchange rate was 20.60 schillings to the pound, how many pounds sterling did she spend?

33. Newbury is 44 km due north of Winchester, and Oxford is 40 km due north of Newbury. Guildford is 60 km on a bearing of 069° from Winchester.

Make a scale drawing using a scale of 1 cm to 10 km.

From your scale drawing, find the distance and bearing of:

(a) Guildford from Oxford,

(b) Guildford from Newbury.

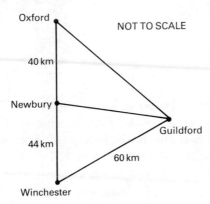

445

34. Draw a pair of axes as shown.

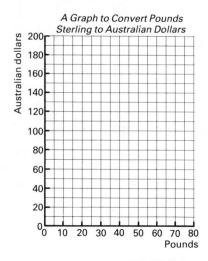

Draw a conversion graph to change pounds into Australian dollars. Use the exchange rate of 184 Australian dollars to £80. From your graph, find:

(*a*) the number of Australian dollars in:
    (i) £50   (ii) £30   (iii) £20

(*b*) the number of pounds sterling in:
    (i) 92 dollars   (ii) 161 dollars   (iii) 138 dollars

35.

90 mm

100 mm

150 mm

The swallowtail butterfly has a wingspan of 75 mm.

A drawing of a swallowtail is shown, together with an enlargement. If the full-size drawing is 90 mm long, and the enlargement is 150 mm long and 100 mm wide, find:

(*a*) the width of the full-size drawing,

(*b*) the wingspan of the butterfly in the enlargement.

446

36.

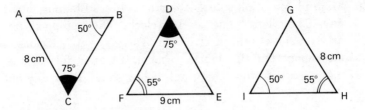

(a) Name the two congruent triangles.

(b) Name two similar triangles that are not congruent.

37.

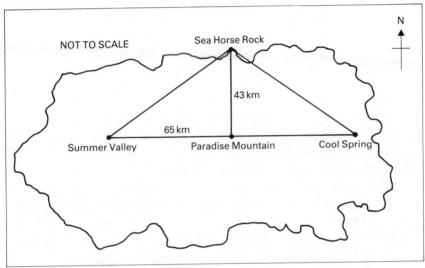

A sketch map of an island is shown.

Sea Horse Rock is 43 km due north of Paradise Mountain, while Summer Valley is 65 km due west of Paradise Mountain. Cool Spring is on a bearing of 143° from Sea Horse Rock and is due east of Paradise Mountain.

(a) Calculate, to the nearest kilometre, the distance of Sea Horse Rock from Summer Valley.

(b) Calculate, to the nearest degree, the bearing of Sea Horse Rock from Summer Valley.

(c) Calculate the distance of Cool Spring from:
   (i) Paradise Mountain,
   (ii) Sea Horse Rock.

38. Mr and Mrs Colby took their daughter, Eleanor, out for the day. They left home at 10 o'clock. They stopped for lunch at 12 o'clock and arrived in Torquay at 2 o'clock in the afternoon. On the journey home, Eleanor felt sick so they made a short stop. The graph below shows their day out:

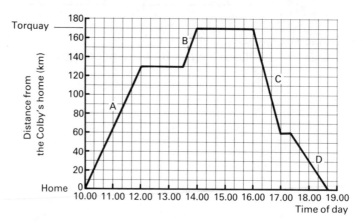

Use the graph to answer the following:

(a) How far is the Colbys' home from Torquay?

(b) How far did they travel before having lunch?

(c) How long was the lunch-stop?

(d) How long did they spend in Torquay?

(e) How long did they stop on the way home?

(f) What was their average speed between the lunch-stop and Torquay?

(g) Parts of the graph are labelled A, B, C and D. Put those letters in order of speed, from fastest to slowest.

(h) How far did they travel altogether on the day out?

(i) If the car averaged 14 km per litre of petrol, what was the smallest whole number of litres of petrol needed for them to travel from home to Torquay then back again?

39. A car driver had to drive through two sets of traffic lights, A and B. The probability of A being green was $\frac{2}{3}$, while the probability of B not being green was $\frac{1}{4}$. (The driver was only allowed through the lights on green.)

(a) Copy and complete the following tree diagram to show all the probabilities and outcomes.

448

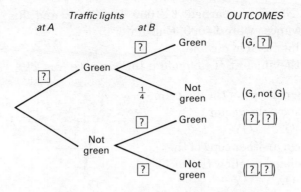

(b) Find the probability of each of the following:
   (i) The driver went through both sets of lights without having to stop.
   (ii) The driver stopped at A but not at B.

40. The bar chart shows the number of points obtained in a quiz game by several people.

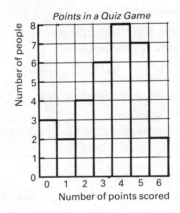

Find:
(a) the modal number of points scored,
(b) the median number of points scored,
(c) the number of people who scored 2 points,
(d) (i)   the total number of people in the quiz,
    (ii) the total number of points scored by those in the quiz,
    (iii) the mean number of points scored.

41. Mr Needham earned £12 680 last year and his total tax allowances were £4090. Calculate:

(a) his taxable income,

(b) the amount of tax paid if the tax rate was 27%.

42. (a) On a copy of the diagram, show the vector $\overrightarrow{OX} + \overrightarrow{OY}$.

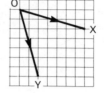

(b) On another copy of the diagram, show the vector $\overrightarrow{OX} - \overrightarrow{OY}$.

(c) Write as column vectors:

(i) $\overrightarrow{OX}$ (ii) $\overrightarrow{OY}$ (iii) $\overrightarrow{OX} + \overrightarrow{OY}$ (iv) $\overrightarrow{OX} - \overrightarrow{OY}$

(d) Find the magnitude (to one decimal place) of:

(i) $\overrightarrow{OX}$ (ii) $\overrightarrow{OY}$ (iii) $\overrightarrow{OX} + \overrightarrow{OY}$ (iv) $\overrightarrow{OX} - \overrightarrow{OY}$

Miscellaneous Papers

Paper 6

1. (a) Estimate: $9.7 \times 9.8 \times 10 \times 10.2 \times 12$
(Work with one significant figure.)

(b) $98 \times 100 \times 102$ is closest to:

A. 10^3 B. 10^4 C. 10^6 D. 10^8 E. 10^9

2. (a) If 16 g of drinking chocolate contains 12 g of sugar, what percentage is sugar?

(b) If 20 g of fruit gums contains 12.5 g of sugar, what percentage is sugar?

3. The volumes of the following cylinders were calculated using the formula $V = \pi r^2 h$. By *estimating*, find which of the given volumes is not correct.

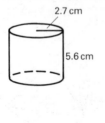

128 cm³

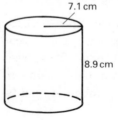

1410 cm³

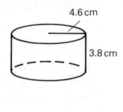

393 cm³

4. The larger of the two angles between south-west and east is:

    A. 315°   B. 135°   C. 285°   D. 225°   E. 240°

5. Copy and complete the electricity bill:

        685 units at 5.700 p = £⬚⬚⬚

        Quarterly charge   = £6.60

        Total now due   = £⬚⬚⬚

6. A spinner has the numbers 3, 3, 3, 4 and 5 on it:

    (*a*) When it is spun, what is the probability of a 3?

    (*b*) If it is spun 350 times, how many times would you expect to get a 3?

7. Which is larger:

    (*a*) 10^4 or $\frac{1}{1000}$?   (*c*) 10^{-4} or 0.000 01?

    (*b*) 10^{-3} or $\frac{1}{100}$?   (*d*) 10^{-3} or 0.01?

8. The table shows what 30 people paid to attend a concert:

Amount paid	Number of people (frequency)
£8	5
£6	10
£5	7
£3	8

    (*a*) Calculate the total amount paid by the 30 people.

    (*b*) Calculate the mean amount paid by the 30 people.

    (*c*) Which amount is the mode?

    (*d*) Find the median amount paid.

    (*e*) Write down the range.

9. Calculate the value of *m*:

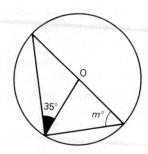

10. A net of a solid is shown:
- (a) Write the name of the solid.
- (b) When the solid is made, which points meet point F?
- (c) Which edge will join CD?

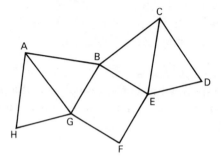

Paper 7

1. (a) How long does it take the hour hand of a clock to rotate through 30°?
- (b) How many minutes does it take the minute hand of a clock to rotate through 210°?

2. What is the next whole number after 4099?

3. Mr Stocks bought 1800 shares at 50 p each then sold them at 72 p each:
- (a) How much did he pay for the shares?
- (b) What was the total selling price of the shares?
- (c) If Mr Stocks paid 1.5% commission on the selling price of the shares, how much commission did he pay?
- (d) Mr Stocks had to pay VAT at 15% on the commission charge. Find the VAT payable (to the nearest penny).
- (e) How much money did Mr Stocks actually receive from the sale of the shares?
- (f) How much profit did Mr Stocks make from the sale of the shares?

4. A cake weighing 760 g is cut into 8 equal pieces. Find the mass of each piece.

5. A circle, whose centre is at the origin, passes through the point (4, 3). Draw a pair of axes where both the *x*- and *y*-values range from ⁻6 to 6. (Use a scale of 1 cm to 1 unit.) Draw the circle, find its radius, then calculate its area ($\pi = 3.14$).

6. (*a*) Write in figures: Six thousand, seven hundred and eight
   (*b*) Write the number 14 023 in words.

7. 5 pieces of cord each measure $1\frac{3}{5}$ m. What is the total length?

8. The diagram shows the plan of an L-shaped room.

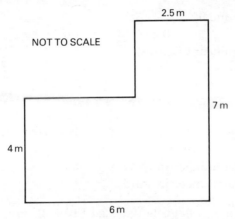

NOT TO SCALE

2.5 m

7 m

4 m

6 m

Calculate: (*a*) the perimeter of the room, (*b*) the area of the room.

9. Colvin called at Harriet's house:

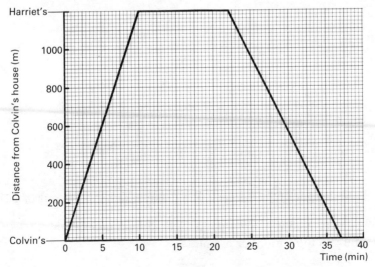

453

(*a*) How long did he stay there?

(*b*) How long did the journey to Harriet's house take?

(*c*) If he walked to Harriet's house, what was his average speed in:

(i) metres per minute?   (ii) kilometres per hour?

(*d*) How long did it take him to return home?

(*e*) What was his average walking speed on the journey home:

(i) in metres per minute?

(ii) in kilometres per hour?

10. Find the value of:

(*a*) 5^2 (*b*) 0.5^2 (*c*) 7^3 (*d*) 5.73^2

(to four significant figures)

Paper 8

1. 12 489 people visited the flower garden. Write the number of visitors correct to the nearest 100.

(*a*) Write the number in figures.

(*b*) Write the number in words.

2. In the diagram, a flagpole (labelled FB) is 29 m high. It casts a shadow (labelled BS) on horizontal ground. The length of the shadow, BS, equals the height of the flagpole, FB. Find the size of angle FSB.

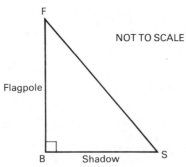

3. Anabelle got 56% in a test. What mark did she get out of 25?

4. The average number of points scored by 5 people was 14. Find the total number of points.

5. The door shown measures 1980 mm by 840 mm. The wood at the top of the door and at the two sides is 110 mm wide, while the wood in the middle and at the bottom is 170 mm wide. The height of the lower pane of glass is 540 mm.

(*a*) Write the height of the door in metres.

(*b*) Express the width of the door in metres.

(*c*) What size is the upper pane of glass?

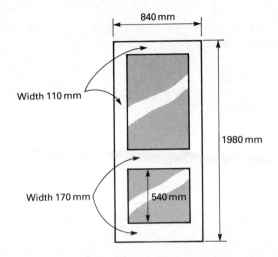

6. A youth club committee consisted of 4 females and 3 males. From these, a chairperson, a treasurer and a secretary were to be chosen, in that order, by drawing names out of a hat and not replacing them.

(*a*) Copy and complete the following tree diagram:

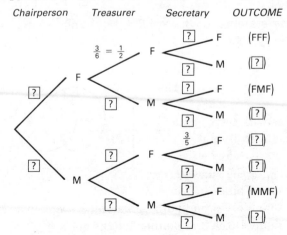

(b) Find the probability that:
  (i)   Females hold all three positions.
  (ii) The secretary is male.
  (iii) The chairperson and treasurer are male.
  (iv) The chairperson and secretary are of opposite sexes.

7. Work out the exact value of: $\dfrac{4.2 \times 7.9}{6.2 - 2.7}$

8. In each diagram below, part of a shape is shown, the broken lines being axes of symmetry. Name the complete shapes
  (a)   (b)

9. Multiply out:
  (a) $3(6w - 7)$ (b) $-4(5m - 2)$ (c) $z(z + 6)$

Paper 9

1. (a) In the statement, the area of the lawn $< 150\,\mathrm{m}^2$, explain what is meant by the symbol $<$.
  (b) In the statement, $3 + 5 \neq 9$, explain what is meant by the symbol $\neq$.
  (c) In the statement, $3.2 \times 4.9 \approx 15$, explain what is meant by the symbol $\approx$.

2. A survey of bikes was made. The Venn diagram shows the set
$B = \{$bikes with bags$\}$ and $L = \{$bikes with lights$\}$.
  (a) How many bikes were checked in the survey?

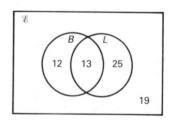

  (b) How many bikes had lights?
  (c) How many bikes had both lights and a bag?
  (d) How many bikes had neither a light nor a bag?

3. (*a*) If I toss a coin, what is the probability of getting a head?
   (*b*) If I throw an ordinary die, what is the probability of getting:
       (i)   a 6?
       (ii) a 1?
       (iii) a 3?
   (*c*) If I toss a coin and throw a die, what is the probability of getting:
       (i)   a 3 *and* a head?
       (ii) either a 3 *or* a head *or* both?
       (iii) either a 3 *or* a head but *not* both?

4. Fergus, who has a day off work every 9 days, wants to go out with Ida who has a day off every 6 days. If they are both off together today, after how many days are they able to spend another day together?

5. A rectangular yard measures 7 m by 4 m, both measurements being correct to the nearest metre:
   (*a*) Write the limits between which the length lies.
   (*b*) Write the limits between which the breadth lies.
   (*c*) Calculate the minimum perimeter of the yard.
   (*d*) Calculate the maximum area of the yard.

6. Calculate the value of *c*:

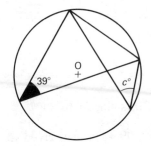

7. Simplify:
   (*a*) $y^7 \times y^3$
   (*b*) $4 \times 2x$
   (*c*) $8x^2 \times 3x^5$

457

8. A bus and a cyclist set off from Ingle at one o'clock. The bus was going to Stanton.

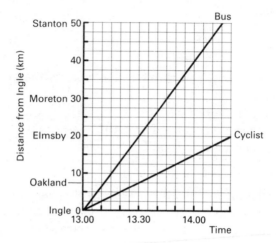

(a) What is the distance from:
   (i) Stanton to Elmsby?
   (ii) Oakland to Moreton?
(b) What was the average speed of:
   (i) the bus?   (ii) the cyclist?
(c) At what time did the cyclist arrive at Elmsby?
(d) When the bus was at Elmsby, how far behind was the cyclist?
(e) At what time was the bus 25 km ahead of the cyclist?
(f) At what time did the cyclist have 7.5 km left to travel to Elmsby?

Paper 10

1. Which multiple of 9 is closest to 200?

2. A bus departed at 09.45 and arrived at its destination $2\frac{3}{4}$ h later. At what time did it reach its destination?

3. AB is a diameter of a circle, centre O.
M is the mid-point of OA.
PN is perpendicular to AB, and crosses AB at M.

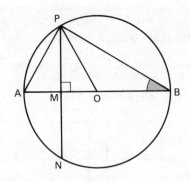

(a) Write the size of angle APB.
(b) What type of triangle is △AOP?
(c) What type of triangle is △BOP?
(d) If AB = 10 cm, find:
   (i) OA (ii) OP (iii) AP (iv) BP

4. The calculator display shows the answer to a calculation. Write this answer:
(a) correct to three decimal places,
(b) correct to three significant figures.

$$26.1548$$

5. The daily temperatures for a particular week were:

   14°C, 12°C, 9°C, 11°C, 15°C, 14°C, 16°C
(a) Calculate the mean temperature.
(b) Find the median temperature.

6. The circular top of a fruit cake is to be covered with marzipan.
Calculate the area of the top if it has a diameter of 24 cm.
(Use $\pi = 3.14$.)

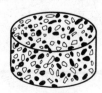

459

7. Describe fully the single transformation that maps the shaded trapezium onto trapezium:

(a) A   (b) B   (c) C   (d) D   (e) E

Which single transformation will move:

(f) A onto C?   (g) A onto B?   (h) C onto D?

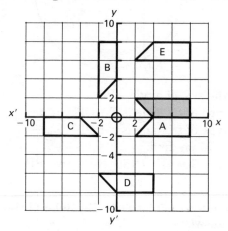

8. Shona, Cynthia and Gareth had saved some money. Shona had saved £190 more than Cynthia, while Gareth had saved three times as much as Cynthia.

(a) If Cynthia had saved £t, express the amounts each of the others had saved in terms of t.

(b) If Shona and Gareth had saved the same amount of money, find the total savings of all three people.

9. From an ice-cream van it was possible to buy two different-sized cornets. The sizes of the cornets are given in the diagram. If the cornets are similar in shape, find the height of the larger one.

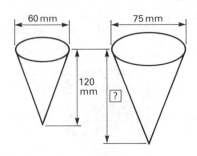

460

10. Out of an ordinary pack of 52 playing cards, the first card dealt was an ace. What is the probability that the second card dealt will also be an ace?

Paper 11

1. Philippa worked out $15 + 7 \times (9 - 3)$ on a calculator:
    (*a*) What answer should she have got?
    (*b*) If Philippa forgot to key in the brackets, and her calculator gave her the correct answer to what was keyed in, what answer was shown on the calculator?

2. A drill bit is turning at 240 rev/min:
    (*a*) How many revolutions does it make in 5 min?
    (*b*) How many revolutions does it make in 1 h?
    (*c*) How many minutes does it take to make 6000 rev?

3. Twenty-three thousand, eight hundred and seven spectators watched the match. Write that number in figures.

4. In a diagram, $a = 40$ and $b = 75$.
Calculate the value of c.

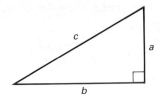

5. Write, correct to the nearest kilometre:
    (*a*) 8.684 km   (*b*) 3946 m   (*c*) 23.496 km

6. In an election A. Winner obtained 60% of the votes:
    (*a*) Write the percentage as a vulgar fraction.
    (*b*) If 27 475 people voted, how many votes did A. Winner get?

7. I have six coins that have a total value of 88 p. What could the six coins be?

8. Calculate the value of x:

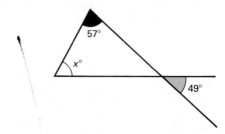

9. Part of the pattern on a wall tile is shown. The pattern is symmetrical about the broken lines.
Copy and complete it.

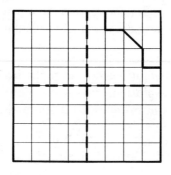

10. Construct a parallelogram with sides measuring 7 cm and 3.5 cm, where an angle between those sides measures 121°. By taking suitable measurements, then by calculating, find the area of the parallelogram.

11. Draw a pair of axes where x ranges from $^{-}10$ to 6 and y ranges from $^{-}2$ to 6:
(a) Draw the graph of $y = \frac{1}{2}x + 3$.
(b) Label the point where the graph crosses the x-axis as X and the point where the graph crosses the y-axis as Y.
(c) Write the co-ordinates of X and Y.
(d) Calculate the length of XY (correct to one decimal place), giving the answer in the units used for the graph.

12. A label of length 91 mm goes half-way around a jam jar. Calculate the diameter of the jam jar giving your answer correct to the nearest millimetre. (Use $\pi = 3.14$.)

1. Which whole number when multiplied by itself gets closest to 350?

2. Two whole numbers are divided. If the display shows:

$$0.3333333$$

   (a) What could the numbers be if neither of the numbers is a 1?
   (b) What could one of the numbers be if the other number is 12?

3.

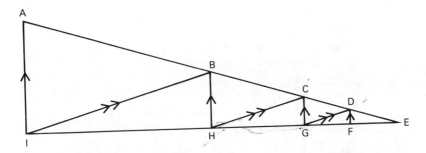

   The diagram shows a framework. The lines IA, HB, GC and FD are parallel. The lines IB, HC and GD are also parallel.
   (a) Which triangle is congruent to triangle CGH?
   (b) Which triangle is congruent to triangle EFD?
   (c) Which triangles are similar to triangle CGH?
   (d) Which triangles are similar to triangle BHC?

4. Eam averaged 59% in 6 exams. What mark does he need in a seventh exam for his average to become 61%?

5. The number 28 367.4871 correct to three significant figures is:
      A. 28 400   C. 28 367.487
      B. 28 300   D. 28 300.0000

6. There were two matches. For each match, wins, draws and losses were all equally likely.
   (a) Copy and complete the diagram.
   (b) Find the probability of:
       (i)   two draws,
       (ii) the second match being a win,
       (iii) both matches having the same result,
       (iv) the first match being a win or a draw,
       (v)   the second match not being lost.

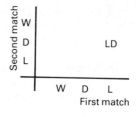

7. Factorise completely:
   (a) $2e + 14$ (b) $4t + 10u$ (c) $5x^2 - 25x$

8. The plan shows a rectangular garden. It is divided into a lawn and a triangular shrubbery.
   (a) What is the total area of the garden?
   (b) What is the area of the shrubbery?
   (c) What is the area of the lawn?
   (d) Find the perimeter of the lawn.

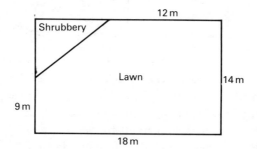

9. The legs of a pair of dividers are each 10 cm long. They are opened to form an angle of 41°.
   Calculate the distance between the points.

10. If it costs 16p to run a fire for 2 h, how much would it cost to run the same fire for 5 h?

464

Appendix 1
Calculators

(pp. 32, 35)
Clearing the Display

$\boxed{C}$ $\left(\boxed{ON|C} \text{ or } \boxed{CE} \text{ or } \boxed{CE/C} \text{ on some calculators}\right)$ On many calculators, $\boxed{C}$ is used to clear the last number that was keyed in.

$\boxed{AC}$ This key usually clears everything from the calculator except for the memory. On certain calculators, $\boxed{AC}$ may also clear the memory. Some calculators do not have an $\boxed{AC}$ key. On those, pressing $\boxed{C}$ $\left(\text{or } \boxed{CE/C} \text{ or } \boxed{ON|C}\right)$ twice normally clears everything from the calculator except the memory.

The Memory Keys

$\boxed{MR}$ $\left(\boxed{RCL} \text{ or } \boxed{RM}\right)$ This key $\underline{Re}Ca\underline{L}ls$ what is in the calculator's $\underline{M}$emory and shows it in the display. The number that was in the display is lost, but the number in the memory remains. Some calculators use the key $\boxed{MRC}$ or $\boxed{M_C^R}$ which work in the same way as the $\boxed{MR}$ key when first pressed, but usually clear the memory when pressed twice $\left(\text{see } \boxed{MC}\right)$.

$\boxed{Min}$ $\left(\boxed{STO} \text{ or } \boxed{MS} \text{ on some calculators}\right)$ This key normally $\underline{STO}$res $\underline{in}$ the $\underline{M}$emory the number that is shown on the display. Any previous number that was in the memory is lost, but the number in the display stays the same. On some calculators, possibly older models, this key stores the calculation so far.

Key in: $\boxed{AC}\,\boxed{8}\,\boxed{\div}\,\boxed{2}\,\boxed{Min}\,\boxed{AC}\,\boxed{MR}$

If the display shows 2 then $\boxed{Min}$ stores the displayed number.

If the display shows 4 then $\boxed{Min}$ stores the calculation so far. (Throughout this series of books, I have let $\boxed{Min}$ store the number shown on the display.)

465

To store the calculation so far,

key in: AC 8 ÷ 2 = Min
                    ↑
           This key causes the
           calculation so far to appear
           on the display

Min stores this result in the memory.

Keying in AC MR should now display 4. The sequence AC 9 Min AC 4 Min AC will store 4 in the memory and leave 0 on the display (9 is lost). Try it. (Depress MR afterwards to check that 4 is now in the memory.)

MC (CM on some calculators) This key clears the memory without clearing the display. Other ways of clearing the memory are: AC Min or MRC MRC or M$_C^R$ M$_C^R$, but these methods affect the display. (Remember, on calculators without an AC key, AC can probably be replaced by C C or ON|C ON|C.)

M+ (SUM on some calculators) This key adds the displayed number to the number already in the memory. Clear the memory first then key in:

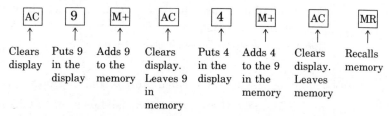

AC	9	M+	AC	4	M+	AC	MR
↑	↑	↑	↑	↑	↑	↑	↑
Clears display	Puts 9 in the display	Adds 9 to the display memory	Clears display. Leaves 9 in memory	Puts 4 in the display	Adds 4 to the 9 in the memory	Clears display. Leaves memory	Recalls memory

The last key MR in the above sequence should cause 13 to appear in the display.

Make certain you know the difference between Min and M+ (that is, STO and SUM on some calculators).

Note M+ can be used instead of Min as long as you

CLEAR THE MEMORY FIRST

So: MC M+ is the same as Min

$\boxed{\text{M}-}$ This key subtracts the displayed number from the number already in the memory.

Note $\boxed{\text{MR}}$ $\boxed{\text{M}-}$ should clear the memory and $\boxed{\text{MR}}$ $\boxed{\text{M}-}$ $\boxed{\text{AC}}$ should clear the memory and the display.

If your calculator does not have the key $\boxed{\text{M}-}$, but has $\boxed{\text{M}+}$ and $\boxed{+/-}$ then $\boxed{+/-}$ $\boxed{\text{M}+}$, can be used instead of $\boxed{\text{M}-}$.

Appendix 2
Annual Percentage Rate (APR)

(p. 189)

The following formulae can be used to calculate the true rate (APR), if a rate per cent per week (or per month) is given.

I   Annual Percentage Rate, $\text{APR} = 100 \times \left[\left(1 + \dfrac{r}{100}\right)^{52} - 1\right]$
      (true rate)

where $r\%$ is the rate per week.

II   Annual Percentage Rate, $\text{APR} = 100 \times \left[\left(1 + \dfrac{r}{100}\right)^{12} - 1\right]$
      (true rate)

where $r\%$ is the rate per month.

e.g. 1   1 p per pound per week is 1% per week $(r = 1)$.

Then, $\text{APR} = 100\left[\left(1 + \dfrac{1}{100}\right)^{52} - 1\right]$.

One way of working this out on a calculator is to key in:

| AC | (| 1 | + | 1 | ÷ | 1 | 0 | 0 |) | x^y | 5 | 2 | = |

| − | 1 | = | × | 1 | 0 | 0 | = |

This sequence should give 67.8% p.a. (to one decimal place).

e.g. 2   2% per month $(r = 2)$.

$\text{APR} = 100\left[\left(1 + \dfrac{2}{100}\right)^{12} - 1\right]$

Key in:

| AC | (| 1 | + | 2 | ÷ | 1 | 0 | 0 |) | x^y | 1 | 2 | = |

| − | 1 | = | × | 1 | 0 | 0 | = |

This should give 26.8% p.a. APR.

Glossary

counterfoil (p. 178)

This is the slip on which the person who has the bank account keeps a record of a transaction. There is usually a counterfoil for each cheque in a cheque book or with each paying-in slip. In the example of a paying-in slip given below, a counterfoil is shown on the left-hand side.

Account Number	THRIFTY					
0,2,3,5,1,6,4,7	BANK	**Deposit**	Sort Code 4,4,1,8,1,2,0	Account Number 2,3,5,1,6,4,7		
			Cheques	£50		—
			15 45	£20	40	—
			12 80	£10	30	—
				£5	65	—
				£1		
Till/Crossing Stamp	Till/Crossing Stamp			£1 coins	13	—
	Account Name			50p	4	50
Total Cash 158 86	R.O.B. BANKS			Silver	3	90
Cheques 28 25	Paid in by (signature)			Bronze	2	46
Total £ 187 11	R.O.B.Banks			POs		
				Total Cash	158	86
			28 25	Cheques	28	25
				Total £	187	11

Mach number (p. 91)

This is the usual way of giving the speed of an aeroplane. The Mach number shows how fast the aeroplane is travelling compared with the speed of sound. Mach 1 is the speed of sound, Mach 2 is twice the speed of sound and Mach 0.9 is $\frac{9}{10}$ the speed of sound. Note that the speed of sound does vary with the altitude (height above sea level). At sea level, Mach 1 is about 1200 km/h (750 m.p.h.), while at 12 000 m, Mach 1 is about 1060 km/h (663 m.p.h.).

no-claims discount (p. 393)

This may be called *no-claims bonus* by some companies.

self (p. 180)

When using a cheque to withdraw money at a bank, the cheque may be made payable to 'self' or the word 'cash' may be used instead. *e.g.*

Pay *Self*

or

Pay *Cash*

subtended (p. 56)

to be opposite to

In fig. 1, the line XY subtends the angle P. We can also say that angle P has been subtended by line XY.

Fig. 1

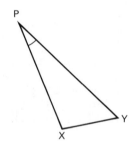

In figs 2 and 3, angle P has been subtended by arc XY.

Fig. 2

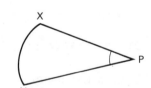

In fig. 3, arc XY subtends an angle P at the circumference of the circle.

Fig. .3

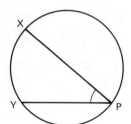